THE BANKRUPT BOOKSELLER

THE BANKRUPT
BOOKSELLER

BY

WILL. Y. DARLING

" Because a man has shop to mind
In time and place, since flesh must live,
Needs spirit lack all life behind,
All stray thoughts, fancies fugitive,
All loves except what trade can give ? "
ROBERT BROWNING

EDINBURGH
ROBERT GRANT & SON LTD
1947

THE PRIVATE PAPERS OF A BANKRUPT BOOKSELLER
First published by Oliver and Boyd 1931

THE BANKRUPT BOOKSELLER SPEAKS AGAIN
First published by Oliver and Boyd 1938

COLLECTED VOLUME 1947

PRINTED IN GREAT BRITAIN
BY R. & R. CLARK, LIMITED, EDINBURGH

FOREWORD
TO THE FIRST COMBINED EDITION

Many booksellers have gone bankrupt in the history of this precarious profession, but in the world of letters there is only one Bankrupt Bookseller, the author of this collected edition which is now presented to the public in one volume. The book was begun as a jest, and the cream of the jest is that the author was neither a bookseller nor a bankrupt, and though he now owns two bookshops he is still, perhaps to his own surprise, not yet insolvent.

In 1931 there appeared under the aegis of Messrs Oliver & Boyd of Edinburgh a finely printed octavo volume entitled *The Private Papers of a Bankrupt Bookseller*. It purported to be the occasional writings of a bookseller who, after a struggle to make a living, went bankrupt and gassed himself in the oven. The papers had been rescued by his neighbour, a draper, who acquired his assets and his shop, and had put the bookseller's papers into some sort of order. The book attracted wide attention, not only for its knowledge of books and bookselling, but also for the flashes of wit and wisdom with which it was illuminated. Reviewers praised it in nearly every paper of note, and there was much speculation about the identity of the unfortunate bookseller. Gradually it leaked out that there was " no sich a person " ; that the book was the imaginative work of Mr Will. Y. Darling, a partner in the firm of Darling & Company, the drapers of Princes Street, Edinburgh ; that he had created the character out of nothing, and had hung on this peg his own knowledge and experience of literature and life. True, he had a bookshop for neighbour, but the cap of the Bankrupt Bookseller fitted no one there, nor did it fit the head of any of the many bookshops he was wont to frequent. There was all the more merit in such an achievement and this merit was the more generally acclaimed. The book was indeed a *tour de force*.

Mr Darling followed the book by bringing out in 1938 a further collection of the alleged papers under the title *The Bankrupt Bookseller Speaks Again*, and this book also had its success, not only of esteem. One special point it had that differed it from its predecessor was a section giving the Bookseller's memories of the last war, and especially of the 1918 Retreat, which it would be idle to pretend were not Mr Darling's own. These memories give the book an exceptional distinction because of their essential truth.

The long arm of coincidence now plays its part. In 1940 the bookshop next door to Darling's went into liquidation, and after negotiations Mr Darling acquired it in order to keep in being a century-and-a-quarter old business for which he had always shown a regard, amounting indeed to affection. In his hands the business was lifted from the pit of bankruptcy into prosperity, and shows every indication of continuing to flourish.

Both books have been out of print for some time and as the demand for them has been continuous, it has been thought desirable to issue them complete in one volume. They are issued without alteration as they appeared first, with the original prefaces. The only differences are that because of war economy standards they must be printed without the handsome margins and open spaces of old, and that it seems right to state now that the author "and onlie begetter" is Sir William Y. Darling, Lord Provost of Edinburgh from 1941 to 1944, and Member of Parliament for South Edinburgh since 1945.

HAROLD FORRESTER

EDINBURGH
July 1947

CONTENTS

1

THE PRIVATE PAPERS OF A BANKRUPT BOOKSELLER

2

THE BANKRUPT BOOKSELLER SPEAKS AGAIN

1

THE PRIVATE PAPERS OF A
BANKRUPT BOOKSELLER

FOREWORD

As the discoverer of the pages which form this book, I have been asked to write a few words of introduction.

It is the general wish that the author's name, place of business and town be kept a secret. I agree to this as I have now taken over the premises of the deceased for the extension of my business as a ladies' outfitter. I do not intend to take the opportunity (although I am tempted to do so) to clear my own character from some of the comments made by the deceased.

I merely wish to inform readers as to facts.

The deceased came to our town and bought a bookselling business. The business he bought was not in a good way when he bought it and he paid too much for it. The rent he paid was absurd and he had fancy ideas as to what books he would keep and even what books he would sell. I heard of him refusing to sell a book because he said he wanted it for himself.

I am told he was a good man at his trade but I never saw it. He got into trouble with the bank and his creditors in the end. They were going to sell him up and he was found in his back shop with his head lying on a cushion on the gas stove. The gas was full on and not lighted. The stove was one of the new kind—more like an ordinary grate than the upright sort.

The place was sold up and I bought some of the fixtures, including the back shop furniture. In the kitchen cupboard there were piles of sheets of white window paper, torn roughly into squares. On these was a lot of writing, all in pencil, all about books. I kept these papers and showed them to his relatives, who told me that they were manuscripts for a book. They belonged to America and only happened to be in the country when they saw the paragraph in the papers about his death. They asked me to see if I could get some of them published, and I have done so.

I can only say that I think the failure was due partly to lack of capital and partly to lack of business experience. He also had been hit on the head in the War. He was a man I was always sorry for. It is hoped the book will interest those who care for booksellers and their point of view, and that it will have a good sale.

X. Z. E.

ACHIEVEMENT

This is achievement and I want no higher.

> " I will not think how far I came,
>   How fasted in the rebel wilds remote,
>   How rode down Folly, gripped with shame,
>   To reach yon Hill of God. . . ."

Some day I will think how far I have come, but not to-day. It is achievement that fills me, and follies ridden down and shames outlived are behind me. I have reached the Hill of God on earth for me and now I can contentedly look out through my open shop door and see the trees on the other side of the street—green and glad—and on either side of me—books.

I am a bookseller. I am not a bookseller born and bred. I am one who has come late to the craft, but, if late, not less lovingly. Books are a transcript of life, they say, but to me they are more than the transcript. They are Life itself, for as it was in the Beginning—is now—and ever shall be, " in the beginning was the Word."

I don't remember my first book. I was always a reader of books. I never was a student. I loved books in bulk and the strain of the collector is stronger in me than the savant. I love books for themselves. As a naturalist loves all nature, so I love all books.

And to-day is the day of achievement. I stand and look down the little avenue of books which is my shop. On each side there are shelves and on these shelves are my books. All day long, I live my life between these two parallel straight lines, which I know, from my recollections of Euclid, may be extended into infinity and yet will never meet. I stand between these lines that lead to infinity, and I, myself, am buttressed by these protecting walls.

There might have been other achievements, but none could

have given me my present happiness. After all, what more can the reasonable man ask of life than I have? I had my call, and now have my calling. Like Joan of Arc I have my voices, and though others do not hear them, my happiness is in this, that I have heard. I am among the Chosen—my chosen —and these chosen are my children. Like children too, they will leave me.

That dreadful pleasure—that pleasurable dread that the mother knows is mine. With infinite labour I have got these children of mine and my happiness will be in their going out into the world, just as a mother's happiness lies in her children's going forth from her fireside.

The mother's misery, too, is mine. I will not part with any of my darlings without a pang. It may be, none will go without a prayer. But all will go—nay, all must go—for these have no permanent abiding place with me, if I have to live— and if *they* have to live out their usefulness. It is my achievement, this housing of the infinite for a time, this laying of hands on all that is to be—God grant it—hopeful and helpful to that world that I am to meet—here, as I stand between these serried shelves of books.

Writing these words I remember a print of the French bookshops in the Palais Royale. I would like my shop to be like that, well-filled bookshelves and graceful ladies. I aim at elegance. I hope I am going to attract pretty women from my neighbour next door.

BEAUTY

" Tell me where is Fancy bred,
In the heart or in the head."

I can't answer Shakespeare's question but I want an answer to the question, " Whence comes Beauty?" Keats tells me that " a thing of beauty is a joy for ever," but what is Beauty? Bacon declares " that is the best part of beauty which a picture cannot express." Masefield has it that "the loveliest things of beauty God ever has showed to me, are her voice, and her hair, and eyes, and the dear red curve of her lips." My own favourite—God is Beauty in this instance—is in Maurice Hewlett's *Open Country*, a book which ought to be a classic if only for the character of John Maxwell Senhouse. Here is how he puts it in one of his letters to Sanchia:

"The flush of dawn—there'll be a lot of that still wonder in your God; the wrath of a storm; music; the rhythm (endless, world without end) of running water; children's voices; an old man blessing a young one; a young man louting to an old one (a beautiful thing); a windless evening in autumn, when the sky is translucent violet, fainting to white, and the moon rides out, colour of an old coin; the sun on a brown hill; hares at play in young corn; a mother cat in lazy ease (all her troubles over), gravely watching her kittens, and purring entire contentment; any mother of any baby, and any father of any fine young man ready to go out into the world; any girl with her sweetheart, any boy on his first adventure; day and night; rain; spring sounds—lambs in the pasture, the cuckoo over the copse; the sea asleep and the sea in a rage. . . . There's no need to separate them. They are indistinguishable and well for us that it is so."

Robert Bridges has, however, the final word in the passage from Plotinus translated by him in *The Spirit of Man*.

"For the absolute good is the cause and source of all beauty, just as the sun is the source of all daylight, and it cannot therefore be spoken or written, yet we speak and write of it, in order to start and escort ourselves on the way, and arouse our minds to the vision."

SHOP WINDOWS

My shop looks across a street along which traffic roars and subsides during the long hours but, on the far side of that street, there are trees and they nod a blessing on my venture.

They have put forth the green leaves of hope, and my spring and their spring are one. At first I thought them too old to care, but now I know they are not indifferent. After all, we have a common ancestry—and a common destiny, and they feel there is room for us both—green trees and greenhorn together in the communion and the commerce of things.

On either side of my shop door I have a window. My windows are not large. No bookseller wants large windows. He offers infinite riches in little room. My neighbour, who is a ladies' draper, has great glittering sheets of glass, but I hardly dare look into his windows. There is to me a lack of reticence in his displays of the intimate. I could not be a draper—purveying "not one necessity of the soul."

My windows are small and some would "dress" them as they call it. I would not "dress" windows. There are no trimmings wanted for books. I am fond of colour, but I am not sure I am wholly in love with the "jacket" which the new publishers wrap round their books. Some jackets I like. Some, indeed, I have cut out and pasted inside the book—so fine—so pretty have I thought them; but my more usual feeling is for the naked truth—just plain cloth and plain lettering.

Some would put pencils and playing-cards among the books in the shop window, but I would not even if I kept such things. I do not bother about the "stationary" trade. I am an auxiliary of progress. I am a proud bookseller.

My windows show the backs of the books close against the glass. Shelf rises above shelf to the top where the blind used to be and where the blind-roller still is. The other day—dusting the top row of the books in the window—I found several spiders. I was glad to give them such security as they have between the old blind-roller and the window top. I have always liked spiders. It was the story of the Bruce, perhaps, that endeared them to me early in life—and then Fabre has shown them to be more than ever deserving of human admira-tion and pity. Pity—of course—they must be accorded, though Heaven knows we want all our pity for ourselves, were not self-pity such a narrow, melting, soul-sapping potion.

Anyway I am now something of a business man and though the rôle does not become my fancied idea of myself, yet I am tempted to remember Pope's lines :

> " The spider's touch—how exquisitely fine !
> Feels at each thread and lives along the line."

That's me—in my new calling—responsive to anything that stirs me ! What an excellent sign for a bookseller, " The Sign of the Spider," but I daren't do that ! I have shocked commerce enough already by changing my yellow painted number of 47 to the lettered way of writing it. I have it " Forty-seven."

Am I not a man of letters rather than an arithmetician? What would my neighbours say if I outraged any other canon of commerce? I cannot imagine. What would my customers think? I care not to prophesy. The spiders will stay. I alone among humanity know of their presence and their plans for the flies are safe in my keeping. The thoughtless would have cleared them out but I am not thoughtless. Bookselling is a thoughtful affair and mere cleanliness is—after all—only *next* to godliness. We booksellers, I have already said, have little to do with those who are next door—and those who are merely *next* to godliness are too far away for us to take into our cognisance.

I remember a bookseller who always hung a book in his window on a card on which was written, " The Book of the Week." That was to my mind a poor service that he did our profession even if he sold hundreds. That notice declared the ephemerality of books and that is the unforgivable sin. How many books have been condemned as " Books of the Week," only to find that the judgment day for them has not even yet really come? No bookseller ought to pronounce a sentence, and that is nothing if not a sentence of death. That Book of the Week may indeed be the Brain of a Lifetime and generations yet unborn will assuredly read it if only to know what strange books we read in this our Year of Grace.

For me, I will have no labels or tickets or cards and only

once I was tempted to lure trade in this fashion. I prepared a card and printed on it in my best characters these words :

> A BOOK
> NOT FOR TO-DAY
> BUT FOR ALL TIME

For all that, I never used that card. I saw it was a sentence too, and Heaven forbid that I should be a judge of anyone or anything, let alone a Judge of Books. I would not make any book—if I could—the Wandering Jew of Literature. So there they are—my shop windows—not too clean, for, too brilliantly polished, they do not afford a reflection for my neighbour's customers, who can see their figures reflected as they pass my door. I cannot serve them with books, so I hold the mirror up to what is Nature and their self-assuring glances of admiration.

The bookseller, I hope, is always a gentleman, and most chivalrous and gallant at that.

DOUBTS

The *London Mercury* is good to booksellers. It believes OURS to be a worthy profession and I get pride from its pages. (Without pride I am naked in the world.)

In the issue which I have just been reading, there is a note of Ellis of 29 Bond Street, W.1. This bookshop has attained its bi-centenary but it is eclipsed in years of honourable trade by Bowes & Bowes of 1 Trinity Street, Cambridge. Its history can be traced back—says the *Mercury* writer—to 1581.

I write it all, out of sheer egotism and preoccupation.

I dally with the bi-centenary of other bookshops.

My problem is, Will I last, not two centuries, but two years?

THE SHOP DOOR

The door is an all-important feature in any building and the door into a bookseller's shop is no mean portal. Mine is an ordinary door and, winter and summer, it is always open. Sometimes I stick a publisher's announcement on it, but, as often as not, I let the glass remain unobscured. The door itself I swing back, and it is held in place by a brick which I have covered, first in newspaper and then in strong brown paper. Nothing is unimportant. Everything has significance, and it is significant—although the significance eludes me—that my shop door should be held back by this brick—first wrapped in printed paper and covered again with brown paper.

The door is held back thus, and those who pass by on the pavement are thereby permitted, when they deign to look, to see a sight, not for sore eyes perhaps, but a sight worthy of a second glance. If such passer-by halts in his progress and steers across the wide pavement, he will find he must rise in the world to enter. That, too, is significant. To enter a bookseller's is indeed an elevation in mental station, but it is an elevation which is not for the host but for the elect. There is one step at my door, and I learn that in other places the one step has become a fashion. My shop was over a hundred years ahead of that fashion, however, for dignified men, of a generation now gone and designated for ever as Victorian, did the one step over my entrance before such a simple movement had won itself its modern name.

Having raised themselves in the world by taking the one step, my customers are now on my level, and they can enter—

shuffling or striding—as they will or can. But it is at the
door I leave them for the present. I do not ever go forward
to greet a customer. The play is the thing and not the actor
—the books are all-important and not the seller of books.

I hate these modern shops which employ shop-walkers (the
name always suggests the squalor of the street-walkers without
the romantic colour of their calling), who pounce on one as one
enters a shop. Who are these men who do this work? How
are they caught and trained for such a calling? What service
do they think they render as they escort their charges to
counters where mincing minxes demand again one's wants.
I would have none of them and I will not attempt in my shop
the faintest, most remote imitation of them. My shop door
is no mouth of a mouse-trap. Free come—free go—is my way,
and, if I am poorer in consequence, my conscience is lighter
by the thought that none ever bought from me for any better
reason than that he wanted to buy and could find what he wanted
for himself.

But my shop door has other implications than those which
are associated with those who come to look at my books and
perchance to buy. It is the entrance into my shop, after all.
I am not one of these cosmopolitan merchants who want the
public to make a rendezvous of their shops. My place of
business is first mine. It does not belong to all the world,
and I have felt, more than once, that I might some day, in
some towering rage of anger, take the whip of knotted cords
and lash the unbelievers from my door. My customers have
their entrances, but they have, too, their exits—and even the
most wearying go at last.

Then, and I am often glad of that closing hour, the shop
door gives itself exclusively to my hands. I, who unlocked it
with hope—when the day's business is over—close it with
calm contentment. It is my shop door in the morning, and
when the evening is come it is mine again—to guard my books
until I relieve its vigil with the coming of the new day.

THE FUTURE

A customer has been a regular buyer of the To-day and To-morrow Series by Kegan Paul. He commenced with *Wireless Possibilities* by Professor A. M. Low, and bought in succession, for half a crown apiece, *Icarus, or the Future of Science*, and *Tantalus, or the Future of Man*.

He then bought *Dadalus, or Science and the Future* by J. B. S. Haldane. He was surfeited apparently to-day. He does not like the Future any more. He toyed with books such as these from the Oxford Press—*The Legacy of Greece*, *The Legacy of Rome* and *The Legacy of the Middle-Ages*. He toyed with them but bought none.

I was serving when he went out and he handed me a card, one of my shop postcards, on which he had written

NOW

is all we

KNOW

The observation is original as far as I know but the thought behind it led me to two books. The first is *A Modern Symposium*, the best thing Lowes Dickinson has done. There —I found the passage quite easily, though I read the book before the War—there I got Cantilupe's expression of feeling which seemed to follow on the repudiation of the Future which had been made that afternoon. Cantilupe reminds one of Baldwin a little, though Baldwin in 1905 was still a man of business rather than a man of politics. He is made to say in his apologia for Toryism : " I am a Tory, not because of any opinions I hold but because that is my character. . . . The England that is, will last my time ; the England that is to be, does not interest me." My edition is published by Brimley, Johnson & Ince, but, oddly enough, was printed in America.

And after Cantilupe, let us have Lamb. (The Pun is resisted.) Hear Charles Lamb : " I care not to be carried with the tide, that smoothly bears human life to eternity. . . . I am in love with this green earth : the face of town and country : the unspeakable rural solitudes : the sweet security of the streets : I would set up my tabernacle here. I am content to stand still at the age to which I am arrived, I and my friends, to be no younger, no richer, no handsomer." Who would want a future who could find so much joy in the present as Charles Lamb? His joy in life, however, transmitted to us through his Essays, has given *him* a Future he never imagined.

The Discovery of the Future by H. G. Wells has a considerable sale with me. *Looking Backward* by Bellamy has not been so good lately, but I still recommend *A Modern Utopia* and even *News from Nowhere*. Now, however, that the Architects of the Future (with plans complete) are our rulers, even the short-lived among us may hope to see the New Jerusalem

" In England's green and pleasant land."

I wonder.
Palestine looks a more likely site after all.

BOOKSHELVES

I think my shop is exceedingly well planned. The door is plumb in the centre and the windows, which flank it, are of an exactly identical size. I like the symmetry of the place. I am no longer terrified by that awful phrase which Alfred Russel Wallace gave to his book, *Man's Place in the Universe*. I have shuttered out the vastness of things and find, instead, Man's Place in the Shop. My place in my shop is fixed almost with geometrical exactitude. The door and I are at the respective ends of it—the door supported by the windows, I supported by these parallel shelves which join me to the street—on either hand. Both walls are lined with shelves. They do not vary except for widths, and from the floor to within a foot and a half of the ceiling there is nothing but books. What gigantic buttresses these two walls are! They are—for the wise—buttresses against the arrogance of knowledge. For the simple, they are buttresses against the crushing despair of ignorance. They are—for the proud—buttresses against pride. For the lowly, they are buttresses proclaiming that the meek are blessed indeed in the larger inheritance. They are the walls of Jericho and neither the mouth organs of the multitude nor the trumpets of the tyrants can bring them low. They are the shelves of my books.

I don't arrange my books much. My customers—I persuade myself—have catholic tastes and prefer them as they are, but perhaps the deeper reason is that I do not know how to classify them. I admire the writers of publishers' catalogues—the way they classify. I simply couldn't do it. Who can classify books unless it be the new type of Public Librarian, who has made a trade of this business of classification. If I did classify, it would be in alphabetical order. Any other classification would lead to absurdity, as far as I see. Is *The Pilgrim's Progress* a religious book? What is *Gulliver's Travels*? Is it a novel—a political satire—or a child's fairy tale? How shall I place Shakespeare? What was the man? A playwright—a romantic historian—a philosopher—a poet—or a text for the upper classes in our schools? Where do I put dictionaries? I ask you—are they not more fascinating than fiction and more alluring than any anthology? No, let it be an alphabetical classification, if any, but then there are difficulties. Will classification be by authors (what of pseudonyms?) or by titles? If by authors, William Shakespeare and Samuel Smiles might lie together and I would not—could not—compass that!

And then the pseudonyms. What is a painstaking classifier of books on the alphabetic plan to do with Mark Twain, who was baptized Samuel L. Clemens, or how can he place Marian

Evans Cross or Lewes, who called herself—most wisely—George Eliot?

If one attempts classification by titles—no fewer difficulties beset one. *The Spanish Gypsy* finds itself beside that fine new book *The Spanish Farm*, and wonders why. *Trilby* would be less shocked perhaps to lie alongside *Twenty Men and a Girl*, but I—for one—would never plan such a forgathering.

My arrangement of my shelves may earn me a reputation for untidiness among the unthinking, but I am indifferent to these. From natural laziness—if you like—from sheer inability to discover any congruity between one book and another—I will not classify. There they are—as they come—as they go—in serried shelves—all happy with the fortuity of things—there are my books from the lowest shelf—to reach which the seeker must go (as he ought) on bended knees—to " the dust and silence of the upper shelf," as Lord Macaulay put it—there they are—awaiting the touch of the discerning hand and the light of the critical eye.

I am proud of my shelves and no happier man is there on this spinning sphere than I, when I see six or seven seekers after books—seeking they know not what—and finding not what they sought—but still seeking among these well-stocked shelves of mine and getting the sure satisfaction promised to those who seek—and find.

NINE

I have Brewer in two volumes by Cassell, and I was reading it over my tea. There are two pages—two columns in each—devoted to the word NINE and its significances, and yet the most significant significance of NINE is not mentioned.

Nine is one of the mystic numbers of the Greeks ; *nine* consists of a trinity of trinities. *Nine* is a simple representative of plural perfection ; we may go dressed up to the *Nines*, there are *nine* orders of angels, there are *nine* Gods and there is the *ninth* heaven. 'There are *nine* muses. *Nine* tailors make a man, and there are *nine* days' wonders. There are *nine* crowns in heraldry, and there are *nine* rivers in hell. Possession is *nine* parts of the law and the law's most unpleasant punishment is the cat-o'-*nine*-tails. There are *nine* planets, and a cat has *nine* lives.

The Reverend Doctor Brewer gives them all—these—and many more, but I have made a discovery which he has omitted.

For you who may read this and for me who write it, there is a more important *nine*.

It is the *Ninth* letter of the alphabet.·

LITERARY AFFINITIES

If " man, know thyself " is the first counsel of wisdom, " man, confess thyself " is an important stage on the journey to self-knowledge. My literary ancestry are the self-revealers. Samuel Pepys gives me shamelessness : Amiel's *Journal* the desire to go deep as I can in my shallownesses : Barbellion has taught me to see value in the trivial and deem it worth while to set it down for myself, if not for others ; Henry Ryecroft gave me calm resignation and a love of nature and the country : Bagshot made me a commentator. on men and politics : Richard Jefferies hints of an infinite that I may know.

These are my principal ancestors and I affirm strong grounds for my ancestor worship. They have a common characteristic—none was happy in life. They had their dearest joy in self-examination and in self-revelation and so have I. Their books alone make me glad I became a bookseller.

If the world—my world—ends to-night I count myself as having lived well, these men being my friends.

They are all dead.

THE BOOKSELLER AND THE BOOKS

It is to St Thomas Aquinas that the saying is attributed—
" Beware of a man of one book." The Saint gives me his
blessing by implication. The world has nothing to beware of
in me. I am no man of one book—but a man of many books.
I am a bookseller, with shop and shelves all complete.

It is a fine calling and one which, as far as I ever heard or
knew, never yet begot malicious envy. Envy it has begotten
. . . for years I envied those who were booksellers, but it was
an envy which did not seek any ill or loss to the envied. I
swear that I only wanted to be as these happy mortals were.
I did not covet my neighbour's goods, but I thought his circumstances fortunate and longed to be as he was—always allowing
that no detriment befell him in my attaining my ambition.

I am an unrepentant book lover, and so soaked am I in
the love of books that I feel—poor twentieth-century shopkeeper that I am—I feel that Pliny is a man I know, for all the
eighteen centuries and more that lie between us. Pliny used
to say (you will see it in a translation I have on my shelves)
that no book was so bad that some good might be got out of
it, and that is my feeling. I—and Pliny—born and bred so
differently, feel the same about books and it gives me a flattering
sense of rightness—sitting here in this shop among books that
Pliny could not have imagined—books written in a language
which was not then evolved—the thought makes me feel
thrilled. There is no other word for it, but I dare not tell it
to anyone. It is an astonishing secret to me that I must enjoy
alone.

Does my neighbour—important man and full of civic
honours—does my neighbour have his calling in life endorsed
so classically? I can't think so. He wants the Royal Appointment, he told me once, but he would laugh if I told him that
Pliny was my patron.

I savour every hour of every day the good fortune that
made me a bookseller. It might have made me anything but

it could not have made me happier. I was destined—if the
purposes of eager and ignorant parents can be dignified by the
name of destiny—for some aspiring respectable clerking, but I
loathed it always and left it soon. If I am to write books it
will be books into which I can put more of myself than ledger
entries—debtor and creditor. Not that I—thinking it over as
I write—disparage even ledgers. Ledgers have written the,
tragic and comic history of many a life, and even the very name
of a " Day Book " suggests the solemn transience of men. That
American writer—Joseph Hergesheimer—makes a counting-
house book the repository of a most moving episode at the
conclusion of *The Three Black Pennys*. Howat—the Last of
the Pennys—rummaging among the remnants of his past,
comes on " a full ledger, bound in crumbling calf with stained
and wrinkled leaves." It had been the forge book in 1750
and he noted the faded entries . . . " what flourishing pale
violet initials, what rubicund lines and endings." He marked
—this last of his line—" two handwritings listing commonplace transactions now invested by time with an accumulated,
poignant significance, one smooth and clerkly, the other abrupt
with heavy impatient strokes. Youth probably "—he ruminates
—" held at an unwelcome task." As he turned the pages, the
book fell and from it dropped " a note, obliterated by creases
but with some lines still legible, hurriedly scrawled by a
woman." It was a note signed " Ludowika "—but where
have I got to? I am away from my thought about books
and am now even glorifying ledgers !

I replace Hergesheimer's book and feel again the immensity
of my little business—how it makes its master willy-nilly a
veritable time-traveller though he never leaves his shop !
Where is there a day's work that can connect Pliny and
Hergesheimer as mine has done without an effort this afternoon?

Bookselling is the very kernel of the romance of commerce,
I feel, though for that matter shopkeepers never have seemed
to me to make the most of their business. I wonder if the
Chambers of Commerce would not do more for the advance-

ment of the shopkeepers in the esteem of the public if they
published in pamphlet form—handy to give to customers—
these wonderful interviews which Adam Wayne had with the
shopkeepers of Notting Hill. The Grocers' Federation—or is
it the Ancient Company of Grocers?—I don't know—what
have they done with the grand tribute which Wayne gave to
their trade when he talked to Mr Mead? Or the Pharmaceutical
Chemists—how does Mr Bowles stand with them? Or where
is Mr Turnbull among the Association of Toyshop Keepers?

I never read the *Napoleon of Notting Hill* but I wish that
its author had found a bookseller among its magic streets and
let Adam Wayne talk to him. It is the only defect in a wonderful book, and yet it is a book, I find, that is little known and
little read among my customers. But I am an indifferent
literary guide. I have occasionally allowed my enthusiasms to
run away with me, and their running away was the immediate
prelude to my customer doing likewise. I find my need is
temperance. I find I must cling fast to my determination to
let my customers look where they like and buy where they like.
I must not proselytise although it is ever hard on a believer to
suppress the good tidings that have given him great joy.

I must be restrained. I will out to my doorstep and smell
the evening—with my books for the moment behind me.

The night is coming on fast and there is a blue among the
blackness of the sky. There are a few stars and—fretting the
sky on the far side of the road—these trees sway gently. Life
strikes me suddenly as being too overwhelming in its perfection
—in its completeness—in its beauty—and in its unspeakable
and untellable wonder. Books are small now that my back is
turned on my shop—and the mind of man is great, but beyond
both—unfathomed and unfathomable—is a greatness passing
all understanding—yet with it all—a greatness of which I am
a living, feeling, pulsing particle.

" CACOETHES SCRIBENDI "

Why do I scribble away in this back shop? What hopes have I?

John Milton wrote—" By labour and intent study (which I take to be my portion in this life), joined with the strong propensity of nature, I might perhaps leave something so written to after-times as they should not willingly let it die."

Is that why I write? Or does Thomas Carlyle explain? " Produce! produce! Were it but the pitifulest infinitesimal fraction of a product, produce it in God's name! 'Tis the utmost thou hast in thee : out with it, then."

John Keats felt something like that a generation before.

> " When I have fears that I may cease to be
> Before my pen has glean'd my teeming brain."

John Keats wrote that sonnet, but its conclusion does not explain it to me—

> ". . . then on the shore
> Of the wide world I stand alone, and think,
> Till Love and Fame to nothingness do sink."

Is it inspiration that bids men write? The answer is in the tale of an earlier John than John Keats. " I was in the Spirit on the Lord's Day and heard behind me a great voice . . . saying . . . What thou seest, write in a book." Thus wrote Saint John the Divine.

What I see I write—not to the Seven Churches which are in Asia, nor yet unto Ephesus, nor Smyrna, nor Pergamos, nor Thyatira, nor Sardis, nor Philadelphia, nor even Laodicea. . . .

I write for my own satisfaction, a bookseller among his books. Saint John the Divine—surely a patron saint of all writers—will understand.

A BOOKSELLER'S CUSTOMERS

It was one of these economic books (of which I have to-day discovered I have only a very meagre stock) which set me thinking of my human relations with the world at large. We are a nation of shopkeepers—though why Napoleon should have selected us especially I never clearly understood. The French—at any rate in the spacious years from 1915 to 1918—seemed to require little to complete their knowledge of the art as far as my recollection serves, and they showed such skill—hampered as they were by limited stocks—as leads me to believe that theirs was an inherited rather than an acquired quality.

However, shopkeepers all the world over don't last long—and never long enough to tell a 'tale, if there are no customers.

It is an odd word the word " customers," and as the stock copy of the Concise Oxford Dictionary of Current English points out—a customer is a buyer—but more than that. The oddness of the word, as I sense it—has a dictionary justification, for the meaning given is expanded with a reference to the colloquial use of the term as implying " queer " or " awkward." " A rum customer " (long before the Great Free American Republic dreamt of Volstead or dreaded his Act) was " one "—so another book of reference declares—" better left alone, as he is likely to show fight if interfered with." Truly an odd word but one which fittingly describes *my* customers at any rate. The philological origin of the term eludes me but it may have its roots in the ancient suspicion which the owner of property feels towards one who may be seeking to acquire it.

Genovesi, the Italian economist, declared that " exchange consists in giving the superfluous for the necessary," but an older teaching announced to a sceptic world before Genovesi, that " fair exchange is no robbery." The world doubted that dictum then—and I fear still stands with Saint Thomas.

A *fair* exchange is so difficult to understand. How much do these inscrutable customers of mine desire my books? What would be a fair exchange? There are no balances in which such bargains can be weighed, for I don't think I ever parted with any book from all my stock but with a feeling of regret—without a sense of loss—even although I knew that I might replace the dear departed with another by return of post from the publishers. Habit dies hard and possession—and especially pride of possession such as I have—is an ineradicable thing from which a million Carnegies with their municipally-aided plans for book lending could never wean me. I want possession, and even though I must sell to live—to sell—to lose possession—wrenches at something in me older than my memory can recollect.

Some of my customers frankly are a mystery to me, and the darkness of their mystery is not lightened by the books they buy.

Some superficial space-filler has written, " Tell me what a man reads and I will tell you what manner of man he is."

He was no bookman who wrote that. If ' clothes oft do proclaim the man ' to some, they leave me in darkness and books certainly give to me—no clearer clue. I have a panel doctor who reads every detective story he can lay hands upon, and he must be no rare type, for I see more than one publishing house is issuing a series of detective or mystery stories. What does that taste in books proclaim in him? Has he an analytical mind? Does he love problems for their own sake? Is his life dull—and do such books give him a thrill—a much-needed thrill in the monotony of panel patients, pills and plasters?

Who can tell? I can't, and I have sold him six such books with never a syllable from him as to why he reads them. I only know that he would buy a book like John Ferguson's *Stealthy Terror* or one of Isabel Ostrander's amazing yarns every week if I could provide one, and yet I cannot fathom what manner of man he is.

There is the draper, too, next door. Heaven knows what his mind is, for he buys a most astonishing variety of books. He believes there is a book about everything. He was a gramophone enthusiast when I first met him and he must subscribe to *The Gramophone* of course. He had, too, *Learning to Listen by Means of the Gramophone*—a book I looked at but really couldn't read. Then he had a book by Archibald Marshall and Compton Mackenzie on *The Appreciation of the Gramophone*, and I almost was convinced I knew him by the books he read.

But I was wrong, for his versatility broke out in a different vein when an unwanted General Election burst in on an astonished people. He took to politics and displayed an equally industrious devotion to that topic. He became greatly interested in the Capital Levy and read Dalton—for—and Pennefather—against. He bought *Coal and Power* and Sir Lynden Macassey's book. He tried to get me to discuss *The Hope of the Worker* by Austin Hopkinson, and even offered to pay for a copy of *The Case for Capitalism* if I would only read it. My resistance was weakening—for he is a good customer of mine—when he threw over politics as dramatically as the Rt. Hon. Mr John Burns or Lord Morley did at the outbreak of the War, and was off into the *History of Costume and Dress*.

What can the most profoundly analytical mind make of such a customer? What do his literary tastes reveal except diversity, and what does diversity show in a draper any more than in any other son of man?

There is no conclusion to be taken from what men read. Man is not so simply manifested. Man is a mystery and the key to that mystery is not given to the seller of books. . . .

So I wrote days ago (I find) and it does not matter (much) if I agree or disagree with what I wrote then. This I remember, that my writing was broken off by the historic happy incident in the life of a shopkeeper. As to the shop of John Gilpin—so to mine—" a customer came in " and I laid down my pencil to attend to him. He disproved my theory altogether, for he was a man from whose inquiry I learned something. He was a man who that very morning had sought—and bought—a guide-book of the city. He came back at three—and it still rained—and he wanted to buy a time-table. From his purchases—morning and afternoon—even so purblind a shopkeeper as I could glimpse something of his mind, and what I saw of it did not seem to rate very highly the beauties of this very beautiful city wherein I have set up shop, for he sought no more from the Bradshaw than information as to when the next train left for home !

LOVELY WOMAN

Sometimes I have been a little contemptuous of my friend, the ladies' outfitter, next door.

I have been wrong.

The blue stocking I served to-day was a freak, for all her erudition. Women without beauty are unnecessary.

The world needs beauty. It can do without knowledge from women.

The props of a lovely life are the beauty and elegance of women and the courage and knowledge of men.

Foppish, brainless men and inelegant brainy women are encumbrances.

The two needs for men are war and literature ; for women love and clothes.

Good-looking women don't bother about books. They go next door. I am convinced that they are overwhelmingly right. The instinct that makes them do it is as old as the world.

No wonder their fathers (and husbands) forgive them although they know not what they do.

TITLES

Handling F. W. Bain's books in the new small edition which Methuen are offering at 3s. 6d., I am enthralled by the titles.

A Digit of the Moon, A Heifer of the Dawn, An Essence of the Dusk, what poetry there is in these titles for me!

How different the new vogue in titles! *Good-Bye to All That* is one I see announced; *Liquor, Loot and Ladies* is another; *Nigger Heaven* is a third.

They don't enthral me, these titles, however the contents of the books may attract.

I thought of some titles in the same vein as F. W. Bain's. *The Dust of a Star* was my first attempt, and *The Echo of a Dream* was my second, but I gave it up.

I have no title even to be a title-writer.

THE BACK SHOP OF THE BOOKSHOP

Battling along the street—out for an early walk—with a south-west wind blowing—it seemed—a hundred miles an hour—I thought all the time of the back shop of my bookshop. I saw the plashing rain and the wetted pavements. I saw the blown skirts of the girls shopbound (and shopward-bound) like myself. I saw on the far side of the street, too, these heaving, waving trees that are the only bit of nature I have learned familiarly enough to love . . . but none of these things did my mind dwell on. Like Byron's Dying Gladiator who heard but heeded not, I saw but heeded not. Turning like a corkscrew, wriggling, persistent, I thought of my back shop and especially of my new gas fire contrivance which only yesterday I had fitted. It was with a sense of having with much difficulty arrived, that I hastily opened my shop door and got inside out of the rain. I was glad to get into the shop—although I was an hour before the usual book-buyer is due to appear. I put my door weight against the door and presto ! my shop is open.

I don't sweep my shop every day. It doesn't always need it and sweeping raises dust which settles on the books.

If I had not found these good reasons for not sweeping my shop, I would be unhappy because I would reproach myself for being lazy. I don't reproach myself, and the man who is free from self-reproach is freest of freemen. I believe—as Stevenson has said—in the importance of the grim condition of keeping friends with oneself and a somewhat dirty shop (perhaps) is the grim condition in my case. To the back shop, therefore, I go.

It is really, I suppose, what some would call a scullery or a back kitchen. Certainly a sink with a tap suffering from a chronic (but not unmusical) running at the nose faces one as one enters. A window with twelve panes on two sashes lets in the light from my neighbour's yard. It reveals a dingy room —some would think—but I find it a veritable haven.

. I write " Haven " and recollect—such is the haunted memory of a bookseller—these eight lines by Gerard Manley Hopkins. I often say them in this room, for though the writer thought of something unimaginably remote from me—and this place—yet somehow they apply :

> " I have desired to go
> Where springs not fail,
> To fields where flies no sharp and sided hail
> And a few lilies blow.
>
> And I have asked to be
> Where no storms come,
> Where the green swell is in the havens dumb,
> And out of the swing of the sea."

I have that sense of " Haven " here and the new gas fire gladdens me. It is a new type fitted to fill my grate and is shaped like a cushion, throwing up its comforting, glowing warmth into the room and up to my face as I sit writing before it. Beside it I have another attachment on which I can boil a

kettle and even—if I want to do so—cook food. Above it is
my mantelshelf on which lies an ever-changing assortment of
books. I have a leather chair for comfort, a camp bed and two
wood chairs with rush seats. Beside the leather chair I have
a most handy and convenient stool—on which I have papers
and a pipe or whatever I have had in my hand when called to
duty from the comforts of the chair. Students of Cowper will
observe that mine is an incomplete accoutrement.

> " So slow
> The growth of what is excellent : so hard
> T' attain perfection in this nether world.
> Thus first necessity invented stools,
> Convenience next suggested elbow-chairs,
> And luxury th' accomplished sofa last."

I am satisfied with my stool and elbow-chair. A sofa is
unfashionable nowadays and I do not blame the fashions. I
have never wanted a sofa. It seems too commodious for one
and too crowded for two, I have always thought, and, anyway,
this room wouldn't hold one. There is barely room indeed
for the big table and the cupboard which completes its furniture.
The table—I eat at—do my accounts at occasionally (for I
hate them)—read at and at times have even bowed my head on it
and gone to sleep ; it has supported much—my table. May it support my needs as long as I require it—certainly I want no better.

But my cupboard is an interesting feature of my back
shop. It is unconnected with books except in so much as
the bookseller eats and drinks—uses dishes and spoons—like a
Christian. I have an excellent stock of cups, saucers, plates,
bowls and basins. The ware is coarse white stuff with a most
attractive blue pattern on it. I have the necessary cutlery,
assorted, it is true—but I can appreciate the variety of a knife
with a cracked, stained, yellow bone handle and an efficient,
businesslike fellow—thin and almost wiry—with a corrugated
metal handle. Some knives are bred for breadknives and others
seem to be born with a blood-thirsty intent. I am fortunate.
I have both kinds—and a variety of others suitable for every
variety of occasion.

I have also decanters, glasses and tumblers, for I drink beer, whisky and wine. This morning I make myself tea—I make it very weak and drink much of it—flavoured with slices of lemon and sugar. I don't take milk : it is inconvenient to have about a room such as mine and I have weaned myself as well as my cat from it.

I remember a tea planter I met once railing at the enormity of mixing a fine oriental vegetable decoction or brew like tea with the vulgar animal product of a cow's udder. I feel the appropriateness of the Anglo-Indian's objection.

I put in a lot of time in my back shop. I have no chairs in the front shop at all. When I mind the shop I read lying over a counter—a restful pose—and one studiously bookish too—if one lets one's head rest on one's hands—elbows on the counter. Digestion, too, I think, is rendered quiescent in this way. The ridge of the counter bisects the stomach and makes for repose. A Scots tramp, whom I met in my previous existence, told me of a lodging-house, a "kip" he called it—in which he had stayed on the Glasgow Road—or was it York? It was an old house anyway which had seen better days, and its large rooms held " dossers " all round—each lying on the floor on mattresses, heads to the wall. Down the middle of the room a rope was hung about four feet from the floor. Those who could not pay fourpence for a bed on the floor could have a " tuppenny hing." This consisted in hanging over the rope, head, shoulders, arms and the trunk on the one side—thighs, buttocks and legs on the other. The discerning—and those who had lost things before—made a pad of their coats, but the bare rope (my friend said) was not uncomfortable. It helped sleep, too, the head being turned down—although the morning was a rude awakening, for the keeper of the house (who was no trembler) brought the strong men low by unshackling the rope. Then all the " tuppenny hingers " knew the night's rest was over and another day had begun.

I sit in my chair when I want rest and retirement, and from it—through the half-open door—I can see my shop. I always have a meal at mid-day, for I don't trouble about breakfast except for my morning tea. My midday meal I usually prepare myself, but preparation is only getting out the dishes and the food. Bread, onions, cheese, beer is my staple, though I do eat pies and roast beef at times. I often make soup too, but lately I have thought it bad form for a bookshop to smell like a soup kitchen. I content myself with simpler things and these entail practically no dish-washing which—reduced to the minimum as it is with me—is still one of the greatest of the wearinesses of the flesh.

I always read at meals. It promotes digestion in spite of what the doctors say. It has a greater virtue too, for no reader at meals was ever a glutton for food. " For one general who died of overwork, nine died of over-eating." The Duke of Wellington is alleged to have said that and—fond though I am of food—I am glad book-reading never allowed me the time to be a gourmandiser.

A few of my customers have discovered me in my back shop and occasionally I have a pipe and a glass with them. But not often. The same scruple which makes me feel the incongruity of soup, makes me feel the incongruity of turning this annexe of my business into a bar. I am a public man but will not make my shop a public-house. I think there is something of the backwoodsman in me, for I have a lively sense of the necessity for this retreat from the public. I suppose I am really shy—but whatever my motive, I like the back shop no less than the shop, for if in the shop I am reminded that man does not live by bread alone, in the back shop I cannot forget how good it is for man to be alone—to be able to shut out all the world and commune with that darkness within him which he is pleased to call his own soul. Then I can answer Whitman's question—

> " Hast ever come to thee an hour,
>   A sudden gleam divine, precipitating, bursting all
>   these bubbles, fashions, wealth ?
>   These eager business aims—Books, politics, art,
>   amount to utter nothingness."

And my answer is an affirmation, here, as I write in the back shop behind the bookshop.

FELLOW-FEELING

Pity took me this afternoon looking out of my shop door. A man stood with a card—

> " Four Years' Active Service,
>
> No Pension,
>
> Unable to obtain Work."

I saw his case and mine were alike. Honourable death had passed us by and dishonoured graves were our destiny.

For all the tons of metal that were hurtled about for four years one splinter each might have been our fortune. Then we would have had peace in one of these most peaceful cemeteries.

Instead he stands with his card, unemployed, and I peer out at him no less unhappy.

Pity made me give him a penny, but whose image and superscription will be on the penny which would buy my thoughts?

PEN PICTURE OF A BOOKSELLER

It has been said that the true artist is revealed in his art, that the man can be seen in his books. My books are a confused revelation of myself. The lingerie next door veils the character of the dyspeptic draper, and the cheeses and pork pies dissemble the parsimony of the grocer further along the street no more completely.

Man is a mystery.

It is the staggering commonplace of our lives.

I can draw no word picture of myself. I see myself many

men—depending on the day and the hour of observation. To the public I am mean-looking. My face is not intellectual— nor noble. It is common. I look like a member of the lower middle classes and I am that. God knows what my ancestry was. I know—but it is a boast any of us can make—that it includes kings, popes and priests (I am sure of that—my faith in human nature is not less than my knowledge and understanding of it), prostitutes, pimps, decent farmers, day labourers, Roman legionaries, Norse Vikings, fighting men and cowards of all ages and generations, saints and sinners, a mixed lot, but no better and no worse than the best pedigree that was ever elucidated by the Court of Heralds or printed in the pages of Burke. These ancestral influences all work in me—unrecognised—but potent—as I follow my calling as a bookseller.

I am happier than most in my ancestry in that I can only imagine and conjecture its composition. I never knew my father. He was a clerk of various sorts and—failure all his life—he failed to continue living after thirty. My mother died two years ago—a curious soul. She gave me everything but I never understood her. She had no philosophy of life—no theory of existence. Left with me an infant, she apparently narrowed whatever had been her previous existence down to one purpose and poured her life force along that narrow channel. I believe she was left with a small house in Bristol and, partly by day work and partly by keeping lodgers, she struggled to bring me up and keep herself alive. She had a hard battle but she won. When she died she left me nearly eight hundred pounds and it is that capital that made it possible for me to be a bookseller. She had insured her life within a few years of my father's death, and the payment of the premiums on that was—I see now—the desperate victory she set herself to win year by year.

She worked as I have known no creature ever work. She moved from smaller house to larger house until she had at length six lodgers—and single-handed she served these until, happily I think, she fell down from heart failure one morning as she was about to begin the unending toil of another day.

I have often thought that the sacrifice was not worth the end achieved. I am not worthy of anything so highly conceived—so magnificently sustained—yet the effort she made for me filled her life and gave her intense happiness.

She was a frugal woman. She never bought a dress that I noticed. Her clothes were always indeterminate and characterless. She, in her later years, hardly ever went out. For two years before she died she never crossed the door. She saved—and saved—and saved and yet was no miser. She gave to beggars and bought laces and notebooks and studs which were worthless because she could not refuse a creature her pity.

She had come from the country, but her folk had died—gone to America—or dropped her—before her marriage. She had nobody but me—me—and her plan to leave me five hundred pounds when she died. She was the finest creature I ever knew—or read about—or heard of . . . she was that to me anyway and I am what I am because she was what she was—so single-minded—so quietly determined—so confident and sure in her purpose.

I am not like her in appearance. I am like my father. She had fine eyes and smooth hair and such quietness and firmness in her look. I am of a different cast of face. I get excited—show pleasure—cannot conceal displeasure. She was a Stoic. Her face masked her attitude toward life. Mine expresses emotions as they come and go—and bewilderment mostly.

They—people—would say I have a weak face. I am not a thing of beauty to others any more than to myself. I console myself with the biographies of ugly men but it is a poor consolation. I think, sometimes, I will cultivate a great soul but common sense tells me I have not the materials. I am what I am—and at best—make myself content.

> " None answer'd this : but after Silence spake
> A Vessel of a more ungainly Make :
> They sneer at me for leaning all awry;
> What ! did the Hand then of the Potter shake ? "

I don't know—and it is some consolation to know that nobody does.

I had a good enough education but did not make much of it. My mother got me a job as a clerk in her insurance office when I was fourteen and there I stayed until the War. I never liked the work but I could plan no better. I had horizons too remote for realisation—and I could not leave my mother.

The War came and I was among the first. They had me over in France early. I was hit on the head after Loos, and it has made me more fanciful than I was, but I am happy with it. " My mind to me a kingdom is "—I can write that truly. Perhaps many of us would be the better of a knock on the head. I certainly have been improved, to my mind. I think now, and I don't remember thinking at all before. Ideas jostle each other in my brain. I have found myself thinking and expressing myself as I could not have done before.

The War made me—undoubtedly. It deserves that tribute if I am the only one who can make it—for all the misery it has been alleged to have caused.

My mother died a year after I came home and with her money I felt free. I did nothing for over a year. I stayed in different towns and looked up old acquaintances of the war time. Then I came here by chance and bought this business. I would not have anything, I see plainly, but for my mother's insurance policy, her determination to leave me a sum of money, the War and that smack on the head at Bully Grenay. It is strange how destiny works out and brings this little act before the public.

I sit at my table with my paper in front of me and my pencil in my hand. My bookshop fills my glance as I look leftwards and lo ! I see myself a miracle. Who would have believed it ? Had one been told the story one would have said it was a fiction. How romantic it all seems and how true was that remark of O. Henry's when someone asked him to read some new novel. He replied that everything seemed commonplace compared with the romance of his own life. I feel that too and that may be the Inner Secret. God must love those who love their lives. It is His Drama—His Comedy—His Tragedy we are acting, and the Producer cannot but be gladdened when His players feel they fill the bill. At bottom that is the real thing in life. I seem—suddenly—to see God's purpose with us—to feel we have got the part we want to play—that is the beginning of the happiness the Saints and Martyrs had in doing God's will.

The Lord's Prayer comes back from childhood to me in my bookshop and " Thy will be done on earth as it is in heaven " is seen to be a great stage direction from the Master Producer to those of us who have the wit to see indeed that " all the world's a stage."

A BOOKSELLER'S HOLIDAY

A day in the country is good for a bookseller but it is trying to get back to worry and business. I don't mind books and I can even stand bookselling, but I have never understood book-keeping !

It is a profane name to give to ledger-keeping and debtors and creditors. It has made my head dizzy and to give myself relief I thought of yesterday. My mind turns to the woods and I make this poor piece of verse.

I call it " Trees."

Shops and dust and clatter,
    Trams and cars and a crowd,
Roaring turmoil, chatter . . .
    And something cries aloud.

Something just remembered—
    Something that's full of ease—
Ease for souls dismembered,
    A memory of trees.

Grim Scotch firs at twilight,
    And willows by a weir,
Poplars like some Stylite,
    Great oaks that men revere,

> Ash and birch and beeches
>   And sweet limes wooed by bees—
> God ! how far their reach is—
>   These memories of trees.

THE BOOKSELLER'S CAT

I have written that I am all alone in my shop but, these last months, I have had a cat for company.

A cat is the ideal literary companion. A wife, I am sure, cannot compare except to her disadvantage. A dog is out of the question. It may do at a butcher's—it would be out of place in a bookseller's. A cat for a bookseller is a different creature temperamentally from the same animal at a fishmonger's or a baker's. In these shops the cat is a useful animal—I suppose it is employed to eat fish entrails or to keep down rats and mice—but in my shop its function is that of a familiar. It is at once decorative—contemplative—philosophical, and it begets in me great calm and contentment.

My cat has discrimination. On Sundays—it will hardly be believed—she lies on a large old-fashioned Family Bible. This Bible I bought most uncommercially from a woman who had had it bequeathed to her. She was no scoffer at sacred things or one of those who undervalue the Holy Writ. Her lot was different. She was the survivor of a pious family and had heired the Family Bible of her parents through her eldest brother and in turn four other Bibles—no less ponderous than the one I bought from her—through the successive deaths of her two brothers and two sisters. With such a cargo of Holy Books and a further blessing of many children she sought to lighten her load of both by commerce with me. She heard— Heaven knows what gossip—about my pliable and simple character from the greengrocer and it was armed with an introduction from her that she sought me. I bought the heavy tome. It measures a foot by a foot and a half and is—from a bookseller's view—a real book. No bookshelf would hold it. It is made to lie—I imagine—if no lectern had been made for it, on some lace-edged cloth of bygone days on top of some high and stately chest of drawers.

This Bible is described on the title-page as " The Practical and Devotional Family Bible " and is of Scottish origin. The date is in Roman figures—1858—and it was " printed by William Collins & Co. and sold by William Collins, South Hanover Street, Glasgow." It contains the Old and New Testaments " according to the Authorised Version, with the Marginal Readings, and original and selected parallel references, printed at length, and the Commentaries of Henry and Scott, condensed by the Rev. John M'Farlane, LL.D., Glasgow."

That is a digression, but I went to my front shop and brought the Book that I might write down its proper description. This Bible lies on top of a fixture of smaller shelves nearest to my west window and it catches the sun. This fact —and the softness of its leather binding—may have led the cat to choose it for a resting place—I don't know—but anyway on many a Sunday—entering my shop in the afternoon to see that all was right (really because I can't leave the blessed place a whole day unvisited) I find my cat curled up on top of this noble book.

I am not claiming that my cat is a pious cat, however, though I am perhaps as serious a devotee of its species as the ordinary Egyptians were reputed to be. I admire the cat for its independence. It has no slavish faithfulness like a dog. It does not fawn. The nearest approach to a manifestation of affection that my cat attains is to rub itself against my legs when I come in with my purchase of liver. I love its languorous grace then—like the seductive, alluring wiles of some wondrously beautiful, entirely selfish woman that I can imagine, but will never know.

I can believe that cats were in Egypt considered sacred animals. I read that they were held to be under the special protection of PASHT—a great goddess—and that again, they were held to be servants of Diana. They behave to-day certainly as if they owe no allegiance to mortal master or mistress, but either have already pledged their souls away or hold them aloof from all earthly entanglements.

I have few books on cats, I find. The reference books tell how hated cats were in the Middle Ages and how their association with old women who were believed to be witches brought many to horrible deaths. Indeed it was part of some medieval processions to imprison a number of cats in a wicker cage and slowly roast the squalling crate of misery over a brazier as the masque went through the streets. Well may my cat with these race memories find peace in our time reclining on the Sacred Book!

There is an excellent book which I got once specially for a customer on the cat. It is by Carl Van Vechten and is called *The Tiger in the House*. It is an American book and I kept it long enough to see that it was a very elaborate compilation of all that was known, imagined and written about cats. The pictures—some of them anyway—were good, but I have no longer the book by me.

Cats have always been favourites with remarkable men (I bow to myself)—from Richelieu who had many of them always by him to Dr Nikola, to me quite as real a character —on whose shoulder a cat always sat. (I trained mine to do that at meal times and it is an entertainment to watch her reach out her paw and detain my hand—fork-laden—on its way to my mouth. I rarely can resist a reminder so gentle.)

I like my cat in all the aspects of her mystically obscure personality, but now—at this time—she is almost terrible. She is in the throes of passion—and all my efforts are required to keep her from escaping from the shop on some adventurous amour. I play the stern parent and deny her what she hardly knows she is seeking. I seek to compel her contentment—as mine is compelled—by the bookshop we live in, but hers is a straining nature—determined—daring—ready to risk all—and I fear that somehow she will elude me—defeat me—and win her heart's desire on the house-tops.

STILL LIFE

Why shouldn't it last for ever?

Here we are, my cat, my books, my fire and my table and chair—after my mid-day meal on a Sunday afternoon in October.

We are all happy—the sun pours a solid bar of gold across the room—and everything is placid—peaceful—still.

Why shouldn't it last for ever, like the figures on Keats's Grecian urn?

I could be content with life like this—life that is " Still Life."

A BOOKSELLER'S NEIGHBOURS

I have been reading Pope's *Essay on Man* (I can't but think there will be a revival in favour of Pope some day) and I find this :

> " Whate'er the passion, knowledge, fame or pelf,
> Not one will change his neighbour with himself."

In these days (no different perhaps from any other days)—what a damnable habit the parenthesis is !—in these days, that seems a strange doctrine. Everyone covets his neighbour's ox or his ass, and many I know delude themselves into believing that they would be better if they were someone else.

It is not true. We are not misfits in life. We get what we deserve. I am a rude determinist in that, if for no better reason than that to believe the contrary would rot my self-respect. I may be a poor thing but I am I, and that undaunted self-assertion forbids me the desire to cower into somebody else's apparently more comfortable circumstances and strut abroad—deceiving the world as to my inferiority—but concealing no shred or scrap of my own pitiable meanness from myself.

I will not be as my neighbours—I envy none of them—
but I will do what I can to love them as I love myself. Pliny
the Elder—I find him again apposite to my purpose—advises—
" Always act in such a way as to secure the love of your neighbour." I try—but it is a sore trial.

My friend the draper is a likeable enough soul for all his
being a literary weathercock, answering so promptly to heaven
only knows what strange winds. He is a hearty-looking fellow.
I suppose his wife thinks him handsome and many of his
customers certainly do.

He is about fifty, I imagine, and has a daughter, who,
caught up in schools and colleges, has soared above her father
and her mother both. He is a solid fellow and it is this instinct
for solid things that makes him look on me as a curiosity. He
has no pleasure in his business and marvels that I find all my
life in mine. He aims at getting out of his business into something else. It is sometimes a farmer, when he has just read
Poultry-Keeping for Profit or _Profits from Pig-Farming_. Sometimes it is the motor business—_Motors in a Nutshell_ is his
mentor then—and again it is politics. Politics usually, I
imagine, are his dream in the business. Like many men he
imagines he has something to say—something to give—to his
fellows when, of course, he has nothing that could not well
be done without.

He brought once to me a boyhood friend of his—a depressed
and dyspeptic commercial traveller—who bought one or two
books and stayed in the back shop to discuss his friend. This
commercial traveller said that the ideal of Man—the creature
a little lower than the angels such as we all think we are—was
merely a disordered yet widespread dream of a generation of
monkeys. " We are not yet men," said he, " and the fault in
us—the tragedy of our lives—is that we try to live too closely
to this ideal concept of ours."

Havelock Ellis in his Third Series—_Impressions and Com-
ments_—confirms this commercial man in his idea. " There
are thinkers," he writes, " who have occupied themselves with
the problem of the exact mode of man's ending. Some imagine

it will be by an epidemic of collective insanity, of which," he adds with terrible and scientific calmness, " germs may already be detected."

My customer thought the draper—and he had known him all his life—a monkey with a disordered mind, and his opinion was sincere, for he knew himself to be no better. Robert Browning must have felt the truth of this bitter thought— the thought that we are incomplete and yet often blind enough not to see it—when he cried, "Make no more half-men, God ! "

But the draper is not my only neighbour. There is the fruit merchant who, though no customer of mine, yet is my neighbour in God's sight and the municipality's. He is a young man—and like me—he loves his art. He is as miserly as I, and often—long after closing time—I see his fat figure, a silhouette on his drawn blind—counting his bananas, polishing his pippins, or it may be blending the raisins with the almonds with all the skill of a connoisseur. I love him as myself. He is my neighbour. Is it not seemly so to do?

I buy my fruit from him but he buys no books. I arrogantly think I am superior, but he—I am suddenly illumined by the humbling thought—may rightly think me a dealer in second-hand things. Fruit—fruit of the earth—is the direct miraculous work of God. Books—alas ! God help us !—are too often the fruits of all kinds of mental disorder and disease. " All that's *writ* is marred," and he handles more wholesome stuff than I, perhaps. I think of them—Chatterton, Keats, Dr Johnson, Edgar Allan Poe—Charles Lamb—O ! Lord, what diseased fruits are these, and yet it is their handiwork I handle so lovingly. I see I have no stones to throw—not even plum stones—at my neighbour, the fruiterer, who, I arrogantly thought, was my inferior.

There is the baker. He buys books on astronomy, I believe, but I have only sold him one. It was Camille Flammarion's *Astronomy for Amateurs*—a book I sold with more willingness than most. Its figures startled me, and the illustrations appalled me, especially that of one of the comets.

Astronomy is a lovely science. If I were a baker I might take to it—rising above ovens and pastry to the infinite, but I make answer to that possible craving in a quotation from a most likeable book which I have been thanked for recommending (O! rare pleasure for the bookseller!)—*The Comments of Bagshot*. It is out of print now, I believe, but it was written by J. A. Spender and published by Archibald Constable & Co., Ltd., as they were then.

Here is my answering quotation—and let me say that I cannot translate the Latin, but it gives a loftiness to the whole, I feel, so let it stand.

" Life's great irony is that achievement defeats itself in the moment of its victory. *Tantae molis erat Romanam condere gentem.* The poet has scarcely finished before the historian takes up the tale of the Decline and Fall. Our Paradise may be lost and regained, but never held and enjoyed. We develop our brains and pay by the decay of our bodies; we refine our tastes and pay by the decay of our morals; we become humane and find that we have lost our endurance, we enjoy the blessings of peace and find that our bones are full of water. There is stupendous energy of building up, stupendous energy of tearing down, but no moment of repose for the atom or the planet or the human spirit. The city of the soul whirls and vibrates like a machine-shop fitted with dynamos. Yet, somewhere in the heart of it all, the individual can make his own peace on his own terms and deny the whole universe to disturb it. It still matters nothing to me that the earth and the solar system are whirling through space at the rate of sixty miles a second from no one knows where to no one knows whither, if I may sit in my garden and listen to the bees on a summer afternoon."

I like that about the " earth and solar system are whirling through space at the rate of sixty miles a second."

What a thought—and what a counter-thought! Counter-thought—what a shopkeeping compound that is! It recalls me to my counter. I have written here too long and must out to the front to see what is doing and what may be sold.

That is the neighbourly mood. I recollect the great example of the one who was neighbour to him who fell among thieves.

This afternoon I would be the Good Samaritan to any who want books—written by diseased minds for the healing of diseased minds if you will. I have such books for all who come—for all, that is—who are my neighbours.

EVERYBODY'S DOING IT!

Everybody nowadays—if a poor bookseller of very limited capital may be admitted to be a judge—writes books or at least a book. It is a bad business for the bookseller. He has to buy them, for his customers ask for them and he must sell books to live.

In revenge, I sometimes think I will write a book but I am deterred. I will not inflict myself on others. I will keep my little, locked within my breast. I will be sunk without a trace.

Piles of books which I shouldn't have bought provoke these reflections. I turn them over—the women are the worst—and remember Edward Gibbon. He writes of the time when he meditated authorship, sane words which every publisher might print on the back of his letters, which he has to send, when he declined with thanks.

" Unprovided with original learning, uninformed in the habits of thinking, unskilled in the arts of composition, I resolved to write a book."

Edward Gibbon adds that the discovery of his own weakness was the first symptom of taste. . . . It would make an excellent title for an essay. " An Essay on the Discovery of One's Own Weakness as an Evidence of Taste " would be a good title for those authors who follow the reviving fashion of long titles.

But what a restraining influence there ought to be in the experience of Edward Gibbon ! Alas, the lesson is lost !

A wicked generation seeketh ever some new thing and the publishers must publish and the bookseller must book-sell in order to live.

ANTHOLOGY BUYERS

For a desultory reader the anthology is the gateway to literary ecstasy. I like the very word. Its etymology delighted me when I turned it up in one of the dictionaries. An anthology is a collection of choice poems, especially epigrams. The origin of the word is in the Greek *anthologia*—from *anthos*, a flower, and *logia*, a collection. Isn't that really pretty? A collection of flowers.

I am fond of anthologies and rarely resist buying them. I have a lot, I am afraid, I will never sell. Anthologies do " date," as the Ladies' Fashion Specialist next door said surprisingly once about some outrageous hats which compelled a comment even from me.

For all that, the first anthology I ever grew fond of is one which now, I imagine, is out of date. I have a copy, but care not either if I sell it. I read it often, from the four bold lines printed on its cover to the notes at the end. It is *Lyra Heroica* —*a Book of Verse for Boys*, and the lines on the cover are the noble lines quoted by Sir Walter Scott in *Old Mortality* :

> " Sound, sound the clarion, fill the fife,
>   To all the sensual world proclaim,
>   One crowded hour of glorious life
>   Is worth an age without a name."

The preface, written by William Ernest Henley who made the collection, is in keeping with the book, and this passage of prose I think matches anything really—fine though the contents are—that the book contains. Henley writes :

" My purpose has been to choose and sheave a certain number of those achievements in verse which, as expressing the simpler senti-

·ments and the more elemental emotions, might fitly be addressed to such boys—and men, for that matter—as are privileged to use our noble English tongue. To set forth, as only art can, the beauty and the joy of living, the beauty and the blessedness of death, the glory of battle and adventure, the nobility of devotion—to a cause, an ideal, a passion even—the dignity of resistance, the sacred quality of patriotism—that is my ambition here."

I wonder if any better preface has ever been penned to any book. I know of none certainly. The contents range the evergreen and lovely fields of English poetry from Shakespeare to Kipling. Some of the pieces I have in no other book on my shelf. This from the Marquis of Montrose was a deciding factor in the decision that made me become a bookseller. Little could James Graham have thought of that consequence, yet—please God—I am not the last any more than I was the first who was thrilled to *act* by the challenge of these four ringing lines :

> " He either fears his fate too much,
>   Or his deserts are small,
>   Who dares not put it to the touch,
>   To gain or lose it all."

I have always liked this book for that passage. It proves that poets are the real legislators of the world, for James Graham made my fate as surely as he sang his own in that very verse. The book is full of good things, but I cannot make an anthology of this piece of writing by transcribing the whole book, verse for verse. For the love of it, I read again and, having re-read, write Note VI. Henley comments on those lines of Beaumont, *In Westminster Abbey* :

> " Here is an acre sown indeed
>   With the richest, royall'st seed
>   That the earth did e'er suck in,"

and his comment includes that wonderful passage from Sir Walter Raleigh's *History of the World*—a book I have never seen but would buy for these lines alone—even if it lay a life-time on my shelves :

"O Eloquent, Just, and Mighty Death ! Whom none could advise, thou hast persuaded ; what none hath dared, thou hast done ; and whom all the World hath flattered, thou only hast cast out of the World and despised : thou hast drawn together all the far-stretched Greatness, all the Pride, Cruelty, and Ambition of Man, and covered it all over with these two narrow words, *Hic Jacet*."

To me that is just wonderful.

My stock of anthologies does not stop at *Lyra Heroica*, though there is none I like better. I have *Songs and Ballads of Greater Britain*, compiled by E. A. Helps, formerly one of H.M. Inspectors of Schools. This is a good collection and an eye-opener—and a heart-opener too—to those who think English poetry was all written in England. To me it is curious how prolific the Australians have been. The poetry in this collection is little known. Hardly a name is even familiar, but much of it deserves to be.

This, to a sentimental bookseller, is delicately lovely—

> " The song that once I dreamed about,
>   The tender, touching thing,
> As radiant as the rose without
>   The love of wind and wing—
> The perfect verses, to the tune
>   Of woodland music set,
> As beautiful as afternoon,
>   Remain unwritten yet."

That is by Henry Kendall.

The standard anthologies of poetry and my best sellers in " books of pride " are two Oxford books—the *Oxford Book of English Verse* and the *Oxford Book of Victorian Verse*. These are always in demand and for the lover of poetry they are indispensable. It may be morbid, but my favourite poem (it is in both) is " Non Nobis." The Victorian verse book gives the author as Henry Cust but in the earlier book it is classified as " Anonymous."

" To us thou givest the scorn, the scourge, the scar,
    The ache of life, the loneliness of death,
    The insufferable sufficiency of breath."

That last line—can anyone read it without feeling the tug of the chains that link him to the hours?

I look among my shelves and on my display tables and see that I am well provided for the buyer of anthologies. I know the contents—or some of the contents—of them all. I have Palgrave's *Golden Treasury*—a Routledge edition ; *Heroic and Patriotic Verse* in the Everyman Series ; *The Realm of Poetry*—published by Harrap ; a most interesting introduction to poetry—*The Hundred Best Lyrical Poems* ; and also, for I am up to date, *An Anthology of Modern Verse* which Methuens published last year.

With these I am ready for any customer—if not to sell, at least to tell how good each book is.

I confess I am a modern in poetry in spite of my first loves. If I were young again and I could choose my anthology for the twenties, my choice would be the *Anthology of Modern Verse*. It is modern, for the voice of the men who went to the War is over it, but it is not a voice with a martial note. It is the voice of the fuller experience—the voice of men who saw life so greatly, that they beheld life greatly. It is an anthology of large horizons, and so, I think, I would make it mine if I were twenty to-morrow, and not—an ageing and amateurish seller of anthologies.

I wish I might have a customer now.

I wish it were a youth aged twenty.

I wish he would ask for an anthology.

I wish that I might sell him one, and—perhaps—I would be making history.

POETRY—AND A PUN

A special show of most of my stock of poetry this week has proved a failure. People will buy poetry when it suits them apparently and yet a great paper like the *Observer* prints the following to-day. I have read it twice—once aloud—and I don't make much of it. I will now transcribe it, for writing, says the learned Bacon, maketh an exact man. It is from the *Apology for Poetry* by Sir Philip Sidney, and let it be noted that I haven't the book in stock. It is for my education's sake that I transcribe the quotation.

" Since, then, Poetry is of all human learning the most ancient and of most fatherly antiquity, as from whence other learnings have taken their beginnings ; since it is so universal that no learned nation doth despise it, nor no barbarous nation is without it ; since both Roman and Greek gave divine names unto it, the one of " prophesying," the other of " making " and that indeed that name of " making " is fit for him, considering that whereas other Arts retain themselves within their subject, and receive, as it were, their being from it, the poet only bringeth his own stuff, and doth not learn a conceit out of a matter, but maketh matter for a conceit ; since neither his description nor his end containeth any evil, the thing described cannot be evil ; since his effects be so good as to touch goodness and to delight the learners ; since therein (namely in moral doctrine, the chief of all knowledge) he doth not only far pass the historian, but for instructing, is wellnigh comparable to the philosopher, and, for moving, leaves him behind him ; since the Holy Scripture (wherein there is no uncleanness) hath whole parts in it poetical, and that even our Saviour Christ vouchsafed to use the flowers of it ; since all his kinds are not only in their united forms but in their several dissections fully commendable, I think (and think I think rightly) the laurel crown appointed for triumphing captains doth worthily (of all other learnings) honour the poet's triumph."

Very clotted stuff that !

If poetry were as dull there would be less sale for it even than there is.

My studies go further. Referring to Brewer (2 vols.: Cassell), I add the following to my stores of knowledge. Poet is derived from Greek *poieo*, to make. Poetical justice is that ideal justice which poets exercise in making the good—happy, and the bad—unsuccessful in their schemes.

And now what do I know of poetry?

Nothing.

And what is nothing? Brewer—the Reverend E. Cobham, LL.D., to boot—helps me to the perfect answer, by a poet, too.

" Nothing," wrote William Shakespeare, " is a tune played by the picture of nobody."

" Thou art nothing," says another poet, " thou shalt not be less."

The poetical justice is done and the " ayes " have it.

And I am going to change my window to-night. I will put in biography, war books, a recent purchase of the *Historian's History of the World* in twenty-five volumes, and the *Hundred Best Essays*, by the Earl of Birkenhead. Before going to bed I will put up a prayer for a good sale, the bookseller on his knees for his needs . . .

.   .   .   .

" A pun," said Dr Johnson (was it Dr Johnson now?). . . . " He who would make a pun would pick your pocket." . . .

Happy augury! I will pick pockets to-morrow and give good books in exchange.

AMERICANS AND THEIR BOOKS

America has been getting into my way a lot these last few days. The papers tell me we have signed an agreement with America which will lower the standard of living for a generation. Without being a politician, I would hazard the opinion that that may not be at all a bad thing. " Plain living and high thinking are no more," deplored Wordsworth, but what Wordsworth deplored as gone may be restored by the unwilling act of the signatories to our acknowledgment of the American Debt.

Is it not true anyway that more nations have risen through adversity than through good fortune? Look at the Scots—for example. Anyway, I am not disposed to be alarmed. Alexander Hamilton's descendants may have remembered that he said that " a national debt if it is not excessive will be to us a national blessing," and I hope it will not prove too good a prophecy to be true. But my interest in America is not a banker's interest, although it may be a debtor's. My interest is in American books and to-day I am making a sort of survey of my stock. My survey brought me to recognise how far we have moved from the days when Sydney Smith wrote demanding " Who reads an American book, or goes to an American play, or looks at an American picture or statue? " Pictures we do not have to any extent unless it be on these calendars which American publishers send over here or the picture magazine covers of Harrison Fisher and the cartoons of Bud, but American plays —by what I see when I go to London—are by no means so rarely seen.

And books—American books in my small shop are surprising in number. I have the poets, of course, and sell them to young college girls mostly. Longfellow still sells well—sells best—I think—but there is Whittier and Poe, Whitman and Russell Lowell, all still well to the fore. Poe ought to be more read than he is—and he is the least read of all. " The Raven " and " The Bells " are fine pieces of poetry and surely " Annabel Lee " ought to be known by heart by every lover if he would make the most of the fine—and fortunately fleeting —mirage of love. I would like to have been able to recite such a romance, if I could, about my life as that contained in these four lines :

> " I was a child and she was a child
> In this kingdom by the sea,
> But we loved with a love that was more than love—
> I and my Annabel Lee."

They are magic lines and the whole poem is magical. The

challenge of love to separation and dissolution and death never
rang more clearly in literature than in—

> " But our love, it was stronger by far than the love
> Of those who were older than we—
> Of many far wiser than we—
> And neither the angels in heaven above,
> Nor the demons down under the sea,
> Can ever dissever my soul from the soul
> Of the beautiful Annabel Lee."

Poe, I fear, is old-fashioned and is eclipsed by Ella Wheeler
Wilcox as a " best seller." Her poems—and I am not one of
their deriders for I often read them—are among the best selling
poetry I have. All sorts buy them—men as well as women—
and I am sure they are always worth—and more than worth—
the price they pay for them.

Among the essayists Oliver Wendell Holmes has only had
one inquirer since I came to take over this business. I have
him in the " World's Classics Series." He is worth reading,
and I write a special plea for his remembrance. He would like
it and I will please his memory by recalling the passage from
the " Poet at the Breakfast Table " where he perhaps foresaw
his own dwindling fame and had philosophy enough to face it
and discount it as nothing. " I suppose we all," he writes,
" those of us who write in verse or prose, have the habitual
feeling that we should like to be remembered. It is to be
awake when all of those who were round us have been long
wrapped in slumber. It is a pleasant thought enough that the
name by which we have been called shall be familiar on the
lips of those who come after us, and the thoughts that wrought
themselves out in our intelligence; the emotions that trembled
through our frames shall live themselves over again in the
minds and hearts of others."

And so on—a very gentle—almost lamb-like passage—
discussing the pros and cons of being forgotten and balancing
the two thus : " To become a classic and share the life of a
language is to be ever open to criticisms, to comparisons, to the
caprices of successive generations, to be called into court and

stand a trial before a new jury once or more than once in every
century." The other side is thus put: " To be forgotten
is to sleep in peace with the undisturbed myriads, no longer
subject to the chills and heats, the blasts, the sleet, the dust,
which assail in endless succession that shadow of a man which
we call his reputation. The line which dying we could wish
to blot has been blotted out for us by a hand so tender, so
patient, so used to its kindly task, that the page looks as fair
as if it had never borne the record of our infirmity or of our
transgression."

And again before I leave him, take these sweet waters for
the consolation of most of us: " Not unwelcome shall be the
baptism of dust which hides forever the name that was given
in the baptism of water! We shall have good company whose
names are left unspoken by posterity. Who knows whether
the best of men be known, or whether there be not more
remarkable persons forgot than any that stand remembered in
the known account of time. The greater part must be content
to be as though they had not been: to be found in the register
of God not in the record of man." I do not grudge the transcribing of that, for I want to do my share in keeping the
memory of Oliver Wendell Holmes green on this green earth
for yet a little while longer. He is worth it—and I must
speak to some of the comprehending who come to this shop of
mine about this gentle essayist of the west.

Emerson and Thoreau are favourites still—though not what
they were when I was young. I would make all the schools
have " Self-Reliance " and " Compensations " read regularly.
They inspire me—and I am weak and need the first, sceptical
of providence—sometimes—and need the second—and I am
always the better of re-reading them. Emerson's poetry too,
I have liked since I was a boy, though I have known none
who has shared my liking. I have lost a piece beginning—

> " Teach me your mood, ye patient stars
> That climb each night the ancient sky,
> Leaving no shade, no space, no scars,
> No trace of age nor fear to die."

I have mis-quoted, I think, but that passage somehow links up with Matthew Arnold's

" Calm soul of all things ! make it mine
To feel, amid the city's jàr,
That there abides a peace of thine,
Man did not make, and cannot mar ! "

I have a lot of these mental affinities. I can't account for them. They may be deep calling to deeps across the void of the native emptiness of my own mind.

Anyway they make me humble and grateful.

. . . .

It is days since I wrote these words and I come back to these scattered sheets of shelf paper with a further knowledge of the books of America. I have had an American—a man —who has commended my selection of American novels. Curiously enough, he had never read two of the older American writers and I sold him a set of the Breakfast Table books as well as Nathaniel Hawthorne's *Scarlet Letter*. It is part of the regular recurring surprises of life that an American born and bred should buy his first copies of these authors' works from a simple-minded book vendor in a provincial English town. It has restored my feeling of self-importance and it has made me self-satisfied—a condition I find almost essential to my happiness. This customer put me wise to Edna Ferber and I got her two books, *So Big* and *Fanny Herself*. They sell and I can recommend them. He confirmed my enthusiasm for Joseph Hergesheimer and I offer his books with renewed confidence. Jack London's *White Fang* and *John Barleycorn* have always been books I felt I could speak favourably of to my customers as well as enjoy privately. The first is surely unequalled as an animal book, and the second seems to have had its part in helping to plant prohibition in the States for all the good things it has to say about drink.

I am reminded—another example of one literary allusion leading to another—I am reminded of Mr Dooley's dictum about drink. The Mr Dooley books I haven't got, but they

C

were good and this I always remember. "Drink," said
Mr Dooley, " never made any man better, but it's made millions
of men *think* they were better." I think that is the best case
for Drink I have yet heard, and it is tragic to think that it did
not—with all its sweet reasonableness—stem the tide of frothy
soda-creams and sundaes which is, at present, threatening to
engulf the thinking faculties of our American cousins !

The Letters of a Self-Made Merchant to His Son seem no
longer to be in print and that's a pity. They were good and
they compared well with their successors—the *Five Minutes
Sermons*, does he call them, of Frank Crane? I think that
penman is wise in recognising his readers' patience is limited
to five minutes but he is mistaken as regards me. I have
literally and actually *no time* for Dr Frank Crane—nor indeed
any of his works. There are two American books that I ought
to have mentioned had not Dr Crane awakened my doubtless unwarranted enmity. They are *Walden* by Henry David
Thoreau, and *Jurgen* by James Branch Cabell. I have read
them both. I recommend them often and they are worthy of
any British bookshop and indeed of any British reader. My
shop calls me forth and I go—the thought of a republic of letters
glimmering in the brain of a bookseller whose ideal is to serve
that republic with worthiness and understanding. I am a prig.

Walden and *Jurgen* : what I have written about *Walden*
and *Jurgen* reads fantastically. Surely there was never a more
extraordinary accidental juxtaposition.

Henry David Thoreau pushes off with the mentality of
a Greek philosopher and takes up his abode in the woods
by Walden Pond. Pushing, thrusting, striving, newly born
America goes back—goes farther back—into nature and back
into history as far as mind can take it.

James Branch Cabell, a generation later, in a still more
thrusting, pushing America than the one that Thoreau knew,
goes back too, but not so far back. He goes back to the happy
days of medievalism and there riots gorgeously. Apparently
America-as-it-is is never tolerable for Americans. Thoreau
goes back to Greece—in mind at any rate ; Cabell goes back

to the Middle Ages; and all their fellow-citizens, whenever they have the money, pack up to go east, west and everywhere with all the speed that they can acquire.

I am afraid I am getting to dislike Americans and I must check this weakness in my temperament.

NOTES ON SUICIDE

The subject of suicide is one on which I have no books—not that I have been asked for them—it is my own curiosity which prompts my investigations. The reference books in the Public Library are my only authority, and it is doubtful if such should be made available in a public place if the law is to maintain its consistency.

I have fancied sometimes in these sore days, when the world is too much with us, that a Temple of Euthanasia ought to be erected for those who feel that the time has come for them to go, they having few illusions left. It would be—need one say —a beautiful building, for all who paid their final devoir there would leave, if not all, something substantial to its maintenance. The poor to whom even free justice is denied would have freedom there at last. They would pay no fees.

I plan a temple in a garden. There would be outer courts for those who wanted to say farewell, but these would be a minority. To preserve the peace, a spacious garden—trees surely—would shut off the temple from these and the outer world. There would be no moaning at the bar for those who set out on the deep waters.

There are difficulties in devising the arrangements.

I understand from my studies and inquiries that hanging is the most popular or most frequently practised. Of recent years, gas poisoning has become rather a vogue, but hanging, at least for men, is still the favourite mode.

Women avail themselves of gas and drowning, and it is stated that the highest number of suicides who take to the water is to be found during the months of May, June and July.

Since the War ex-soldiers have resorted largely to firearms, but recently the Home Office has taken very special steps to ensure registration and the giving up of war weapons. Soldiers —serving soldiers—in all countries show a high rate of suicide. It is held that the high rate among men-at-arms is due to the facility with which the means for suicide are available.

The Salvation Army has a Suicide Bureau but no details are made public. There are no other organisations dealing with the problem.

The Church has never been kind to suicides. To die intestate was a grave sin in the Middle Ages—the man who went into the Unknown unshriven had no opportunity to make a gift to the Church before going. They were—these hasty ones—denied Christian burial and the only sign of the cross they knew was the lonely grave at the cross-roads.

Nowadays we are less squeamish. Respect for property is waning, and perhaps it is some consolation to know that there is an increasing inclination among ordinary folk to allow us to do what we like with that most personal of all properties, our breath.

The Law, and then the Church, will come into line before long too, and man will be able to go to his long home when he likes.

I recollect Dr Johnson on suicide. He was asked whether a criminal should commit suicide to avoid arrest.

" Sir, let him go abroad to a distant country : let him go to some place where he is not known. Don't let him go to the Devil where he *is* known."

The quotation is from *Sir, said Dr Johnson*, published by Duckworth. It is a collection of some sayings arranged by C. Biron, published at 6s.; the book is offered at 3s. 6d. by me.

I don't like Johnson on this point. The discussion with Goldsmith on the same subject shows that Johnson did not consider suicide an unmanly or a cowardly act. The subject ought to be discussed more than it has been.

Socrates really committed suicide.

Christ might be said to have set the great example of Willing Death.

He died at the right time.

His work was done.

Did he not say " It is finished "?

Willing Death and this suicide question keep recurring in my mind. I ought not to allow it. It is the sort of road, I imagine, that people go before they actually decide to take their lives. What Dr Johnson has said on suicide is really of no importance to me, and I should really not have troubled to re-write it. Of course, I never asked for life—it is an unsought-for boon as far as I am concerned, and I have been in nothing but trouble since it was given me.

I must break this thread of thought, and to do so I am going to take out my window this morning. It has been in long enough. I will get my cloth, my pail and some water and wash out the bottom of it. These tasks are good for me ; they take my mind away from suicide.

ADDITIONAL NOTES ON SUICIDE

Simpkins publish *Epigrams, compiled by Walter Jerrold*, a handy book to read between times.

This chimes with the mood that caused me to write the foregoing.

ON SUICIDE : *from Martial.*

" When all the blandishments of life are gone,
The coward creeps to death, the brave lives on."
GEORGE SEWELL.

I don't agree.

The man who lives on may be brave but he may also be a glutton.

The suicide says finally to the banquet of life, " Enough."

.   .   .   .

I am demanded by a tall, angular Anglican gentleman for a copy of Dr F. W. Farrar's *Lives of the Fathers*. I have not a copy of this work, which I have subsequently discovered was published by A. & C. Black in two volumes some years ago. The angular Anglican was very severe with me. Apparently through no fault of my own, I did not know of the existence of the work, and he was not as patient with my ignorance as perhaps his profession ought to have made him.

I am revenged, however, in the idleness of an empty forenoon, for I have written twelve lines of verse which I have dedicated to him. Here they are :

> My pride it is my poverty,
>   I own but what I need ;
> A virtue of necessity,
>   It is my only greed.
>
> I have nothing but my longing,
>   My all is my desire ;
> From me thieving is no wronging,
>   Take then what you require.
>
> So rich then is my lowliness,
>   I'm filled with what I've not ;
> Keep you your heights, your holiness ;
>   Mine is the happier lot.

I feel better.

I won't think of suicide again to-day.

A BOOKSELLER ANALYSES HIMSELF

Last night there were fireworks in the street and I slept badly.

How I hate noise ! It was the War that brought it home to me as an intense conviction. The wantonness of it amazes me ! Does it please anyone—really *please* anyone—to let off what they call Chinese Cannons ! I can't believe it, yet so fearfully and wonderfully are we made that hundreds last night congregated in the streets and heralded every explosion with loud shouts of appreciation. A lot has been written about noise and its effects on health, but the writers write in vain. Every day the world around me becomes more and more a *mélange* of clanging and banging, of shouting and grinding, of barking and groaning, of chattering and clattering. The machinery of our modern life obviously creaks, and there is not enough oil in all the wells of all the world to bring it peace and lubrication. Veritably the whole creation of God groaneth and travaileth and there is no Saviour but the hope of a duller sensibility than that with which I have been endowed.

At six I could lie in bed no longer, and with a cup of tea for internal comfort I was away with an apple in one pocket and a book in another. The shop, as I passed through it and out, was close-smelling of print and binding glue and the dust of yesterday, and I did not linger. By seven I was on the crest of the lower ridges of the hills that surround us here and gladness possessed me. The quiet which the night had denied me was here with the morning, and I said aloud, " Here, now in this moment I am at one with the best in the universe. I am happy."

I analysed that feeling. Where was it ? Whence did it come ? Would it have been mine without the Chinese cannonade and the sleep—the bad night and the early rising and the cup of tea and the breath of fresh morning air that met my face as I issued from my shop door ?

I wondered, and wondering left the miracle unsolved in the enjoyment of it.

Back in the shop I have more time (for the book-lookers and book-handlers and book-buyers are not yet about) and I reflect how rarely do we find perfect bliss and happiness. How rarely do we say, " Here and now I am happy "—and yet how often are we visited by unearned, unexpected transports of pure joy.

Do we seek the life ever more abundantly as we should— do we strive once a year even to achieve the Perfect Day? We don't, and yet we should if we are to deserve immortal bliss. How can we deserve eternal happiness living as we live?

I see in a Bunyan-like vision the end of it all. I come after much tribulation before the Great White Throne and before the Judge of all the world. The Recorder reads my record and I am ashamed. The very reading of it sounds like doom and, in my apocalypse, a voice deliberate, slow, inexpressibly final, pronounces my fate.

" Threescore years were yours. You had health enough to be happy. You had time enough to achieve anything. How did you spend your health and time which were the fabric of your daily life?

" I covered my eternal hills in winter with stainless snow : in summer I clothed them in lovely greenness. You heeded them not.

" I filled the skies by day with sunshine and by night I lit them with stars. You heeded them not. The pageant of the seasons I presented year by year for your delight and happiness and every wonder of the world was yours to see.

" You heeded them not.

" There is no need to pronounce your doom, O mortal. You have doomed yourself. You doomed yourself to blindness, to darkness, to oblivion. You doomed yourself to see nothing of the greatness and the glory of God. I do not doom you. Get to that Hell which is your self-appointed, self-chosen, self-desired place."

And so the vision of that Day of Judgment comes and goes. It is the blinding light for me and in its light I make resolution.

I resolve to seek the good life with all the freshness of a new hope. No longer am I going to be satisfied with the second best and the second-hand. I am going to get down to bed-rock. I am going to search for reality. I am going no longer to self-condemn myself to the uttermost oblivion of the uttermost darkness. I will—like Henry David Thoreau—seek " to live deliberately, to front only the essential facts of life . . . I do not wish to live what was not life. Living is so dear. . . ."

I want to " live deep and suck all the marrow of life, to live so sturdily and Spartan-like as to put to rout all that was not life, to cut a broad swathe . . . to drive life into a corner." That's me. . . .

Someone is in the front shop. I know who it is. I know what he wants. I hear him moving about attempting to attract my attention by shuffling his feet and coughing. I know what he wants. He is a small lawyer and he can wait till I write this about him. He is developing schemes to buy up estates cheaply and cut them up and sell them to town dwellers, small farmers and the like. He is an immortal soul and God will damn him for what he is making of his life.

I can't help it. I must go and speak to him. The second-hand copy of *Debrett's Peerage and Titles of Courtesy* is ready for him. The price second-hand is a pound. It is cheap and he will take it. . . .

That was all in the morning at the beginning of the day. Now it is nine and I am an entirely different creature from the man who looked down on this collection of halls, houses, churches and slums in which I live and have what may be called my being. Ten hours have passed since I attempted to put down the ecstasy of the freshness of the new day which so began for me.

I can't see myself as I was then at all. Food has done it. I shut the shop at seven and read parts of a parcel of new books

that came in by the afternoon delivery. What a lot of rubbish
is written and what a lot of that rubbish is laboriously read
by publishers and printed by compositors and sold by booksellers! I will not add to it. That ambition is dead whatever
else lives, dead—still-born if you like—as a result of the unsuitable mating of Too Big Ambition with Too Little Will.
Content—gross, fleshy, material—now possesses me and food
begat it.

At eight I tired of reading trash and put the smaller of my
two pans on the gas stove. I cut up four tomatoes into segments
and put them into the pan, with a piece of butter. I take
two eggs and break them into a cup, switching them up with a
fork. The tomatoes and the butter sizzle agreeably and a hot
sparkling of fat rises up into the air from the heated pot. I
pour my switched eggs over the tomatoes. Quickly the mixture
solidifies and I tip it out on my plate. It is delicious, and now
with a pipe in my teeth I am as sublimely happy as I have
ever been.

It all eludes me as it has eluded all of us who have ever
thought of the strangeness of being.

What am I?

Filled with the wonder and the beauty of nature, I am at
one with the joy of the universe. Filled with tomatoes and eggs,
I am at one with life and am content. . . . It comes to me
and it will do for an ending to these sheets I have written
to-day.

"Only the infinite pity is equal to the infinite pathos of
human life."

A HIGH CALLING

I am sorry for my neighbour, the draper. His trade is a dis-
enchanting one. He cannot feel romantic about women. He
only sees them, at worst, as creatures seeking to adorn them-

selves ; at best, as naked obscene animals to whom shame has come, seeking to clothe themselves and hide their indecencies.

I am sorry for my friend, the butcher. His trade is a dis-enchanting one. Food, the three times repeated daily joy, is for him a dull affair. The ecstasy of appetite is an affair of trade. He only sees mankind as a mob of perambulating bellies needing to be filled.

I am proud of my trade of bookselling.

It is enchanting.

It is romantic.

It is as wonderful as the world and as illimitable as the universe.

It makes lovely women lovelier.

It makes the commonest victuals the very food of the gods.

It is a high calling.

POETRY BOOKS AND POEMS

" I want a book—a book of poetry—something for a girl." The request was put to me rather diffidently for all the bluff ruddiness of the speaker. It left me speechless for a moment. How do I know what books of poetry young girls like? How do I know that girls like poetry at all? My hesitancy was apparent to my customer and his words went on again. " She is a junior hockey international," he added. There is no reason but decision came with the abruptness of the falling of the guillotine. " *Masefield*," I said, " the new complete edition of *Masefield*."

He looked at the book. " I don't know his work at all," he said. I turned the pages—for I knew the book well. I hesitated at " Sea Fever "—passed by " Cargoes "—and stopped at " Beauty." " Read that," I said. " I think any girl would think that wonderful." I took the book out of his hand and showed him " C.L.M."—the thing that begins :

> " In the dark womb where I began
> My mother's life made me a man."

He read it through—and some of his ruddiness seemed less coarse when he got to the end. I could see, though he held the book above the level of my eyes—I could see when he read " O grave, keep shut lest I be shamed." I knew he had no wife now. I knew he had only one daughter. I knew I would sell him *Masefield* for that daughter.

" I'll have it," he said quite shortly.

" There is just one other I would like you to look at : it is quite short."

I turned to " The Centurions " and took his eight and six away to my till while he read it. There was one and sixpence change. When I handed it to him he took it quite blankly. He turned on his heel. His finger in the book at the page on which " The Centurions " is printed—he walked out of my shop.

Who would believe it—the emotions that may come to struggling booksellers? I don't know the man. He was a stranger—come, I fancy, to see his daughter at the Young Ladies' College here, and Masefield and I marked him to-day.

What is in poetry that makes it so wonderful a thing? I don't know, but it makes me feel the awful strangeness of men. How incalculable we are ! If I had said Browning and shown him " Love among the Ruins," would the effect have been the same? Has he read " O Mistress Mine ! where are you roaming ?—O ! stay and hear your true love's coming " ; and if not, would these words of Shakespeare's have had the same effect?

Ought I not to have sold him the *Oxford Book of English Verse* or its companion the *Book of Victorian Verse*?

The responsibilities of bookselling are immense. I shudder and almost cower now down by my shelves of business books. My eyes find repose on a shelf of Sir Isaac Pitman's Industrial Administration Series.

There is no certainty.

There is no sense of the unfathomable immensities. There one can hand out one's wares without a tremor. Whose soul is shaken from now till the end of time by Mr James A. Bowie's book *Sharing Profits with Employees* or Samuel Crowther's *Commonsense and Labour*?

These are not dynamite nor yet quicksilver. They may be the substantial bricks from which the New Jerusalem is to be builded, but they certainly feel no more than mere bricks to my hands. . . .

Poetry—I write the word. The experience is still fresh with me and I come back to this back shop of mine to turn over my mind. I see myself : a collection of moving molecules, I suppose mostly putrefying : a sort of thickish slime on the surface of matter in which moves and stirs an emotion—a thought—a dulled formless radiance responsive and throbbing still to the moments when I turned these pages for my customer. It is quite inexplicable. I sit buttoned in my clothes, thatched over inadequately with hair, faintly moist.

My little room is too painfully cramped and little, and I go out again restless to my shop . . .

I always like Arnold Bennett for recommending *Aurora Leigh*. It is good poetry to me and suits what literary stomach I have rather better than his other recommendation, *Paradise Lost*. His book *How to Live on Twenty-four Hours a Day* was one of the great stimulants of my disordered youth. I have my own edition, published by the New Age Press in 1908. I get it down to read again. " Poetry," says Bennett, " is the highest form of literature. It yields the highest form of pleasure and teaches the highest form of wisdom."

I am all for the narrative poets in a way. What better than the *Lays of Ancient Rome* or the *Lays of the Scottish Cavaliers* or the longer poems of Sir Walter Scott?

I am not a *vers libre* man. I like rhyme and recollect Samuel Taylor Coleridge's declaration, " I wish our clever young poets (there were clever young poets then as now) would remember my homely definitions—of prose and poetry,

' Prose is words in their best order. Poetry is the *best* words in the best order.' "

To a bookseller poetry is a problem. There are some poets in regular demand, but there are no very complete series. The *Padded Poets* were very useful stock but folk don't take to these to-day. Macmillan's Globe Library is useful to me, and for a good Shakespeare I sell Dent's Edition in three volumes. As a rule I don't like pictures in books. Leave the ideas to the writer and his reader, I think—but in this instance I can make an exception. The other pictures do not move me, but the picture of the *Histories* volume is an astounding thing. It hasn't been noticed by anyone as far as I have ever heard—I mean by anyone of importance. It attempts and succeeds in showing us the idea behind the sonnets. The traditional William Shakespeare—a young William Shakespeare in high collared cloak and with a doublet with point embroidered cuffs —is pulling a curtain over the face and figure—hiding from us the mysterious " Mr W. H." This remarkable picture is by E. J. Sullivan, a fine illustrator.

For the rest, poetry is a passing thing. Benn's *Sixpenny Poets* was a work of national importance for which Sir Ernest Benn deserved a baronetcy had he not already inherited one. These paper-covered leaflets, I wager, gave and give more joy than all the legislation passed since the War. They must have opened the door of poetry to thousands, and I know in my little way I have sold hundreds.

Instead of raising the school age or raising the pay for teachers or building bigger schools, my politics are to give prizes and subsidies for good books. We have the Hawthornden prize for authorship—why not a prize for publishing? I am all for giving honour to the writer, but I know the courage that goes to make a publisher. These writers think themselves brave figures on the boards of life, but they would be poor ghosts but for the bold publisher who bodies them forth. If poets had to make their living by reciting to living ears, the calling would cease to be a drawing-room one. The publisher saves these shy creatures that shock to their sensitive souls, and they are not always as grateful as they might be for it.

Of the service booksellers render to poets and poetry I will make no claim here. I am going out to walk and recite to myself all the poetry I remember. The flagstones shining after rain will find voice in me. I will be the expression of absolute poetry which is defined, I see, in a book of reference as " the concrete and artistic expression of the human mind in emotional and rhythmical language." In a few minutes, then, one human mind will be expressing itself in emotional and rhythmical language. I will be saying over The Hundredth Psalm from the Scottish Psalter, " The Road to Mandalay," " Cynara," " Non Nobis," the passage from *The Tempest* beginning " Our revels now are ended," Gray's " Elegy " (I can say it all), Swinburne's " The Pilgrims," that shortest poem in the English language by W. N. Ewer, some of the " Shropshire Lad," a good whack of the " Song of the Open Road," Masefield's " Beauty "—I will say all these between the planets and the pavement, and when I come home none surely will deny that I am a qualified bookseller—qualified if not to pen at least to peddle poetry. . . .

My poets' walk ended in a pub last night and I went to bed fuddled. I fear it was a poor ending to a day lived so much with thoughts of poetry.

I commiserate myself. I do it easily.

If only people knew me as I know myself, life would be more endurable. I am not at all a bad fellow, really. I was always the most popular man in my platoon in France. These seemed to be—in the happy halo of the unreturning past— poetic days. I used to recite then, but none of the things I recited last night. The favourite was a piece called " Lasca," which a Scotsman always thought had something to do with Glasgow—a place which for him was the very home of poetry and romance. It was hardly a classic piece, but I must confess that my other piece, the " Speech " by Cassius, " Honour is the subject of my story," used to go as well. For a while I was called Cassius, but the later phases of the Battles of the

Somme took away those who knew my fame, and use and wont returned to my abbreviated surname.

This morning I feel the poetic is not at all a durable fabric. It is not like some of the goods my neighbour is displaying to-day—guaranteed to wash and wear.

It is, alas !—and God be thanked—" the stuff that dreams are made on," but, in Army phraseology, at the worst " it will always do me " in this little life which is so smoothly " rounded with a sleep."

REPRIEVE

How is it that in retrospect the late War seems pleasant to remember ? I was free from anxiety about food or drink or indeed anything. Who worries about a future that seems not at all likely to be his ? We had our hour.

It is stand-to.—We will surely live till they bring up the dixies with the tea and the dirty bacon in the lids.

It is between eleven and twelve.

In the support line, the mess orderlies can be heard putting round the stew.

We will last till then.

It is four.—Tea will be round very soon and cigarettes will come up after dark.

We will live till then.

And so we went round the clock.

Life was an immediate thing and infinitely precious. We had it. We held it. We might part so soon, but we had it and

" Over the past not even the gods have power,
  To-morrow do thy worst—for I have had my hour."

That was very often my feeling. It supported me wonderfully.

But there were other times.

Once in the salient in front of Zonnebeke they plastered

us with the big stuff for hours. We were ordered out into " No-Man's-Land " after many casualties, and I remember clawing myself into the side of a shell hole in terror. My belly was quivering and, if I had had to stand erect, it would have fallen out, I felt.

I prayed.

If I were spared I would be different.

I would repent . . . I would never again . . .

I would be better . . .

I asked in Gethsemane depths that not this time . . .

At six the bombardment stopped, and digging a new trench that night I was chaffing and bold and gay.

I had been reprieved.

BOOKS ABOUT FOOD AND DRINK

There is nothing that I know of in literature that deals with headaches. Burns I know, with his " Address to the tooth-ache—thou hell o' a' diseases " I think he writes—but no one else has impressed my memory with their words on pain. There's a book which I remember Conan Doyle makes Dr Watson refer to in the Sherlock Holmes Series—*The Mystery of Pain* by James Hinton, but I have never handled it. My headaches are the consequence of ill dieting, I sometimes think, and yet I have never been able to find the road to right diet. The doctor I go to see is an excellent fellow but cannot cure anything. He almost admits it. Dr Diet, Dr Quiet and Dr Merryman, in his opinion, are too big a consultative party. He thinks little of Dr Diet—a good varied dietary, some-thing of everything ; he knows nothing of Dr Quiet ; and as for Dr Merryman, one man's jokes are another man's despair.

After a day of headaches I took to looking through my

books for a remedy. My first—not an acrostic—is *Diet for Men*, written by a doctor whose description of himself some-how amused me. (My head perhaps is weak still from the headaches.) Here it is—" *Diet for Men*, by Cecil Webb Johnson, M.B., Ch.B., Major R.A.M.C. (T.F.), late Civil Sur-geon and Officer Commanding Station Hospital, Dum-Dum; Surgeon in charge of Native Cantonment and Followers' Hospital, Dum-Dum; Specialist in Midwifery, Diseases of Women and Children, 8th (Lucknow) Division. With an illustration."

This writer has also written *Diet for Women*, with two illustrations, and *How not to be Fat*, apparently, very mercifully, with no illustrations. According to the publishers' announce-ment facing the title-page, the first of these books wrung from the *Daily Chronicle* the following encomium : " Useful and entertaining, he has done brave service to our sex " ; while the *Daily Graphic* is allowed only one word, an ecstatic one in its description of the work—the one word " Splendid." I haven't *Diet for Women* in my stock, nor yet have I *How not to be Fat*, but I will procure both from Simpkins with alacrity, if any one desires them.

I return to my *Diet for Men* lest before the afternoon is out I sell it to a dyspeptic. It is readable enough, and what more do booksellers expect from their books? It isn't a faddist book —the author disclaiming that on his first page ; but there is not much in it for a man who is laid out and laid low by head-aches once or twice a week. That bang on the head I had in the War may have deranged—or disordered—would that be a better word?—the cortex. It was a funny sensation. I never heard the shell coming. I was blown up in the air and fell— I felt—on the *pavé*. My own impression was that I was bumped on the back of the head but the mark was on my right forehead.

Dr Webb Johnston doesn't help much with such a headache any more than his colleagues did in the R.A.M.C. at the time. In fact they never admitted that the headaches were due to external action—they blamed my liver and perhaps they were right, for the guess of a doctor may be as near the truth as that of any other man !

I am prone to liver disorders, I fancy, for I am fond of food. I am a gorger at times—a glutton—and yet it is a bookman's fault. Hear Macaulay on Doctor Samuel Johnson—a bookman and the son of a bookseller like myself. I quote from the essay in the *Encyclopædia Britannica*, 1881 edition, a set of which I will sell bound, half calf, slightly rubbed, for three guineas. I feel like—and for—Johnson as I write it.

" Being often very hungry when he sat down to his meals, he contracted a habit of eating with ravenous greediness. Even to the end of his life and even at the tables of the great the sight of food affected him as it affects wild beasts and birds of prey. His taste in cookery formed in subterranean ordinaries and *à la mode* beef shops was far from delicate. Whenever he was so fortunate as to have near him a hare that had been kept too long or a meat pie made with rancid butter, he gorged himself with such violence that his being swelled and the moisture broke out on his forehead."

My dear, delicate Thomas Babington Macaulay, how disgusted you were ! I can feel it and yet I forgive you, for you never knew what it was " to contract a habit "—a habit, mark you, " of eating with ravenous greediness."

I am afraid there were other reasons for Macaulay's dislike, though his essay on Johnson is the best thing he wrote, to my mind. He disliked Tories as much as Johnson disliked Whigs. The first Whig was the devil, declares Johnson. Macaulay's counter is a glancing blow but it shows the temper of the mind behind it. " He (Johnson) was himself a Tory, not from rational conviction . . . but from mere passion."

I hope these twain have made it up in the Elysian Fields where hack writers hunger and thirst no more and finicking essayists are at rest.

Food—eaten ravenously or delicately—is a great topic none the less. It is the only pleasure that recurs three times a day and its only equal is sleep which comes too with such satisfying regularity.

My odd lot of books on food is good—mostly second-hand but all worth while. I prefer to sell a cookery book to a novel. I rate my art high.

Here are some of my selection of books on food and drink. *Book of the Table*, published by Kettners, the restaurant people, with a dedication to George Augustus Sala ; *Why not Grow Young?* by Robert Service—a book on diet and health ; Marcel Boulestin's *Simple French Cookery for English Homes ; Eating without Fears*, by G. F. Scotson-Clark—a very jolly book by a *bon viveur* ; and a *Manual of Modern Cookery*—a good practical book published by—no less—the University of London Press.

The *Gentle Art of Cookery* and Lady Jekyll's *Kitchen Essays* I also have. They are good works, and probably these two books have done as much for the post-war homes of England (how beautiful they stand) as the Treaty of Versailles. Joseph Conrad's wife, too, has a good book in my collection—the introduction to which was written by her husband. The opening paragraph in my present phase of industry I will transcribe, for who knows I may sell it on the morrow to one who would win her husband's love for a mess of pottage !

" Of all the books produced (writes the author of the *Arrow of Gold*) since the most remote ages by human talents and industry, those only that treat of cooking are, from a moral point of view, above suspicion. The intention of every other piece of prose may be discussed and even mistrusted ; but the purpose of a cookery book is one and unmistakable. Its object can conceivably be no other than to increase the happiness of mankind."

Conrad admits that he had found it impossible to read through a cookery book (even his wife's), but comes forward modestly and gratefully as " a Living Example of her practice."

Note the capitals.

I think this occasion is the only one where Conrad uses them and, be it noted, he used them to apostrophise himself.

I have a very old edition in my stock, the title-page of which I will also transcribe :

The
Art of Cookery
made
Plain and Easy
to which are added
One hundred and fifty
new receipts,
a copious INDEX,
and
a Modern Bill of Fare, for each month
in the manner the dishes are placed
upon the Table
by H. Glasse
Edinburgh
printed for Alexander Donaldson,
sold at his shops (no. 48) in St Paul's Churchyard,
London and Edinburgh
MDCCLXXIV.

Here is a well told-tale—heading and all—from page 230 :

"To MAKE AN EGG AS BIG AS TWENTY.

"Part the yolks from the whites, strain them both separate through a sieve, tie the yolks up in a bladder in the form of a ball. Boil them hard, then put this ball into another bladder, and the whites round it ; tie it up oval fashion and boil it. These are used for grand sallads. This is very pretty for a ragoo, boil five or six yolks together, and lay in the middle of the ragoo of eggs ; and so you may make them of any size you please."

Isn't that fine? The price of the book is five shillings and cheap.

Old Cookery Books and Ancient Cuisine is an oddity and I am afraid bad stock. A know-all of a school teacher made me get it for him as he thought it was by William Hazlitt. It is by W. Carew Hazlitt and is in the Booklovers' Library, published in 1902. I would sell it willingly. My customer wouldn't take it—and perhaps unfairly I haven't taken to it either.

The best book I have of this eating and drinking sort is George Saintsbury's *Notes on a Cellar Book*. It is a third edition but signed by the Professor himself. It is all so good that I fear the day it may be bought—in fact I doubt if I would part with it. Hear the bold full-blooded honest man :

" There is no money, among that which I have spent since I began to earn my living, of the expenditure of which I am less ashamed, or which gave me better value in return, than the price of the liquids chronicled in this booklet. When they were good they pleased my senses, cheered my spirits, improved my moral and intellectual powers, besides enabling me to confer the same benefits on other people. And whether they were bad or good, the grapes that had yielded them were fruits of that Tree of Knowledge which, as theologians too commonly forget to expound, it became not merely lawful but incumbent on us to use, with discernment, when our First Mother had paid the price for it, and handed it on to us to pay for likewise."

My headache is gone. I have taken my cachet and drunk a cup of tea. I will go out. I feel righteous. I feel good. I will test the prophecy " for he hath filled the hungry with good things ; and the rich he hath sent empty away."

I have faith. I will be filled with good things and will praise the Lord for His goodness and for His wonderful works to the children of men.

BUSINESS BOOKS, BOOKS ON POLITICS, Etc.

Enter a middle-aged man, advance the bookseller into the centre. The bookseller bows. " I want *The Dolly Dialogues*— the best edition." The bookseller gropes around his shelves. He has no good edition of the book—he knows—he only has a good clean second-hand Nelson (pre-war) Sevenpenny and this he produces.

" Good Lord, is that the only edition ? " " It is the only edition I've got," I admit. (I drop the third person.) .·

He was annoyed, but he hadn't time and I couldn't say where a better edition could be got, so he bought the one I offered. Then comes the astonishing thing. He gave me an address to which the book was to be posted, an address here—and further—instructions to stick an inscription on the front of it. Here is the inscription he gave me to put in—I thought it rather nice and wished I knew the recipient.

Lines to accompany *The Dolly Dialogues*—

"Life aches sometimes . . . and always will,
The best of us it cannot fill ;
We crave for more than empty days
Of languor or of vacant praise.

"This book is good ; not great, you know,
But quite well done as these things go ;
I give it ; so when dull care dogs,
Throw in his teeth—these Dialogues."

He was a little abashed and, to prove to me he was really the sensible man he looked, he picked up a couple of books which were in a shilling case I sometimes display. He bought both : Ernest J. P. Benn's *The Trade of To-morrow*, and Arthur Kitson's *Trade Fallacies*. Both books are old stock—I think they were published during the war but my customer paid his half-crown—two shillings for business and sixpence for *Dolly*, and—went.

These business men are wonderful and there should be a market for a British "Babbitt," if there is a British Sinclair Lewis anywhere. Their neat-tailored appearance—and their wild sentimental minds—their dull businesses and entertaining typists—their Rotary societies and their would-be romantic adventures—what curiosities they are ! I would be a collector of them and certainly the one who in his mind married Anthony Hope's *The Dolly Dialogues* (with a poetical presentation on the fly-leaf) to Arthur Kitson's *Trade Fallacies* will take first position and a high place in the prize list.

My lot of business books become more entertaining when I dwell on these possibilities. What may be the upshot of a sale of my others and how strangely are they to be joined by the purchaser ! Of course business books are hardly books at all. I rarely buy them deliberately—they come in the lots I

get at the sales—I have to take them in private purchases—
and not a few I order specially for customers who fail to claim
their orders or who, when they see the book they ordered,
think better of it. I don't blame them !

I had a man the other day—it was more truthfully months
ago—who ordered *Progressive Co-partnership* published by
Nisbet. He didn't like it when he saw it, and yet what is
wrong with it? If one is interested, I am sure Mr Ernest
Walls can tell one as much as any. It is dedicated by the author
to his wife—which is always touching—and he writes in his
preface that a business man, who has written a book, for
example, " is quite certain to be called a hypocrite, if he does
not happen to practise in his own business everything he may
preach in his book." I will not call him a hypocrite anyway.
It was quite entertaining to read of Godin and Leclaire, of the
Gas Companies and Lever Brothers—not that I can fancy a
co-partnership world in which I would care to live. I am for
the individualist camp. I am more taken with the bold *Case
for Capitalism* or the *Confessions of a Capitalist*. These are
more the stuff I like to read if I have to read business books.

Co-partnerships and co-operations at best produce herds of
well-fed contented folk, and this world may have little meaning,
but the best of mankind somehow feel it was not for that we
have dragged ourselves up from the slime of the primeval seas.

Books about business and politics are really toy books.
Business men cannot scan the immensities eternally. Poets do
that and go mad or die of drink. Business men have to plan
the narrow business of food and drink and shelter, and there
is a literature which is all theirs. I do not despise it : indeed
I have definitely often bought books which have that appeal.

In political economy, I have Mill and Adam Smith—both
readable—both books which, if studied, would make any of us
wiser than any Prime Minister I have lived under or seen.

I have another work on political economy, too, of which I
am specially proud. It is quite unreadable and I am sure
unsaleable. I often take it down and look at it. I leave it
about to tempt people but it is as unreadable as a cuneiform

inscription. The book is *On the Principles of Political Economy and Taxation*, by David Ricardo, Esq., Second Edition : London, John Murray, Albemarle Street, 1819. It has a back and covers of green leather—is in excellent condition (never having been read) and it is really beautifully printed. I do like David Ricardo, Esq. No publisher dare write Michael Arlen, Esq., or even Rudyard Kipling, Esq., to-day. The book is on offer at one shilling.

Its companion, although I had it in a different lot—a parcel from Dublin—is simply labelled in gilt *Speeches*. The binding is white vellum : the boards are of faded marble paper on incredibly stout cardboard. It contains the speeches of The Right Honourable George Canning, The Right Honourable William Huskisson, and " the substance of the speech " (so the title-page reads) " of Francis Jeffrey, Esq., upon introducing the toast, Freedom of Labour, but let the labourer recollect that in exercising his own rights, he can not be permitted to violate the rights of others."

The dreary speech was published—it is almost unbelievable—" at the request of the meeting," and printed for Archibald Constable & Company. It is " sold by all the booksellers in London, Glasgow, Leeds, Manchester, Birmingham, Sheffield, Aberdeen, Dublin, Newcastle-on-Tyne, Perth, Newcastle, Hull, and Liverpool." The two Newcastles is not a mistake, and I make bold to say, of all the booksellers who sold it in 1825 I am the only one with a copy to-day.

The price again is one shilling.

I got up from all this writing infinitely weary. Is there nothing of vivid interest in this world of politics and books of business? I read their names over :

An Economist's Protest	Cannan
The State as a Farmer . . ' . . .	Radford
Welfare Work	Proud
The Social Contract	Rousseau
An Introduction to the Study of Prices .	Layton

My knees weaken.

My head is dizzy.

I am overcome with the miseries of mankind and the dreariness of the roads along which they travel in pursuit of the mirage of happiness.

BLUE BOOKS

" I want a set of blue books."

" I don't keep any," I replied, " but I will procure what you want from the Stationery Office. What is the subject? "

" The subject? " the dame echoed, " the subject doesn't matter. I want them in blue."

The conversation was not so intelligible as what I have written but, at length, I grasped, with the help of a piece of blue tapestry which my customer had in her hand, that it was books of a certain shade of blue binding that she desired— books to match her carpet and the curtains of her drawing-room.

I was fortunate and, when my mind had coped with the initial absurdity of the idea of buying books for the colour of their binding, I found her an easy and a profitable client.

My hope is that one day she may look in these blue books and find some of the salvation which I have found in literature.

Here are some blue books, all of which now occupy a neat rack book-box on a drawing-room table which I will never see ! Kenneth Grahame's *Wind in the Willow* (Methuen), *The Moon and Sixpence*, by W. S. Maugham (Cape), *The Misses Mallett*, by E. H. Young (Cape), *The Travel Letters of Lady Mary Wortley Montagu* (Cape), and—to complete the list— the shade of blue is perfect—five volumes of Duckworth's *Popular Library of Art*.

I am a house decorator really as well as a bookseller. I decorate minds and rooms. My friend next door decorates bodies but he is no artist.

BOOKS, BOOKBINDING AND BUSINESS MEN

Re-reading what I have written about business men and business books, I feel I have been too hard on what must be a growing part of the bookseller's business. We ought to be glad that this important section of the community is interested in books. They were not ever thus—pride ruled their will; they could not abide the opinions of others, but now they are like us all, teachable and willing to learn. If they bring their simplicity into the curious and tortuous world of books, we must be tolerant.

An inquiry from a well-known and well-to-do man prompts this attempt at recantation. Among many friends, I have one in the house-furnishing business, and it is at his suggestion that my customer has called on me. He has a library in dark mahogany, with a deep-piled black carpet and hangings,—a rich handsome room with great high windows. His idea is that books should all be bound in vellum—the old yellowing vellum of which I have only one sample—my volume of *Speeches*.

My customer is right—the effect of walls filled with books bound with old vellum will be very attractive and I am to quote for the binding. He has quantities of books and some are unworthy of rebinding—unworthy in paper, printing and contents, but it is his wish and I hope to get the order.

Bookbinding is dear—bookbinding to order, that is—and I think it is a pity. It is one of the trades which might be developed, for most booksellers will agree that some modern bookbinding is very bad.

Apropos of this bookbinding order—or the prospect of it rather—my house-furnishing friend related the story of the self-made man from Glasgow (or was it Liverpool?) who ordered a library. " How will you have the books bound? " asked the bookseller—a better man than I to have thought of that. " Bound? " demanded the buyer, " I want the best binding."

" We will have them bound in morocco," then said the book-seller as if to decide that point finally. " Not at all," thundered the man of business, " bound in Morocco, why the devil should I have them bound in Morocco? I've made my money in Glasgow (or was it Liverpool?) and I'll have my books bound in Glasgow."

I think it a good story but business men are not really like that. I think they don't get the amount of respect the community should give them, but perhaps the community, having given them its cash, feels they are well paid.

Democracy acts always with emphasis, but its acts are often at variance with and contrary to its expression through the ballot box. Democracy at the ballot box repudiates big business, but in its hour-to-hour life it pays tribute. Lord Rothermere (who seems to receive an (to me) unmerited amount of abuse in certain quarters) receives a homage which kings might envy. Every morning over one million and a half citizens say definitely " Here, my Lord, is my tribute." " Here, I render to Caesar the things which are Caesar's by right of conquest." " Here I freely accord you *my* penny for *your Daily Mail*."

The other leaders of democracy may gnash their teeth, but if they are real democrats they will not deny that something less unstable than the popular vote goes—not once in a year or so but every day in the week—to one whom they in their ignorance think only a Press Lord.

The great newspapers command wider suffrages on harder terms than do the great politicians.

Who would pay a penny a day—day after day—to hear what Mr Baldwin, Mr Macdonald or Mr Lloyd George has to say?

ALMOST AN ADVERTISEMENT

How dull and flat was yesterday! It rained. There was a sour smell from my backyard. The cat was out all night and I had to get out of bed to let her in by the door—she scratched and miaowed so loudly.

There were unpleasant letters in both morning and afternoon post.

A man from a debt-collecting and dunning society called on me.

No day could be duller or more miserable.

And yet.

This morning I have read the *Daily Mail* over my cocoa. I am warmed with the feeling how wonderful life was yesterday —to *the young men on the " Daily Mail."*

I was depressed and downcast—but what bright happenings they found in London—in Bury St Edmunds—in Nice and in Tokio—*these young men on the " Daily Mail."*

I was dunned for debt and badgered by creditors but they found men and women gloriously independent—even profligate —*these young men on the " Daily Mail."*

My life yesterday was Hell—and I thought that the whole creation was groaning and travailing with me.

This morning I know it was a foul pestilential illusion. Life yesterday was really large—gay—expanding—glorious—*to the young men on the " Daily Mail."*

Selah.

BOOKS ON TRAVEL AND GUIDE-BOOKS

To-day I have been looking at a book called *The Happy Traveller*. It is written by a vicar and it is sub-titled " A Book for Poor Men." I see it has gone through many editions. I had to get the book for a young man who has great possessions, and as my dead mother used to say, " He doesn't know what he would be at." His, I suppose, is a sad story. His father was a self-made business man who made a big fortune by his own efforts from very small beginnings but who died of overwork and worry in the early 'fifties. He left a wife who is an incurable invalid and one son. They are rich—very rich—but John is bound to his mother's bedside. He was brought up soft—and solitary. He has no calling. He is kindly and affectionate. He loves his mother uncritically—she is the only creature he knows. She is dependent on him for company—indeed, for everything except money—and there they are. John fancies he would travel—he hurled a chunk of Kipling at me the second time I saw him—but his mother can't, and he can't leave her. He is tied to his mother's apron-strings—not literally, for she doesn't wear an apron. (Where are they gone—these lovely aprons to whose strings a man might be happily tied? I remember my mother had a black satin apron—a pleasing thing—so sedate—so comforting—a veritable lap of luxury.)

The Happy Traveller is a good book to read even if one never travels. It seems to be written by a man who knows how. It is practical rather than romantic. It is Baedeker or Muirhead rather than Walt Whitman, but John will never act on its counsels. He will stay and be faithful unto death, and may very probably be married by the capable nurse who just now manages the household for both of them.

Travel books are not in great demand with me. One can't keep everything, and the would-be travellers I see come in so impetuously that I am always taken unawares. Who, for example, among all the booksellers keeps *The Canary Islands : Their History, Natural History, and Scenery*—an account of an ornithologist's camping trips in the Archipelago? I had it a fortnight ago—specially procured for a queer bird (no pun intended) who told me to get it for him. The book costs him (not me!) thirty shillings and I would not have you think lightly of it. The pictures—plain and coloured—are extremely good —ranging from " Washing Clothes at Guimar " to a coloured drawing of " Canarian [strange word] Titmice." It is a book written by an ornithologist but his interests fly wide of mere birds. There is history and geology in the book—a real entertainment for a man like me who now will never travel.

I want to travel all the same. Books—dare I write the

heterodoxy of my trade, the sin for which a good bookseller ought to go to the stake—yes—" Books are a mighty poor substitute for life."

In the dullish hour that followed my tea I went over my travel books—the local guides, the Blue Guides, a few Baedekers, Ward Lock's Tourist Handbooks and so on. Then my pilgrimage took me to *The Sentimental Journey*, and I felt thrilled with Belloc's *The Path to Rome* and John Gibbon's *Tramping to Lourdes*.

Would the real journeying thrill me so much? I doubt it. Too many " Cooks " have spoiled the broth and birds of a feather too much flock together for a lonely and solitary-loving bookseller.

At the end of the day I wrote this poem. The dilemma which lies astride my mind after these thoughts all day on books of travel finds expression. As I wrote it I was a boy again in the house in which I was born, yearning for the big world yet at bottom fearful of leaving the home I knew.

> " I want to travel : see the strange—
> The wonderful : I want to range
> The roads and sail those seas they say
> Are God's—and yet I want to stay
> Here, in this house, so close, so small,
> Marking the fungus on the wall,
> Peering at flies and bumble-bees,
> Staring at birds and watching trees,
> Small mysteries of death and birth,
> All things tiny : all things small,
> I want to understand them all—
>
> " —And yet the great large world, it calls me too,
> What is a silly fool like me to do ? "

What's a silly soul like me to do? Go to bed and pray that that old bird will call for his book on the Canary Islands to-morrow !

.   .   .   .

Some days later I find this sheet of paper partly written on top of what is now a growing pile in this cupboard. He came—

the ornithologist—and got his book. He paid for it, for which I was glad. He might go a long way away and forget about me and my bills which I have to meet for the books I sell. The same day I sold a *Tennyson* by asking a young man if he had read "Ulysses." He hadn't, and I sent him away with the Globe Edition of *Tennyson*. I think "Ulysses" somehow quite out of Tennyson's line though I am sure it is unequalled.

When my youthful customer had gone—he bought an Edgar Wallace and a Phillips Oppenheim—I reproached myself for not having shown him Walt Whitman's *Leaves of Grass*, *The Week-End Book*, *The Sentimental Journey*, *The Footpath Way*, *The Open Road*, *The Path to Rome*, *Tramping to Lourdes*. I have them all in stock. . . .

I reproached myself, but now I reproach myself for greed. It was that desire to sell that made me reproach myself. Damnation! I am becoming a shopman. I must remember my high calling. I am a bookman, not a bookseller.

.   .   .   .

He will come again. With "Ulysses" he "cannot rest from travel."

"QUITE"

Of course I feel life is futile. I feel how little God knows mankind if He offers us as a prize life eternal. Who wants more of what they have already had too much?

I write these blasphemous things because I think them. I feel better now. A lawyer has been in and told me he values my opinion on books more than the reviews. He says I have a feeling for books. I recommended him *Buddenbrooks* and *Magic Mountain* and he enjoyed them apparently.

I am not sure that life eternal would be so distasteful to me. I would be congenially circumstanced. I would be clothed (of course) and in my right mind. I would be understood. It is so terrible not being understood. This man keeps saying to me when I blather about myself and what I think of books, " I understand—I understand."

When I am unusually chaotic and it is obvious I don't at all understand myself, he is equal to the occasion. He then almost unctuously says, " Quite."

And after a pause he says again, " Quite."

Balm in Gilead could not be more gratifying than the benignity of that second " Quite."

THE " LIVES OF GREAT MEN
ALL REMIND US "

Longfellow was great on that—with his " lives of great men all remind us we can make our lives sublime, and, departing, leave behind us footprints on the sands of time."

It has to be rattled off—all in a piece. Footprints on the sands are ephemeral enough but footprints on the sands of time is ephemerality to the uttermost degree.

Yes, to live well, someone has written, one should consult the lives of other men as one would a looking-glass and from thence fetch examples for one's own imitation.

The best biography is Boswell's *Life of Johnson* and I hold perhaps a record for selling him in my small way. Certainly I have sold a hundred in various editions—principally the Oxford one and the Everyman edition.

If I had to go on a desert island with two books I would take the Bible and Boswell. I have no doubt I would tire of Boswell first because he deals with a sophisticated world. I would be hankering after the social life of London and that would make me unhappy by its unattainability.

The Bible is more consoling. Judaea's social customs and social life at no time gave me a nostalgia. There is no happy land in the Bible for which I would hanker. Still I have not to make the choice. I can have in this back shop of a bookshop both the Bible and Boswell, and I am content.

My other Johnsonian biographies are the *Lives of the Poets*. I have a 1794 edition in four volumes with the names of forty booksellers on the title-page. It is an excellent foursome and I plead guilty to having been very capricious about this lot. I could sell the set at 10s. and be paid handsomely, but when I had a buyer, I dissimulated and said they were already sold, though they had not yet been removed by the buyer !

It was a lie.

They are not sold (except to me) but I will not part with them.

Even the most indifferent of biographies is more readable than most novels. I have a copy of *Pioneers of Public Health*, a book done by a woman as a labour of love, I guess, in bright memory of an only son. It tells something of men who have made the world more healthy and habitable and is not pretentious in any way.

Yet it is a book of merit—a likeable book—and one which, for human interest, puts whole libraries of new novels into the shade of things unreal.

Old biographies always attract me. What other bookseller has, for example, the following three books altogether on his shelves ? *George Whale, 1849–1925*, edited by Edward Clodd, Clement Shorter and Winifred Stephens Whale ; *John Mackintosh, A Biography*, by Geo. W. Crutchley ; *Henry VIII*, by Francis Hackett. I am the only one, and what an interest there is in these three books ! They prove my case. Any book is a good book. Any book is worth the money and the booksellers are benefactors.

George Whale was a great rationalist and had—the phrase is—" a genius for friendship." Apart from the editors, E. S. P. Haynes, Augustine Birrell and H. G. Wells all find something worth saying of him in this book. Whale was a good Johnsonian too, which counts for righteousness on earth anyway, and I am sure the Great Doctor will not allow—if words have any meaning—his supporters to be out of it hereafter. He died suddenly at the annual dinner of the Rationalist Press Association on May 4th, 1925, and the concluding part of his speech —a quotation from William Cory—was undelivered by him but will be transcribed by me.

He would have said : "Meanwhile let us reply to the other-worldly."

> " You promise heavens free from strife,
>   Pure truth, and perfect change of will ;
> But sweet, sweet is this human life,
>   So sweet, I fain would breathe it still :
> Your chilly stars I can forego,
> This warm kind world is all I know."

An optimist in spite of it all, you see.

Life went well with him.

The John Mackintosh book is toffee-de-luxe and a good story. Hodder & Stoughton are the publishers. My price is 4s. 6d.

The other companion of George Whale and John Mackintosh is *Henry VIII*, published by Jonathan Cape, but I am nearer the other two than the much-wived Henry. I only mention him because of the company he keeps in my shop and to show how amusing a bookseller's life can be.

Why write Biography? The question is curiously answered by a Mr Laver, who writes an introduction to *Harriette Wilson's Memoirs*. Here is the quotation :—

> " It was no creative impulse that inspired the present book (that is the *Memoirs*) nor even a Casanova-like desire to live over again the scene of her former triumphs. It was a very understandable wish to extract money from the public by a *chronique scandaleuse*, and from the Duke by blackmail."

Note why books of Memoirs are written anyway :

1. Sheer creative impulse.
2. A desire to live a successful life over again.
3. A wish to extract money from the public.
4. Blackmail.

My eyes light on three books of Memoirs and I apply Mr Laver's tests. The first is *Sir Walter Scott's Journal*. There is nothing of the creative impulse there ; he wrote I think— he knew not why. There is no desire to live a successful life over again nor yet to make money either by amusing the public or blackmailing his friends.

Stand down, Sir Walter, you are not guilty !

My second witness takes the stand. The son of a tailor and fond of clothes, women and all good things, Mr Samuel Pepys gives his evidence. Creative impulse? A little puzzled, a slight hesitancy and the Secretary to their Lordships of the Admiralty replies, " I hardly know why—but I would not claim to that."

A desire to live a successful life over again?

" I had a certain gusto in life, I grant you, but the enjoyment I had cannot be lived over again in writing. The waters pass only once under London Bridge."

" No, sir," he concludes with emphasis.

" A wish to extract money from the public? " " Certainly not. If that were my intention, would I have written in cipher? "

The fourth question need not be put—for a man who wrote in cipher, there can be no suspicion of blackmailing, and Mr Samuel Pepys passes down into the merciful gloom behind the dock, having successfully denied all four imputations. His character, as far as Mr James Laver's charges are concerned, is unstained.

The ushers call Edward Gibbon. He asks that all the charges be read out to him. He hears the indictment with grave—almost pompous—dignity, for the greatest historian of any age is not accustomed to cross-examination. " I have no hesitation whatever in asserting that my autobiography was neither inspired by creative impulse nor by a desire to live my life over again nor by the wish to add to my fortune nor yet, it is almost unnecessary to add, surely, by anything resembling in the slightest degree the vile wickedness of blackmail. If before this Court I am to inform the world why I wrote my autobiography, I must admit in words I have used in that work, "Writing my history, I was seduced by the facility of my pen."

Edward Gibbon takes his leave of the Court, and I as one of the jury feel that Mr James Laver has failed to make his case.

We, writers and scribblers alike, are seduced by the facility of our pens.

BOOK TITLES AND POSSIBLE PUBLISHERS

The Psalms in Human Life, I see, has gone through four editions and been reprinted twice as often. It is a book which I have never read through but it always interests me. When I procure a copy (as I did this week of the six shilling edition) I always hold it over for a night or so just to look over it again.

The idea is a good one : it would be most entertaining if it could be followed further. For example, *Shakespeare and his Effect on the Individual, being a Record of Lives Enriched and Actions Inspired by the Works of William Shakespeare.* That might be one book.

Another might be, *Mrs Beeton's Cookery Book and Lives Planned and Damned by Her Influence.*

Why not *The Ten Commandments and Historical Incidents dealing with their Rejection?* That would be an omnibus book.

I must seriously interview a publisher. Who should it be? I think John Murray, or would he be too staid? What about Chatto & Windus? The partnership interests me and I would see either with equanimity. Did they not publish *The Young Visiters?* Faber & Faber, Smith, Elder & Company, Sampson, Low & Company, and Duckworth & Company—all seem forbidding.

Benn Brothers seem friendly, and Jonathan Cape does not appal me, but Victor Gollancz—ah me!—he and Alfred A. Knopf—I could not approach.

Publishers' names are odd, I think, but perhaps it is their bills that really make me feel ill at ease.

I had better give up the idea.

MORE ABOUT BIOGRAPHIES

I am not partial to these omnibus books but, in its way, the big book of Heinemann's *Great Short Biographies of the World* is worth having in stock if only that I may read it myself. I have sold it though, and, as I had ordered a second copy which came to-day, I have been looking through it again.

The book has been made by Barrett H. Clark and, by its dedication to Gamaliel Bradford, indicates that it came from the United States. It is printed in Great Britain but the " big idea " is the star-spangled manner, as Beverley Nichols has it, at its best. Clark tells me—he will tell the world if you will read it, but I like to think he tells me—that the preparation of the book was a delightful adventure. His difficulty was not to make it big but to keep it small, . . . to give infinite riches in little room. In a way that's my task as a bookseller—to select —to discard—to choose and still to be able to offer those who run but also read a collection of books from which they would want to buy at least one.

There are forty-nine biographies in this book and over fourteen hundred pages, divided into six groups,—the Ancient World, Medieval Europe, Renaissance Europe, Seventeenth Century Europe, Eighteenth Century Europe, and Nineteenth Century Europe with the United States.

Some I miss, though I don't complain. I would have liked to see Boswell's *Johnson* for one and Macaulay's *Clive* for another, but the editor has good reasons for the choices that he made. The book is a remarkable achievement, and I will push one or two who would be none the worse of seeing the inside of others' lives to buy this book for 8s. 6d.

Eight and sixpence, I observe, is one hundred and two pence. It would make a good selling point to offer it to the parsimonious for a hundred pence. If I sell a lot I will not mind the loss of profit, and no one will know that I have sold it for half a groat less than the approved price.

The *Louis XIV* by Saint-Simon is new to me. I didn't know either that Saint-Simon was Louis de Rouvroy, Duc de Saint-Simon, although I did know that Voltaire's name was François Marie Arouet. It linked up with a couple of books I bought as remainders, which are good value none the less, Noel Williams's *Pompadour* and *Recamier*. I offer the pair for 5s. I had a talk with the lady milliner next door about them and told her she should study the celebrated courtesans of the past if she would know her sex. She didn't buy either and, on thinking it over, I came to the obvious conclusion that they had not commanded her interest because, as illustrated, they—neither of them—wore hats ! Recamier's picture is the one at 23 by Gerard, and the Pompadour is the familiar one by Boucher, both lovely though they did not secure a buyer.

An unusual book of biography is Will Durant's *Story of Philosophy*, a book which combines the lives and opinions of the philosophers. I often turn its pages. It is a book in which I have found more satisfaction than any on my shelves. Twenty-five shillings is a lot to pay for a book, but I would not hesitate to take twenty-five shillings of anyone's money for it. Some books one buys for their passing interest. Some, one buys for reference. Durant's book would do for a lifetime and leave a large margin for eternity.

The conclusion of the book is very inspiring. One hopes it has begun to seed in the minds of the citizens of the United States. After praising wealth—believing that the abundant creation of wealth must be the prelude to culture—the writer goes on : " To have become wealthy was the first necessity : a people too must live before it can philosophise. We have grown faster than nations usually have grown and the disorder of our souls is due to the rapidity of our development. We are like youths disturbed and unbalanced for a time, by the sudden growths and experiences of puberty. But soon our maturity will come ; our minds will catch up with our bodies ; our culture with our possessions. Perhaps there are greater souls than Shakespeare's and greater minds than Plato's waiting to be born. When we have learned to reverence liberty as well as wealth, we too shall have our renaissance."

All very fine, I agree, but the sense of the shortness of life comes over me as I transcribe it.

And what of it, I demand, what of it if someone called Bunterschamp is born in Walkerville, Ohio, or wherever it may be—one who is nobler in mind than Plato and greater in soul than Shakespeare? What do I care for a future in which I can have no lot or part? How can it avail me if man soars to the empyrean or sinks to the depths? It cannot avail you, I answer myself. Life is only valuable as a personal experience. That brings me back to biography and autobiography—to the curiosity which we have about the lives of others. " Curiosity about their lives " is an echo. It is from Cunningham-Graham's book *Success*, of which I have a copy in Duckworth's old *Greenback Library*. The passage runs : " For those who fail, for those who have sunk, still battling beneath the muddy waves of life, we keep our love and that curiosity about their lives which makes their memories green when the cheap gold is dusted over, which once we gave success." " How few successful men are interesting," he goes on. " Hannibal, Alcibiades, with Raleigh, Mithridates and Napoleon, who would compare them for a moment with their mere conquerors." The essay is good. The defeatism in me is attracted by such writing.

Here is more from another forgotten book published in 1900 by Hodder & Stoughton. I got it—an often read copy—carefully marked at the following passage. " Some of us have to be defeated in this life. We cannot all draw prizes but we can remember that, whatever we may suffer in the buffetings of circumstance, there is still left a wide realm not wholly destitute of beauty, where we may live at least with usefulness and serenity. We can make friends with books. . . ." There is more of it in the opening chapter which is called the " Art of Living." The book itself—Heaven knows what was in the mind that marked the passage—is by W. J. Dawson and can be bought by the man who wants and needs it for one shilling.

Writing these names, I remind myself I have the following :—*The Man Shakespeare*, Frank Harris ; *The Life of Alcibiades*, E. F. Benson ; *The Life of Napoleon Buonaparte*, Sir Walter Scott ; *Life of Sir Walter Raleigh*, Patrick Fraser Tytler.

Frank Harris's book is the best I know on Shakespeare and most enlightening. *Alcibiades* is a new book—I haven't read it yet—published by Benn. The *Buonaparte* and *Raleigh* are old, the first undated and the second a beautiful little book published by Oliver & Boyd, Tweeddale Court, Edinburgh, in 1833.

They are a nice lot. My stock of biographies is good, I think. Man, what do you want to know? Here are the windows which let you see into other men. What more would you? The Searcher of Souls in the Last Great Day will learn little more from the Book of Judgment than you can learn from these biographies. Buy, buy, buy with little money and at no great. price. . . .

Someone may write my biography. I would have him show me as a pathetic figure. Pathos lasts better in biography than mirth. What comic figures have come down the ages? There is nothing more *démodé* than last season's jokes. They hardly bear retelling far less recording. Therefore limn me as a sad case.

There are always sympathetic hearts, and, in such a world, there will be someone who will sigh sympathetically over the sorrows of a simple (and not too successful) bookseller.

PROTEUS

When I read these books of mystery, imagination and horror, I, too, fancy myself as a man of hard, implacable, ruthless cruelty and daring. I see myself track down my enemy— fawn upon him—accept his hospitality and win his friendship. I see myself ensconced in his innermost confidence and in the very sanctuary of his heart.

Then I draw the stiletto—*Then* I point the small gleaming barrel of my automatic—*Then* he dies with horrible, *horrible* suddenness.

I stoop down over his recumbent body. I project my malice and hatred into his fast-fading gaze.

I am Mephistopheles, Cesare Borgia, Tippoo Sahib, Rasputin, Jack the Ripper, Professor Moriarty, Dracula, Dr Fu Man Chu.

I am vice, triumphant, naked, brutal, unshamed.

It is in the early morning when I have slept badly and I have my books to dust that I feel thus, but I am all right again by the time the milk comes.

RELIGION, RELIGIOUS BOOKS AND BIBLES

To-day I went to church. It didn't do me any good. The preacher, for all that he said of any interest to me, might have been speaking of the habits of Crustacea or marriage practices in Nyasaland or the aetiology of rheumatism. The only inspiring feeling I had came to me from a woman who sat beside me in the same pew. When the singing began she sang. How she sang !

I know nothing of music but I felt she felt all she sang. I remember yet the boldness, the fullness, the abounding vitality

of the way she sang. " Summer suns are glowing, over land
and sea."

I saw these summer suns, although astronomy has only
given us one. She made me believe, without effort, in several
suns, multitudes of suns, all glowing—so abundant was her
conviction.

As I came out my friend—my enemy—my neighbour—
came out alongside me. He had enjoyed the service. " Lovely
day," he said ; " this weather makes them all want new hats."

The preacher—what he said—and the draper—what he
said—sent me back to the natural moodiness of mind to which
I am prone. The church is no place for summer suns and
ardent songsters, prosperous drapers and gay millinery. The
church—this church—was a parade of fashions and an exhibi-
tion of complacency. If God is pleased with His handiwork
this morning He had the right congregation. They were
obviously pleased with God and pleased with themselves.

The church in which I should have worshipped to-day
would not have been a church for the contented, a church for
the well dressed and the respectable. The church I needed
was the church of the Man of Sorrows acquainted with grief—
the church of Him who cried : " My God, my God, why hast
Thou forsaken me ? "

Back in the shop, I pottered about my shelves. There is a
great pleasure in pottering about my books on Sunday. My
books are my own that day. Outside, I hear voices and people
passing. I am alone in my library, as lonely as a monk in his
cell. I can hear my voices, as Joan of Arc did, when my shop
is shut. When it is open to the public it is not my own, somehow. It is theirs—the books are either theirs or the property
of the people from whom I bought them or—grim thought—
the property of my financial creditors. I won't think of them
on Sunday.

There are not many religious books nowadays relatively.
Time was when religious books were half a bookseller's stock

in some towns, but we have changed all that. The world is too much with us day by day in the *Daily News* or *Daily Mail* for us to think every day of the life to come.

I remember the excellent Sunday reading of my youth. Old volumes of *Good Words*, a priggish title for most worthy volumes, the *Quiver*, most readable and almost too light for Sundays, *Holy Living and Holy Dying*, *The Pilgrim's Progress*, *The Holy War*, *The Lives of the Covenanters*, many volumes of sermons, particularly the *Sermons of Dr Hugh Blair* in five volumes—these were the books with which my pious relatives surrounded me on Sundays. They did me no ill. Indeed, I would not have been without their influences. My stock contains few of these works to-day, but I have always specialised in Bibles. It is stated that the Bible is still the world's best seller, and so it should be. Carnal and wicked though I am, bookseller and man of many worlds, this book is the book of books for me and, if I dare say it, for all my customers. I don't care what they think they want, I ought to tell them, " This is the book for you." " Not Francis Hackett's *Henry VIII*, sir ; you should read the Book of Kings." " Not *Elizabeth and her German Garden*, madam ; you should read the Book of Ruth." " Not *New Worlds for Old*, sir ; you should read the Book of the Revelation of St John." " Not Compton Mackenzie's *Seven Ages of Woman*, madam ; you should read the story of another Mary in the Gospels." " Not Will Durant's *Story of Philosophy*, sir ; you should read the Book of Job."

It is the commonest of commonplaces to write it, but it is true. The man who has read and re-read his Bible, who has lived his life with his Bible, will be an educated man. He may not be a Christian but he will know the mind of man and glimpse something of what may be the meaning—a meaning anyway—of life.

The stock of Bibles should be varied. There is always the fond father and devoted mother who want to give one on the fifteenth birthday or on the occasion of his leaving home. How frequent that is in my experience—how frequent, and perhaps how futile, but can one do better or do more?

The Comprehensive Teachers' Edition—Bagster—is a popular format, but I sell all sorts. The Modern Readers' Bible by Professor Moulton has taught me much personally, and I sell it sometimes to the discriminating. Dent's Temple Bible is very good and the Apocrypha volumes always evoke interest. I have a good second-hand set which I will sell complete for one shilling a volume. It is a bargain.

Another bargain is my large Family Bible, which came to me in a lot I had from a woman who had had it bequeathed to her. The books, I believe, were the last item on an auction sale list. They followed the poor iron fender from the back bedroom, the bamboo table, beaded cover and aspidistra, and the embroidered footstool. The other books in the lot were *Many Thoughts from Many Minds* by Henry Southgate, Mrs Hemans's *Poems*, Wilson's *Tales of the Borders*, and a collection of old magazines and paper-cover fiction. They had to be turned into cash and I was the buyer.

The title-page of this huge Family Bible is worth transcribing in full—although I have already written of this book before.

THE PRACTICAL AND DEVOTIONAL FAMILY BIBLE

The
Holy Bible
containing the
Old and New Testaments
according to the Authorised Version
with the marginal readings and original and
selected parallel references
printed at length
and the
Commentaries of Henry and Scott
condensed by the
Rev. John McFarlane, LL.D., Glasgow
(Here follows the Royal Arms)
Glasgow
printed by William Collins & Co. and sold by
William Collins, South Hanover Street
MDCCCLVIII.

It is a real book and I often wonder what its history has been and what yet lies before it. Into whose hands will it go —what eyes will read it—what will be the consequences?

Among my religious books I have Prayer Books and Hymnals. The English Hymnary and the Church Hymnary are in good demand and they are both well produced and well-printed books. They are worth studying. I don't think they are studied. They lie on seats and in shelves in churches, but folk ought to take them home.

There is real poetry in many of them and a deep sentiment which one can love and admire in all of them. How graciously beautiful, for example, is that doxology by Samuel Miller Waring beginning " Now to Him who loved us, gave us," and how manly and how confident is John Bunyan's hymn " He that is down needs fear no fall." My own favourite is one I have never heard sung but which echoes all that the struggling part of me sometimes feels.

> " Dear Master, in whose life I see
> All that I would but fail to be,
> Let Thy clear light for ever shine,
> To shame and guide this life of mine.
> Though what I dream and what I do
> In my weak days are always two,
> Help me, oppressed by things undone,
> O Thou, Whose deeds and dreams were one."

That eager poem is by John Hunter, 1848–1917. Who was he? I do not know but he is brother to me—" oppressed " as I am " by things undone." He anyway " has finished his course."

Looking over the names of the hymn writers, I observe they nearly all live long. Godly men do—so an insurance man told me. Clergymen live longest in this vale of tears, and barmen and publicans—no more sinners than clergymen—are for some reason called earlier to the rest beyond.

I pick out names at random . . .

JOHN WESLEY, 1703–1791.
EDWARD DENNY, 1796–1889.

HENRY HART MILMAN, 1791–1868.
JOHN NEWTON, 1725–1807.
ANN LAETITIA WARING, 1820–1910.

" The sweet singers," my cynical familiar irreverently and with questionable taste remarks,—" the sweet singers are not sought early for the choir invisible."

" We need them too much on earth," my younger and better self retorts.

The most popular religious books since I began business are Bruce Barton's. *The Man Nobody Knows, The Book Nobody Knows* and *What Can a Man Believe* have been big sellers and they deserve their success. There has been nothing like them since Charles M. Sheldon's *In His Steps, or What would Jesus Do ?* It is odd in a way that they both came from America. I have had orders for Clutton Brock's books frequently, *The Ultimate Belief* and *Studies in Christianity*. They don't appeal to me so much as Jack's *The Challenge of Life*, which is a steady seller.

Really though, I am all for faith and not argument in religion. I would rather accept than be led by reason and logic to conviction. That is why I am pleased with my prayer books. I sell them by introduction. I tell men who obviously think too highly of their sense of humour to get down and pray on their knees—I tell them to buy prayer books. My favourites are William Law's *Serious Call to a Devout and Holy Life*—not exactly a prayer book but I call it one—*Home Prayers* by Dr Martineau, *The Imitation of Christ, This Day*—a collection of simple prayers published by St Martin's Review—the little purple *A Plain Man's Prayer Book* containing Doctor Johnson's and one published by Blackwood called *Kyrie Eleison*. These prayer books will make men better men and me a better bookseller for selling them.

Perhaps the best work I may do in all my life is to sell *Kyrie Eleison* to some soul who needs it. Casting bread upon the waters is a rash speculation compared with the selling of books.

I am a sower. My field is the hearts of men. My seed is these books.

* * * * * * *

One must never be unjust to books. It would be unjust to omit Dr James Moffatt's *A New Translation of the Bible*. I omitted it from what I have written because it was away from my shelves. I have been reading it and I am untidy. It was in my back room—on what passes for my dressing-table—covered untidily with a handkerchief—not overclean—and a Bohemian necktie which I sometimes affect when my shirts are rather soiled. This new Bible is most absorbing. It is like going to see the same play with different actors. It tests one's old knowledge and makes one critical. It helps one to understand. I love its laconic narrative nowhere better than in that last dialogue between Jesus and Peter in John's Gospel. Peter said to Jesus, " And what about *him*, Lord." Jesus replied, " What does that matter to you? Follow me yourself." But it is all good narrative as well as philosophy.

What could be better than this?

" So I praise pleasure. The best thing for man is to eat and drink and enjoy himself. And to keep this up as he toils right through the life God gives him in this world."

" To keep this up "—one must be a D.D., D.Litt., M.A.(Oxon) to write that—but then I am sure it is just as " the Speaker, David's son, King in Jerusalem," spoke. In fact, is it not just like what David, Prince of Wales and Duke of Rothesay, would say to-day?

Among additional Holy Books I must mention *Great Souls at Prayer*—Allenson—my copy is the seventy-first thousand—and the *Mirror of Perfection* in Dent's Temple Classics.

To both I owe debts and if I cannot repay my debts, I can —decent tradesman that I am—I can acknowledge them.

HYMEN

Near my shop there is a church and to-day there has been a marriage. I saw the happy couple go out under the striped awning and they were happy.

The girl—she was just a girl—was radiant. It made me think I was missing everything in missing marriage.

Things do join up oddly. When I came back to the shop again I picked up *The Defendant*, by Gilbert Keith Chesterton, published by Dent in the Wayfarers' Library. There I read :

" There are thrilling moments, doubtless, for the spectator, the amateur, and the æsthete ; but there is one thrill that is known only to the soldier who fights for his own flag, to the ascetic who starves himself for his own illumination, to the lover who makes finally his own choice. And it is this transfiguring self-discipline that makes the vow a truly sane thing. It must have satisfied even the giant hunger of the soul of a lover or a poet to know that in consequence of some one instant of decision that strange chain would hang for centuries in the Alps among the silences of stars and snows. All around us is the city of small sins, abounding in backways and retreats, but surely, sooner or later, the towering flame will rise from the harbour announcing that the reign of the cowards is over and a man is burning his ships."

I was a man determined to burn my ships. There is a girl in the shop next door . . . exquisite . . . adorable . . . perfect . . . her lips are as fresh as the dew on roses in the morning. . . .

I feel like Gissing. I want to run out and marry the first girl I meet in the streets !

A customer fortunately comes in and I go forward to greet him.

BOOKS FOR CHILDREN AND SO FORTH

" A book for a boy," was one of my inquiries to-day and as Christmas approaches I will have to fill up my stock. As usual a picture of my responsibility comes before me. My choices and recommendations will influence the future in ways untellable and unimaginable. *A Life of Clive* may make a boy a soldier, *The Swiss Family Robinson* may send him to be a planter in the South Seas, *A Life of Kelvin* may make him a scientist, *The Life of Henry Ford* may make him a great individualist.

These are big responsibilities and I feel them all. For boys of fourteen and thereabouts I am all for giving them biographies. *Plutarch's Lives for Boys and Girls* at one end is a good book, and at the other, why not Samuel Smiles's *Self Help*? Monkeys we were, and monkeys we remain—imitative creatures ; let us have the best examples before us while we are very young.

My own youth was greatly stimulated by a good illustrated edition of *Aesop's Fables*. They made me feel an interest in the beasts and helped to awake sympathies with the brutes I might otherwise never have felt. Dent's Everyman edition is good for adults, but a pictured edition—I haven't one just now and don't know of one—is the best for youngsters.

Fairy Tales are not what they were. Andrew Lang's Collections were the best I know, but nowadays the boys and girls want books on motor cars and aeroplanes, books of adventure and pluck and peril, and these are readily available. Personally I can't read them and I often wonder who write them. They are undoubtedly popular—I know that by experience—and that proves that publishers like Nelson's and Blackie's, for example, who make a speciality of the Children's Book business, know it better than I do. The drapers' shops sell more at their bazaars than the booksellers sell and perhaps that is as it should be.

These books with titles such as *The Wolf Runner*, by E. E. Cowper, and *The Smiths of Silver Lane*, by Ethel Talbot, make me feel that I know nothing about books.

The A. A. Milne Books, for all their success, affect me much the same. I am no more able to select and buy such books for children with discrimination than I am able to buy prams or paregorics.

The truth is that the books I—and most folks—think are good children's books are really books for ourselves. *Alice in Wonderland* is a wonderland for children, by all means. It is not comprehension. The mind that revels in Alice is an adult one, as witness the gallant Osborne in that new play *Journey's End*. To him the wonderland of ,Alice is a garden of delight into which the fortunate visitor may escape from the too terrible realities of existence. All the folk I have met who like Alice are grown up and intellectual. To call it a child's book is to bring truth to the prophecy, " Except ye become as little children, ye will in no wise enter the Kingdom of Heaven."

Alice's Wonderland was a veritable kingdom of Heaven in the Wilderness of the later Victorian Era. It even won Victoria herself. She loved Alice and ordered from her bookseller (who were the Royal Booksellers? Bumpus or Hatchards, I suppose) any other works by Mr Carroll. It is not recorded what Her Majesty thought of the other works of C. L. Dodgson on mathematical subjects.

Another favourite of mine which I have sold as a book for children is *Cautionary Tales*, by Hilaire Belloc. It is a work of genius and stands in the same honourable catalogue as *Alice*. The fact is, grown-ups buy quite a number of books which they allege are for children but which really are for themselves. *Alice* is one, *Cautionary Tales* is another, and I am sure *Gulliver's Travels* and *The Pilgrim's Progress* would very rarely be bought by children for themselves. *Lamb's Tales from Shakespeare* is another.

I see I am disclosing myself. I have no real sympathy with children's books, I am proselytising all the time. I want my customers—children or adults—to read the books I like. I am a pontiff in such matters. I ought to cultivate catholicity, although the high organisation of catholicity itself has its "index expurgatorius," so I am not too abandoned a sinner after all!

The most regular buyer of children's books I have buys Scott, Dickens and Stevenson. He says the best boys' books —and he has tried them on his lucky dogs—are *The Talisman*, *The Tale of Two Cities* and *Treasure Island*.

They certainly are a good trio, and now that copyright is out, I might make the suggestion to the publishers who favour OMNIBUS books. They would make a good omnibus for boys. The Crusades, the French Revolution and the Pirates of the Spanish Main are subjects that all proper lads should know. If one wanted others I would suggest a Kingsley Omnibus, Why not *Hereward the Wake*, *Westward Ho!* and the *Water Babies*?

For girls I have no wise matron whose opinion I could seek, but I will venture my own. Louisa M. Alcott's *Little Women* would be first. Lots of girls like it. My second would be *The Mill on the Floss*. George Eliot is always good and is surely due for a revival. My third would be modern, and after a thorough look over my stock and my catalogues, I give the palm to Dorothea Moore. I am sure girls like her books. They know her titles and ask for them. That is the mark of adoring faith.

The older generation of girls' books has passed away, but I remember with affection Mrs Molesworth, Rosa N. Carey and Annie S. Swan, who now writes for the moderns. These were good in their day and still now and then I sell second-hand copies to dames who would renew their youth.

Good A.B.C. books do not exist now, but they ought to. It is a defect. I learned my zoology from an alphabet book with splendid pictures, the like of which I cannot find to-day. A was an ape and all apes to me are descendants of that first ape in the Garden of Eden of my youth. A GNU I never would have known but for this work, for I have never seen one or heard of one since. Yet G, which might have suggested Goose or Goat, brought me through this book to the GNU, which the *Oxford Concise Dictionary* in one line most concisely dismisses as " GNU : ox-like antelope : (Hottentot)."

The Ichneumon is another creature I have met but once and then right early. The compiler of the book knew no other creatures who were so egotistic, so *I* went to *Ichneumon* and my stores of learning have been permanently enriched.

Other alphabets might be made if the idea appeals to publishers as it appeals to me. There ought to be a series of alphabets. The Alphabet of the Bible beginning with Ananias and finishing with Zaccheus would be an easy one : the Z gives no serious thought, and Xerxes might be introduced for the X. The Alphabet of Common Things beginning with Apples and going on down to Zoo would be a valuable introduction to the wonderful world for many minds.

Then why not, in these anti-militarist days, an Alphabet of the Wickedness Men call War?

It would begin with ARMISTICE and end with, most appropriately, ZEPPELIN.

The exercise is a pleasing one. I must address myself, I repeat, to the publishers. They would find me most helpful in their search for " Fairy Gold."

These quoted words are from the decorated title-page of *Granny's Wonderful Chair*. " This is fairy gold, boy, and 'twill prove so "—the dearly beloved Dent has printed them to introduce Frances Browne's book. The book is worth buying for the memoir by " D. R." Frances Browne was one of the heroines. Born poor and blind in Donegal in 1816, she climbed to fame and achievement over every obstacle. Her forgotten novel *My Share of the World*, would be worth recovering. One of the characters finds life intolerable and turns to suicide. Of her she writes, " When the burden outgrows the strength so far that moral as well as physical energies begin to fail and there is no door but death's that will welcome our weariness, what remains but to creep into that quiet shelter ! "

But morbidly though Frances Browne could write there is

no morbidity in *Granny's Wonderful Chair*. It is as good a
fairy book as I know and it can take its place with those popular
aliens the Brothers Grimm and Hans Andersen himself.

Each year sees the old favourites *Cinderella*, *Red Riding
Hood* and *Jack the Giant Killer* revived with appropriate
pictures. They will do for uncles who have three nephews
or nieces and who seek to discriminate none with special favour.
They are a happy lot and it would be difficult to tell which of
the three is the most dearly beloved. The Doctor Dolittle
Series are not to be ignored, and there is also *Little Black
Sambo*.

Few great men of literature have written deliberately for
the young, but Rudyard Kipling is a glorious exception. *The
Just So Stories, The Jungle Book* and *Stalky and Co.* are all in
the highest class and the history he wrote with C. R. L. Fletcher
is calculated to make proud Englishmen. The official neglect
of Kipling always seems to me an outrage, but then William
Shakespeare was never Poet Laureate either. This—amid
much that disappoints and disgusts, including, I have always
thought, the Kipling Society—is one of the consolations of
Kipling. He loves and understands England and Englishmen
too well to expect too much.

I write on and on and I have nothing but rambling thoughts
on books for children. This writing about books under rough
classifications is a task for my trade. I want to confess to myself
as Amiel did to his soul and Pepys to his diary. It gives me
confidence. I have given thought, though it be ever so little
and entirely irrelevant, to the question of what books ought I
to have for children.

It is good. All work, even the great failures like creation
itself, have had that pronouncement said over them. I say no
less of these pages of pencillings.

It is good.

There is no other critic, very fortunately, but myself, and
to-night, complacency conquering, the verdict is with me.

" Good-night, books," I have just said. I had carried back
a pile of children's books—some like *Eric*, or *Little by Little*,

and *A Peep Behind the Scenes*, which I have not, yet would like to have, written about—I have carried them back into the shop. It is late. A few people are in the street. I hear their patter pass the door, the overhead fanlight of which is open. The shop is lit only by the street lamps without.

." Good-night, books," I repeat as I close the door of my room behind.

My reviewing of children's books has made me, for all my heresies, more childlike to-night. I could almost kneel down, long and incongruous, and pray by my bedside.

What hinders me?

A sense of humour?

A sense of the ridiculous?

No! Thomas Hood is right, for—

> ". . . now 'tis little joy
> To know I'm farther off from Heav'n
> Than when I was a boy."

ADVICE TO ELECTORS

A GENERAL ELECTION NOTE

Is the education of the people desirable? It is doubtful. What does society want? What is necessary if we are to live on this planet doing the necessary work to secure for us food, shelter, clothing and entertainment?

The search for the super-man is the folly of the frogs all over again. Let us learn to be content with mediocrity in government. It will be well for us if we never find our betters. They might prove tyrannical masters just as they proved themselves to be in the past.

Anarchism being immediately impracticable, let us have a government which governs as little as possible. Lord Melbourne's attitude of mind should be commended for imitation to all Prime Ministers. On being pressed by less wise members of his Cabinet to further certain legislation, he replied : " Must we really do something—why not let well alone ? "

If I allowed politics in my business I might have a card in my window, something to this effect—

> WHY SHOULD I VOTE ?
>
> Read pages 54 and 55 of
> this sealed volume.
> Price. two shillings.

The sealed volume, in neat brown wrapper with sealing wax, all complete, would be found by purchasers to be *Aesop's and other Fables*, Everyman's Library, Cloth 2s., and on pages 54 and 55 they would read of the Frogs asking for a King.

QUITE FRANKLY

If I were rich and free, I would devote my life to some great cause like the League of Nations or the Society for the Prevention of Litter.

So I think sometimes.

If I were rich and free, I would lead a splendid life of devotion to some splendid woman. I would surround her with luxury. We would yacht in the blue Mediterranean. We would sail tropic seas and view the Taj Mahal in the moonlight. We would be alone on coral islands. We would see the sunrise on the snow of Fuji-Yama.

So I think sometimes.

And then I remember if I were rich and free I would do nothing. I am sure that, fundamentally, neither great causes nor romantic travel nor the beauty of women would hold me for long.

I am born of woman, and being born of woman, I am born lazy. I would, if I had my will, do what the soldiers used to call " Sweet Fanny Adams."

Sweet Fanny Adams would be the Goddess of my Nirvana, nor would I worship her ignorantly.

ANOTHER AMERICAN CHAPTER

I have more to tell about Americans. The Americans are coming into the book trade, and I don't mind at all. I like the American books better than the Americans who come into my shop. Yet they are not a bad folk, after all.

They don't know about us any more than we know about them.

Last week I had one who told his story. He had made a fortune apparently and had come over to Europe and Asia for a year. He wore those silly clothes that Americans wear, in fond imitation, I imagine, of the English. He had a light woollen suit of fine grey texture—the baggy knickerbocker type—and a soft collar with a bow tie, a round hat and the glasses which are the national badge. He was taking a holiday and had made up his mind when he left to travel light. He had brought no books nor had he bought any. He read the papers exclusively, but he wanted to get back to America in a more intimate way than the *New York Herald* could convey him.

" I want a good American book," he said.

So I bustled about and showed him Edna Ferber's *The Show Boat* and *White Fang* and *John Barleycorn*—old editions —by Jack London. He pursed his lips closely and laid them down each time saying, " Piff "—making the word by expelling the air through his lips. I got him Washington Irving and Nathaniel Hawthorne's *Scarlet Letter*.

They awoke the identical emotion that Miss Ferber and

Mr London had done. I went over a lot of names calling them out from behind my counter as I read them from the backs of the books themselves.

" Hergesheimer ? "

No answer.

" Upton Sinclair ? "

Silence.

" Sinclair Lewis ? "

" Read 'em all."

" Van Vechten ? "

Silence.

" Henry James ? "

Silence.

" H. L. Mencken ? "

" Nope."

" O. Henry ? "

" Lemme see it."

I got it down—the new " omnibus " by Associated Book-buyers.

He took hold of it and sat down. I was away and about, attending to others, for a good half hour. I didn't disturb him. He seemed happy. When I got time he had decided to buy it. " This is my homeland," he said, " this is America and, what's more, literature."

He paid up his 15s. 6d. and for once I was apt and ready. I remembered my O. Henry Biography and fetched it out. My copy is a remainder and partly discoloured with water, but I sold it him at full price. He was a Virginian and hadn't heard of Professor C. Alphonso Smith who wrote *O. Henry, A Biography*, which was rather surprising to me. He was very pleased to note—I wasn't pleased at all—that both books were printed in America, though published in England.

I did him a good turn, he told me—O. Henry would cure nostalgia or send him back again for the only real cure—to his home town. O. Henry to me is the biggest thing the United States has done in literature. I think his *Gift of the Magi* one of the finest short stories I know : it and Kipling's *Without*

Benefit of Clergy share an equal place. But I like O. Henry better than I like Rudyard Kipling. I know that Mr Kipling is a better citizen, but O. Henry would be a nearer friend to me. There won't be another O. Henry. O. Henrys are not born of commercial success and world greatness.. O. Henry comes from despair and defeat and from the beauty that shines out from the gutter and the mud.

Alphonso Smith's book is quite good but it is worth gold for the little vignette of the last hours of the hero.

Writing good things down is good for me. I will write it down :

" There was no pain now and just before sunrise he said with a smile to those about him, ' Turn up the lights. I don't want to go home in the dark.'

" He died as he had lived. His last words touched with new beauty and with new hope the refrain of a concert hall song, the catch word of the street, the jest of the department store."

Alphonso Smith adds : " He did not go home in the dark. The sunlight was upon his face when he passed and illumines still his name and fame."

He " touched with new beauty " common things. That's a good epitaph for a great writer, and Americans may yet come to a time when they will be more proud of the fact that they produced in Ohio one who called himself " O. Henry " than of their world-wide commerce with every land.

After O. Henry, there isn't much for me. I've named some of the writers who are represented on my shelves. There are others, but they are not books which lonely, home-sick tourists would take to exactly. Yet they are good.

James Harvey Robinson's *The Ordeal of Civilisation*, published by Harper & Company, has given me lots of pleasure. I rushed through the reading of it just after it came into my stock in case it should be sold. It hasn't gone yet, and I turn its serious pages in serious moods sometimes. The same writer has written the *Mind in the Making*, but I sold it before I read it. H. G. Wells recommends it, and I must get another copy.

The Travellers' Library, which Jonathan Cape published, has three good American books in it which I have sold to less distinctive Yankees than the one who was here this afternoon. They are *Selected Prejudices*, by H. L. Mencken, *Can Such Things Be?* by Ambrose Bierce, and Arthur Mason's *Wide Sea and Many Lands*. The last comes nearest to my bosom, but all are worthy of their place in a good and most saleable series of books.

In brilliant yellow and black, I have another of Mencken's —a fourth edition which I got hold of cheap. I see on the jacket, the *English Review* has a welcome for the American. I don't know. We have iconoclasts enough without importing them.

The book, like all the others, is printed in America. I would forbid it. A people who get their printing done abroad are in a fair way to getting their thinking done there too. These things should not be, quite definitely. I am a narrow nationalist. I would rather that things were done badly by our own people than done well by others. We learn by doing things ill. We despair by seeing them done so well that we can never hope to equal them.

I would protect the right of all peoples to retain poor things but albeit their own. Out of one's own can something better come. There is no hope for the gaping mouth, the accepting mind, the idle hands, the receptive lap.

Poor barbaric peoples are not allowed to learn the road to better things. We dump the finished product on them. We offer them a short cut, which they accept, but they cut out too all the valuable, all the beautiful experiences which would have been theirs had they taken the rough road on their own.

I am, in that sense, a Protectionist.

Poking around I discovered another American book worth mentioning if only as a curiosity. It is dated 1899 and is volume five of Elbert Hubbard's *Little Journeys*. Its full title is *Little Journeys to the Homes of Eminent Painters*. Elbert Hubbard went down on the *Titanic* and was a loss to America and a loss to letters. He made American men—business men—listen, and how much American idealism owes to Elbert Hubbard it would be difficult to assess. There is a good deal of Hubbard in the Rotary Movement—for all its somewhat ridiculous emblem of a cog-wheel. It is less than little that I know about engineering, but a cog-wheel which cogs into nothing is not up to much that is useful. It may turn but it will only turn itself.

Yet this single cog-wheel is the symbol of Rotary. I would have had three cog-wheels and with them—all cogged into one another—and America, having largely—like the rest of us—given up God—might have made a new Trinity. I must write to Vivian Carter about it—that astonishing man who at one time edited the *Bystander* and now runs with the Rotarians.

The Star Spangled Manner by Beverley Nichols—but it isn't an American book. I put it down on the counter again.

That will do for American books, Rotary, and O. Henry, to-night, but the greatest of these is O. Henry.

AN AMERICAN LADY

No one, of course, will dispute, far less deny, that the inhabitants of the United States are the greatest people in the world. I pay tribute to the Caesar who succeeded Columbus. To-day at 3 P.M. precisely, perspiring slightly under the influence of our British July, enters Mrs Sawtherthwaite-Smith. (I did not know her name when she entered, but I have learned it since, and will never forget it. When I stand before the Great White Throne, I will remember many things, and I am not at all sure I will not even then remember poignantly, Mrs Sawtherthwaite-Smith.)

She requires information and she is quite willing to pay for a book which will contain that information. She is proud of her ancestry, and feels that comparatively few people have had any ancestry—at least that seems implied in her observations to me. She will buy a book, but it must contain certain practical information. Her paternal great-great-grandfather, named Job Sawtherthwaite, fought, she is convinced, in the Coldstream Guards at the Battle of Waterloo, and she is anxious to pay me really any price which I care to ask, for a book which will give her some particulars of the deceased Job and his previous life-history. In this way, it is her fond hope, she will establish her claims to a substantial ancestry, and to what other social advantages accompany such an ancestry.

I could not help her; she has gone away sadly. I have sent her to the American Consul; I have sent her also to the College of Heralds, although I was unable to give her the address. She has left me her address, however, in vague detail, but I am unable to say which of the following the concluding portion of the address represents.

It may be Ill., or Wis., or Conn., or Mich., and really I do not greatly care. I think it was Nerissa in *The Merchant of Venice* who said that her little body was awearied of this great world.

God knows, I am weary.

THE EVERLASTING YEA

People ask me such astonishing questions, but I like it.

For instance, a customer, a bank manager, asked me what I thought of business. I see so little of it that I had no difficulty in replying.

Then he went on to talk of how bad things were. The country is on the edge of bankruptcy—a sharp experience for any country—spending power is in the hands of women and no one is saving at all. He said these things and things like these. I agreed with it all. I said, " Yes "—" It's a fact "— " You are quite right "—" That's very true "—" Of course " — " Certainly " — " That's obvious " — " Indisputably " — " Emphatically "—" Assuredly." . . .

We had quite a long talk and I emerged feeling like one who has communed with a great positive mind.

I was an affirmative.

I had pronounced the almost Everlasting Yea in every conceivable sort of way.

BAD TRADE

The steak which I buy and grill for myself seems a hundred times sweeter to my palate than that which I get at the gilded and candle-shade-table-decorated restaurant in the square.

How is it?

Do I prefer my own?

Is the reason why I sell fewer books because men prefer their own thoughts?

A poor thing, but my own, is the most powerful justification of thrift, but thrift among book-buyers is bad trade for me.

I must eat my steak more frequently at the restaurant. The manager is a reader of books and it will encourage him.

Is it not written, " There is that scattereth, and yet increaseth ; and there is that withholdeth more than is meet, but it tendeth to poverty "?-

WAR BOOKS

A Voice from the Past

These war books send me to the old papers and oddments which I brought home—my only loot—from the War. I used to carry odd papers and cuttings in my steel helmet. It was too big for me and I padded out the roof in this way. How creased and greased they are !

The *Times* broadsheets were good—I had quite a lot of them—and it is a pleasure to see Methuen republishing them under the editorship of Geoffrey Dawson. What some soldiers *read* is more readable than what some soldiers *wrote*!

There was a lot of writing during the war which seems to have been lost. The poems of the Grenfells, for example, were only typical. John Lane published a book by E. B. Osborn called *The New Elizabethans*, which contains much that might be reprinted. Tom Kettle is in it and that lovely sonnet, " To my daughter Betty," is printed with the memoir ; Alan Seeger too, although his best poem—as I think—" I have a Rendezvous with Death at some Disputed Barricade," is not printed. Then there are Harold Chapin, Dixon Scott, Donald Hankey and several others.

They all—or nearly all—wrote things worth reading, which is more than I can say of some of the things I am selling just now. The faculty for writing was born for many of us—in the War. I did a little and achieved print in journals such as the *New Age* and the *Daily Express*, but they were disconnected pieces. The moments were few in spite of the timeless idleness which was the lot of infantrymen " holding the line."

My sonnet on " Flies," which the *New Age* published, I wrote in front of Arras—I remember Clump, Cross, Crisp and Cling Trenches and will never forget them. They are off the map now, happily ploughed in or built upon—but they are photographed on my memory as long as I live. The cutting from the paper is among my headlinings and it is a good reminiscence—

Flies

More flies than I have ever seen ;
Flies black and red and bottle-green ;
Grey flies that hum ; blue flies that hop ;
And flies that in the food come flop . . .
Flies that live by stagnant places,
Flies that feed upon our faces,
Flies that line the sides of trenches,
Flies that live and move in stenches,

The flies that live through all the rain
And come—before the sun—again.
The flies that buzz . . . The flies that crawl . . .
Ugh, these I hate the worst of all . . .
   I've seen them thick on dead men's eyes :
   I hate these *tame*—these loathsome flies.

It came out hot after the rain, and how they crawled, these flies, slow, leaden-footed, like drunken bees, over the shiny red-brown-grey faces of the dead !

The early books were perhaps too light-hearted.

Ian Hay's *First Hundred Thousand* is an example, though it only reflected the high spirits of that wonderful Scottish Division in which he served. I saw them often in France. The same lot inspired André Maurois' Book—a customer told me—*The Silences of Colonel Bramble*, which I am pleased to see that Lane are doing in their Week End Library at 3s. 6d.

One of my favourites is the omnibus *Mottram*, particularly the short sketch at the end, "The Stranger." I defy anyone who served as an infantryman to resist the twisted English humour of page 799.

" He is not so far wrong." The post-war visitor to the battlefields is in an estaminet and fancies he hears " the shuffling of feet, the murmur, the grating of heavy boots and rifle butts on the cobbles just as though his platoon were standing easy, waiting the order to move."

" He is not so far wrong. They are waiting for him. They are waiting, ' properly at ease ' in the drill-book phrase, if ever men were. Without even reading the little notice board of the Graves Commission he leans on the fence of the little cemetery and scans the names . . . a mixture of all sorts gathered from one of those last actions in the field below. . . ."

All Quiet on the Western Front doesn't deserve a world-wide sale, but I grudge no book its success. It certainly is as good as any of the other foreigners—I mean *Schlump*, or *Under Fire*, or *Sergeant Grischa*.

Undertones of War is good, and I thought *Death of a Hero*

E

best, one night and morning that I sat up, reading it. That last poem is what the much boomed youth movement are saying to us who served and—not too happily—have survived.

Retreat—for those who knew the Somme from 21st March 1918, and the hectic days and nights that followed it—is a reminiscence that must awake poignant recollections.

Down at Bray I can hear an oldish Captain of some Scots regiment saying—describing the opening bombardment— " First I was afraid I was going to be killed but that was nothing to what I felt later. By the morning of the 22nd I wasn't afraid I was going to be killed, I was afraid I was *not* going to be killed."

He was a little mad and glad of the bullet through his right shoulder which gave him an honourable passport out of the line to the Casualty Clearing Station.

The big retreat was memorable in one way to me, for I won three books in it. I was a collector of books even then and they were an odd lot just as I buy odd lots to-day.

In Nurlu . . . I found a complete set of the Little Grey Books of Mr Pelman. They had been forgotten—no memory system can be guaranteed under such circumstances—by one of the many Generals whom we understood studied these hand-books during the War. I regret to say I lost them too, but I was luckier with a small copy of the *Shropshire Lad*. It is the little Grant Richard's edition and I have it yet—its boards now fallen away from its " innards." There's no name on it, but the ring of a cup bottom is on the cover—a cup of tea has stood on it—by some camp bed I fancy. There is a writing though—

" Barrage lifts on first objective 4.55."

It is written in indelible pencil which has run a little.

The *Shropshire Lad* was a favourite pocket-book. I knew two men who carried it and one—Hooper or Cooper was it?— went out in a raid some time in May up by the Vimy.

The other was a Staff man, but when I saw it and remarked on it he had nothing to say. Was it too much to him or too little? I don't know and I don't suppose I ever will. A. E.

Housman has written the best that has been written about the Old Army.

His " Epitaph on an Army of Mercenaries " does in eight lines what the official histories of the War cannot do in volumes. It is the only thing for me in his volume *Last Poems*. I bought three and am sticking to one for purely personal reasons. It is the First Edition, 1922, Grant Richards.

The New Armies may find a like noble utterance in *Poems by Alexander William Mair*, published by Oliver & Boyd of Edinburgh, at the same price as *Last Poems*. The writer of the introduction—Mair is dead—describes him as " perhaps the last of the Greek Poets," and certainly his epitaph challenges comparison with the best in the anthology itself.

> " Though of their glory all the earth is haven,
>   And though their grave is under every sky,
>   Here lies their youth : here let their name be graven
>   Who, dying, taught men how to die."

The other book I picked up in a hospital in which I lay for a few days—one of these tented field hospitals. It was a *Leaves of Grass*—the Everyman edition, but the cardboard covers were torn off and it was all dog-eared. It was profusely underlined. I was a bit tired sometimes speculating why certain things were underlined—but I appropriated it without compunction and it was a good companion to me for many a day. After all is said and done, Walt Whitman knew something of battlefields and field hospitals.

The histories of the War come and go. I have a set of Nelson's *History of the War* which a bookish friend tells me is written as well as anything that Thucydides wrote. It repays looking at, and on anniversary days like the 21st of March, the 1st of July and Armistice Day I read it. It makes a good Book of Days for those who served.

Last March 21st, when I got up I did say to myself : " Where were you ten years ago to-day? " and then the fog and the shelling, the thirst and the uncertainty, the thrills and the depressions, all came back to me and I am—what God knows I never dreamed I would ever be—a British Soldier of the Line.

" Ain't life a poem? " as a young doctor remarked in my hearing as he injected antitetanus into a succession of walking wounded men.

Shaw Sparrow's book, *The Fifth Army in March 1918*, was good reading to me, but perhaps it is unhistorical. I am a partisan of the Fifth Army, of course, but the quarrel is over. We were the bait that lured Ludendorff to ultimate destruction, and if others caught the big fish we will be sporting enough to wish them joy of their catch.

We know about it all. We know—we who lived and, God willing, they who died. It would be intolerable for those who died not to know, I suddenly think, but Nietzsche demands from the pre-war depths, " Why should not life be intolerable? "

The Prussian has conquered.

REAL SOLDIERS

I heard a story of a picture which appeared in *Punch* during the War. I never saw it, but a man who was buying a War book told it me.

He was quite moved telling it, and so was I, hearing it.

Two men in khaki, cluttered up with rifle and battle kit, are leaving Victoria Station and crossing up towards Buckingham Palace Road. They are unshaven and most unmilitary-like, although they have come straight from the Somme fighting, on leave.

A very smart Guardsman in full dress regimentals passes on the other side of the road.

" Bill," one calls out to his pal—" Bill, look ! *a soldier.*"

Is there—was there *ever*—anything like these Kitchener's Army men?

STRATEGY

Last week I sold Liddell Hart's book, *The Real War*, and on the rebound I caught the buyer. His name is Gorrie and he is a Scotsman. Gorrie told me he was on the staff of some Scots Regiment—the Coldstream Guards or the Gordons—he was very full of it—and in connection with his duties was in touch with the French.

He told me an astonishing story and told it something like this as I recollect it.

Foch was Commander-in-Chief at this time of the French Army. The unity of command had still to be achieved.

Foch said, " This is a pretty business. Here am I a master of open warfare conditions and the most rigid trench and siege warfare the world has ever seen is what I have to face. Nevertheless I am Foch."

Foch resumes.

" I am Foch. Circumstances do not permit me to impose my will on the enemy and so create those conditions of open warfare in which I am a master. Yet I must impose my will on the enemy. I can and must.

" I am Foch.

" I cannot drive in the enemy's front but I can induce him to leave his rigid formations and he unknowingly will then give me open warfare.

" How will I induce him to abandon his impenetrable system of defence. I will offer him a lure.

" Now let me consider.

" Already one part of the soil of France has been overrun by the enemy. He will be encouraged to overrun it again. No need to sacrifice more miles of territory. The land of the Somme, over which he retired in 1917, there will I induce him to open his attack.

" I must have good baits.

" I am Foch.

" The British, ah ! the British—they hold their position

with far too many men. They will take over more of the line.
They will stretch their line so thinly that only one man holds
every twenty-five metres. The enemy will be looking for a
front upon which to attack in the spring. They will find out
the weakest part of the front. They will find out the weakest
part of the front is that held by the British Fifth Army.

" They will concentrate all their force on that sector. They
will overwhelm the British. They will stretch their lines of
communications across the devastated Somme. They will be
allowed to go as far as the ravaged territory extends. They
will create a wide salient and then, but not till then, will I
attack.

" I am Foch.

" When open warfare conditions are presented I must win,
and the enemy will present me with these conditions."

And so Gorrie tells me it all happened. Foch struck when
the Bosches had almost entered Amiens.

It was the first blow of what became the final victory six
months later.

I told Gorrie about Walter Shaw Sparrow's book *The Fifth
Army in March 1918*, which I am trying to get for him. It
doesn't support his theory, but he is one of these men whom
the War has left restless. He admits he died in it—that's how
he puts it. His interests finished with the War. He is a
revenant in a land of ghosts. His body ought to be with the
lads who died at Loos—or the boys who went out in July 1916
on the Somme, or anywhere but in England, carrying about a
patent carpet-sweeper in a cardboard box !

And so he talks sometimes to me of strategy, although the
strategy he would like to master, if he is to do his quota of
sales, is the strategy of getting past the maid in order to show
her mistress his Box of Tricks.

TRADE BOOKS

Two books on my trade have come my way this week and there is something in both worth noting.

These notes are to make me a better bookseller—they aim at clearing up my ideas and the writing of them fills up my time.

My first—like an acrostic—is A for American. It is an American book by Ruth Brown Park on *Bookshops and how to run Them*.

In the first chapter the authoress writes a thing to which my heart warms and which incidentally discloses why a bookshop became my choice of a business. It is worth writing down for my own satisfaction. I can always set these contentions against the bills and financial problems which often outface me.

" Books underneath their square surface value, carry realms of further interior interest. You may not only pick them up and hold their solid circumference in your hands but you may open them, peer into their unfolding pages and bury yourself in the delights of these pages. Then when you have surfeited yourself with those delights, you may pass them on to your patrons for money. We know of no other business where a merchant may both have his cake and eat it at the same time."

The other book is published by Constable and is called *Forty Years in My Bookshop*. The author is Walter T. Spencer, but I cannot write anything about it after all.

Forty years . . . I will not be forty years in my bookshop !

WHEN I AM DEAD

Perfect weather, and I was glad to shut my shop and go up to the hillsides that surround this place where I work and live.

I lay on the grass outstretched. I blinked up at sky and tree and was suffused with sheer physical pleasure. I turned over and peered into the grass. It was living with beetles and ants and small spiders and flies and insects. A wormcast was among the roots of the grass.

What a spate of life—what a squirming, writhing multitude there is of us !

On my back again, hands clasped behind my head—legs sprawled ungainly, I thought, as I often do, of death. This would be the way to die, I thought. Life would just pass away from this body into which it has so strangely breathed itself. That would do.

I would be then as I was when Julius Caesar came to England. I would be then as I was when Queen Elizabeth so strongly told her Captains to do battle with Spain. I would be as I was when Napoleon saw his dream was dust.

I would be content if it can come in that way.

My only misgiving is my carcase. How repulsive is the idea to me of my late housing being lifted—one at the head—one at the feet—with me hanging lumpily and limply between —being lifted and carted away.

They lie so still, these mortuary bodies.

BOOKS NO DECENT BOOKSELLER
WOULD KEEP

My pencil almost quivers in my hand. Certainly I am shaken. I am as Luther at Wittenberg or Latimer at Smithfield. I have made a declaration. I have made a gesture—a gesture with a sacrifice.

Last week I bought at the saleroom some parcels of books. They didn't cost much but I like these purchases. They are as thrilling as the lucky bags of my childhood and contain even more exciting treasures. An earlier purchase at the same sale —twelve books for 4s.—included that forgotten success *The Sky Pilot* by Ralph Connor, four volumes of these exciting romances Wilson's *Tales of the Borders and of Scotland*, and a second edition only—alas!—of *These Twain*. I had four shillings' worth of pleasure out of the parcel and I count on selling the dozen books for not less than twelve shillings. There are one or two which will go for twopence or even, I fear, will only fetch a penny. Who will buy, for example, the *Dignity of Business* by H. E. Morgan nowadays? The proud inventor of the phrase " Business as usual " is not a best seller as far as literature is concerned, but I· may be unduly pessimistic! He certainly was not. Well meant, no doubt—these three words expressed too readily the business man's outlook on the War and perhaps made for us a good deal of our troubles then— and since.

My hand is steadier. I will record what I found and what I did. In a parcel of books I found two volumes of the *What a Young Man Should Know* Series. I burned them with difficulty in the old fireplace in the basement. They stunk actually and metaphorically. They should not have been written. They should not have been printed. They should not have been published. If, however, writer, printer and publisher have failed, I, a decent bookseller, have not failed. I have withdrawn these copies from circulation and I am proud of it. This is no heat about nothing—no storm in a tea-cup. The books are well meant, I will agree, if you like—but they are wrong. Not that they contain anything bawdy or filthy . . . they are just wrong. The impudence of the title offends me. *What a Young Man Ought to Know* indeed—there is nothing a young man ought not to know. In the beginning God said, " Let there be light " and there was light.

He didn't go about striking matches or lighting candles. There was light for those who had eyes to see. The miracle and the loveliness and beauty of life is that it is no fenced-in preserve. All may eat of the Tree of Good and Evil and all may learn by what they experience. The world will not be parcelled up into what is good for young men of twenty-five and what is good for greybeards of eighty.

There is light. He that hath eyes to see and ears to hear, let him—nay, he *must*—use them in fear—in peril—in danger —but he must use them or perish.

I will not distribute such literature, and I swear as a decent bookseller I will burn all unsuitable books which by misadventure I buy. That is the self-denying ordinance of a decent bookseller.

.   .   .   .

Months ago I wrote these lines and I am a different man to-day—not that I go back on my self-denying ordinance. I adhere to it, for I have just burned *Maria Monk*, a violent anti-catholic book, in paper covers and, before the War anyway, of large circulation.

The book is in bad taste and I would not pass it on. I don't mind—I find on examination of my outlook—books which might be called obscene or bawdy. I am fond of quite a few as a matter of fact, but they have a largeness which makes them lovable. *Jurgen*, for example, I have heard condemned. It is a delightful book to me and it has many passages which I have marked, foolishly perhaps, in the volume still on my shelves. I believe I marked it to make it unsaleable, for which sin may heaven and my creditors forgive me! How hot I become on these topics and how unnecessary it all is! From one point of view I ought to keep anything the public want. I am a bookseller, not a censor, but I remember that, before I was ever a bookseller, a woman who was my mother conceived and bore me—a man child. I am not abating my birthright.

This self-examination as to the books no decent bookseller should keep will not let me rest, and I return to it.

I loathe these books which are sold to silly women and sillier business men by instalments. I daren't write the titles but they are sold by companies with high-falutin names through salesmen and saleswomen who call from door to door and from shop to shop.

The manner of selling shows the manner of book they sell. They have half a cover and few pages pasted to it. They have a long story and the subjects of these skeleton books are usually of a very comprehensive character. You can, if their tale is to be believed, buy a book all about the Home or the Dog—you can buy a book about the Universe or the Imperial Inheritance, and you can do this by paying 2s. in cash (or something like that) and an indefinite series of payments thereafter. A shopman the other day asked me to buy his " twelve volumes " and was aghast when I refused to give him even a shilling a volume.

But I must be fair. The manufacturers—they are manufacturers rather than publishers—know that no decent bookseller would have their books. They know that too well, and that is why they advertise for " Ladies and gentlemen of good address to introduce important work to their friends in exchange for generous remuneration." We booksellers are not that sort of ladies and gentlemen, though, Heaven knows, I may come to that yet.

I will do it if fate forces me, but not to-day.

> " O'er the past not even the Gods have power,
> To-morrow do thy worst, for I have had my hour."

I walk up and down my shop. Nelson on his quarter-deck was not a prouder man than I.

THE DEADLY PARALLEL
AND THREE RECOMMENDED BOOKS

There used to be a feature in one of the newspapers called the Deadly Parallel, and this morning I was greatly reminded of it when reading the notices on the life of Arthur James Balfour, following his death.

The Reverend Mr Warr, speaking in Edinburgh, is reported to have said—" Convinced as he was that he himself and his brethren of the human family were destined for an eternal fellowship with their Creator, the pursuit of justice, beauty, truth and goodness was for him the supreme objective both of private and corporate life."

So much for the Reverend Mr Warr, but what did Arthur James Balfour himself write?

I have it.

If you will read on page 202 of *A Treasury of English Prose* in Constable's Miscellany Series, you will find a quotation from *Foundations of Belief*. I am always particular rendering unto Caesar the things which are Caesar's, and I must point out that the quotation there made is " By permission of Longmans, Green & Coy." The extract occupies a full page and it is a poignant summary in a short compass of the inscrutable tragedy of man. Here though is the deadly parallel which challenges the smooth certainty of the funeral oration.

" Man will go down into the pit and all his thoughts will perish. . . . Death itself and love stronger than death will be as though they had never been."

The Archbishop of Canterbury, I see, was subtler and wiser. He said of Arthur James Balfour's position towards the Christian faith, " I doubt not that to the end he would have said in his own way and with his own interpretation, ' I am not ashamed of the Gospel of Jesus Christ.' "

The Archbishop speaks, if not with the tongues of angels, at least with the words of charity.

The *Treasury of English Prose* is one of the best things I have to offer. It runs its course from Geoffrey Chaucer to George Santayana and there is in it nothing that is not superb. I can read it at any time and give thanks to Logan Pearsall Smith, not only because it is a book to read, but a book to sell.

The description of " the response we call literature " on page 210, is a perfect thing in words, and to have found and set so priceless a pearl as these hundred words on LOVE by H. G. Wells deserves a peerage.

There are three good anthologies of English Prose I recommend—

> *Treasury of English Prose*—Logan Pearsall Smith. Constable.
>
> *Oxford Book of English Prose*—Arthur Quiller-Couch. Oxford University Press.
>
> *Prose of To-day*—Compiled by the English Association. Longmans.

UNFASHIONABLE BOOKS

BEING WHAT MIGHT BE CALLED BAD STOCK

It would be difficult to know what is bad stock for a bookseller. Here is the history of a book.

The first stage is when it arrives—after much of *Sunday Times* and *Observer* heralding. It is almost hot from the printers and, if it is a great success, I may sell my three or maybe six. I am encouraged. I believe the book is going to be the big book of the year. I buy another six, and then comes the frost. I am left with them. Strenuously practising salesmanship, I sell—on credit—one—maybe two—more, but the four remain. What can I do with them?

Their jackets—they have always wonderful jackets—coats of many colours—get rubbed and torn and they languish. They become tired and weary. I lose taste of them. I ignore them.

Some Monday I put them into the window. I expatiate to any who will listen on their claims to attention. They are worth buying, if only as representing a phase, I plead. It avails nothing.

I take them out of the window. I try a little longer with them on the counters and then—they are in the old shelves at the back shop incurably, definitely bad stock.

From thence they go to be pulped, or to someone who even buys at a lower price than I do, or . . . they may remain

till that sad day when I am no longer the bookseller and another
makes an inventory of my stock.

It is difficult to imagine, but it has to be faced. One day
a sun will shine on a world in which I don't move about—it
will shine instead on turf under which I lie resting and content.

This shop, too, will hold another, and it is hard to think
what he will say and think of my stock, especially my stock of
unfashionable books.

Unfashionable books are principally of the ephemeral
political kind. Nisbet's published a book *Eclipse or Empire*,
which was a huge success at one time with a full page advertisement in the *Daily Mail*—but it is dead now. I have two
copies. The eclipse has passed and the Empire is still here
yet awhile, though, as the writer of this very work has pointed
out, it is rather precarious.

An earlier book of the same type was Arnold White's
Efficiency and Empire, published by Methuen. It is in my
collection of unfashionables for all its merits. Arnold White
was one of those who, with Lord Roberts and Robert Blatchford,
urged us to prepare for war. It is astonishing that more did
not agree with them. War is a recurring decimator, and as we
finished in 1918 we are due for another in 1930. The South
African War closed in 1902. In 1914, twelve years later, Mars
again commenced his bloody business.

War books of the actual war are unfashionable. They don't
wear well.

On my shelves I have a faded copy of *The Roll Call* which
Hutchinson published for Arnold Bennett—a good enough
book but dead with me. I don't think *Peter Jackson* is much
livelier, though I have not banished it yet from a " shelf with a
view " in the front shop. It is being elbowed out, though, by
the host of newcomers which I can hardly keep out of my shop,
so fast do they come.

I have other oddments on these shelves—the last refuge
of the unfashionable books.

There is a biggish book called *Bolshevist Russia*, published
by Stanley Paul and written by Étienne Antonelli. The price

is 12s. 6d. net, but I will take 2s. 6d. now. The dust wrapper which still protects the maroon covers of the book most effect-ively explains the purpose of the book. It was published in 1920 and, with that date in mind, I can smile at the concluding sentence, " M. Antonelli's conclusions are illuminating and hopeful."

That idea of hope ! It is the ingredient which enables the world to go on ! Duncan Davies, who has bought many books, used to tell me how at first when the world was created it would not go. It remained stagnant, dead. The makers of worlds and men communed together and analysed the problem. They added a new ingredient to the hell's broth mixture which men call a world and, since then, it has spun unerringly, unfailingly, unhaltingly, through space. The new ingredient was HOPE.

W. H. Mallock has a book among the despised and rejected —this *Is Life Worth Living?* It is a painstaking, sincere and very Victorian work which provoked a poem with the same title from the then Poet Laureate, Alfred Austin. Who reads either author nowadays ? and yet there are many less worth while whose works I can sell easily.

T. Werner Laurie have also, I see, a representative. The title stamps it as definitely of the long ago. And yet how engaging it must have been to many ! The book is by Mrs Alfred Praga and is entitled *Love and £200 a-year.*

It is a genuinely valuable social document. It shows not how the poor live but how the Middle Class, at the zenith of their power in Great Britain, sought to live. They planned an ample existence on £200 a year—with—of course—love.

This is the most unfashionable book of all—for love has raised its price. A sonnet in the *New Age*, published about the same time, expresses the costliness of love. I have kept it for years, if only for its unique title and subject matter.

" MODERN LOVE SONNET "

(*A Door-to-Door Canvasser sings to his Love*)

" From door to door, on foot I fare,
Each month a four-bob sole I wear.

My object is a thing to sell
A thing for—well, I must not tell.
I sell it sometimes—oftener not—
I feel, sometimes, I'll chuck the lot.
But then I know, if you I'd hold,
I must get hands each week on gold :
To have you, I must pay the price
And daily peddle this device—
Yes, I who one time really thought
Love was a thing could not be bought.

This is the fee then—that the task . . .
Is it worth while, dear love ? I ask."

I think that there ought to be more poems of the common-place. That sonnet does express the conflict between economic necessity and romantic desire. It ought to be stated, for it is a genuine problem though perhaps now unfashionable.

It has been told me that the young lovers come together now on the " dole " and are very happy too, but they were sterner stuff in 1913 when love would not raise an eyebrow below two hundred a year.

Problems of Reconstruction—there's a genuine antique ! I have a copy, and beside it Buckle's *History of Civilisation* which in a way is only right. It is antique too—the well-meaning, hard-working young man who learned his first thinking from Buckle, has gone. I must go one day to the Working Man's College and see who go there now. From what I hear they are not the same. They are gone—sunk in the mud of matrimony, or the deeper mud of the Somme in 1916, or of Ypres in 1917. Their ideas are unfashionable now. They believed in people who knew more than they did. They were willing to learn.

They were teachable.

They have left no descendants that I know or I would sell not only Buckle but some of my other unfashionable books !

WOMAN A WILD SPECIES

One of my most distinguished customers is a doctor.

He is a celebrated man, but, like Socrates, is married to a shrew. He told me so. " Woman is essentially a wild animal. There is no taming of her," he said once. " She is not yet a domesticated species."

He buys a lot of books and daren't take them home. I had over twenty collected for him when he called this afternoon with his car and chauffeur. " My wife has gone to her sister's," he said, " I will get my books home to-day."

He takes them home and puts them behind other books. He dare not buy more bookshelves, so he double-banks the books he has.

" My wife buys God knows what new clothes and I never notice them. I am not so lucky. She nearly always catches me when I bring a book into the house, so I have to wait until the cat is away."

He likes his wife none the less. " Marriage is inevitable for some men and I have done no worse than most. Marriage is an experience which, if you please, I fear I could not have avoided."

He has a resigned and, I think, a happy and philosophic temperament. He placed me in his debt by directing my attention to the following passage from Joseph Addison :

" I consider woman as a beautiful romantic animal, that may be adorned with furs and feathers, pearls and diamonds, ores and silks. The lynx shall cast its skin at her feet to make her a tippet ; the peacock, parrot, and swan shall pay contributions to her muff ; the sea shall be searched for shells, and the rocks for gems, and every part of nature furnish out of its share towards the embellishment of a creature that is the most consummate work of it."

I showed my gratitude by selling him *Her Infinite Variety* by E. V. Lucas, a book which, as the wrapper will tell you, illustrates " the range of woman's genius and charm."

I think I had the better of the exchange.

BOOKS FOR THE BEDRIDDEN

A person—she was just a person—pottered about my counters and shelves for the best part of half an hour to-day. (Should it be the best part of half an hour or the better part? Is one half better than another? Who can say which is the best part of half an hour? The speculation leads me nowhere.)

This pottering person was approached several times by me, but she shuffled off in another direction without speaking, as if I had the plague.

I coughed at her.

I asked her if there was any special book she was seeking. I said, " This is being widely read " and clutched the three volumes of the *World of William Clissold*. She ignored me entirely.

I just left her and behind my desk read William Law's *Serious Call to a Devout and Holy Life*. I could have cursed her all the same, and I don't mind admitting that William Law's *Serious Call*, as far as I was concerned, barely stifled an audible oath.

What can the woman want? It isn't as if it was raining.

At length the oracle spoke. " I want a book for an invalid," she said.

I beamed.

I had the exact book and, *mirabile dictu*, that lady walked out in a few seconds with *The Bed Book of Happiness*, for which she paid me 5s., being one shilling less than its published price.

It was (for it is gone now) an odd book. I copied its full name and description in the first and only catalogue I made of my stock, and I now write these again as an In Memoriam to the Departed. I had noted the following.

71. (That means the seventy-first book in my stock. I was a methodical man of affairs when I first opened this shop.)

" *Bed Book (The) of Happiness*, being a colligation or assemblage of cheerful writings brought together from many quarters into this one compass for the diversion, distraction, and delight of those who lie abed—a friend to the invalid, a companion to the sleepless, an excuse to the tired, by Harold Begbie : Hodder and Stoughton."

The book was dedicated to Sir Jesse Boot, as if he, the owner of the Boots Libraries, needed such a book !

The dedication I copied in another book of mine, for I thought it neat. Here it is—

> " If in my pages those who suffer find
> Such cheer as warms your heart and lights your
>   mind,
>   Glad shall I be,
>   But gladder, prouder too,
> If this my book become a friend like you."

I thought it good when I copied it, but to-day I think it is a little drawn out and not so neat. It was, of course, before the *Mirrors of Downing Street* had reflected the really domestic character of the Gentleman with a Duster.

There was a lot of Chesterton in it and some good things from Samuel Butler's *Notebooks*. It was very well printed and had wide margins with coloured lines which made it easy to read.

It's away now, however—away along the road to God knows where—and I miss its blue cover. I wish I had made some more extracts from it, but it can't be helped.

The having it and the selling it make me think what other books have I got for the bedridden.

First of all I would put the Bible, I think. When it comes that I must lie long and lie low, I will turn to the Bible and, if I am not too weak for its boisterous argument, I will read much in the Book of Job. There is a primitive quality about Job. The world seems emptier than in these crowded days ; in the great spaces the great argument is conducted. (I have a good edition of the *Book of Job* just now. It is published by

S. Welwood, 34 Strand, in 1907, and has an introduction by
G. K. Chesterton. The page headings are in red and the work
itself in good black letter. I digress, but it is a most attractive
book which I am quite entitled to admire. I am not at all sure
that I could bring myself to sell it, but I haven't had a would-be
buyer yet, so the test has not yet been made between cupidity and
the collector.)

If I were too weak for Job, I would find solace in the
Psalms and comfort too in the Gospel according to St John.
The chapter beginning " Let not your heart be troubled "
would be balm for me in the valley of the shadow. I have
proved it, but I could not tell a customer just how—it would
hardly be a selling argument.

Apart from sacred literature, there is a wide field for those
who are bound to bed and I, in one of my times in hospital,
actually drew up a calendar. I recollect part of it, for that time in
hospital was one of the most serene and satisfying I have ever
known. I was called at 6 A.M.—an early hour out of hospital
but I was usually awake. Early tea followed quickly—a thorough
sponge over—and then a longish wait till breakfast at 8 A.M.

I began my day by reading a chapter of Stanton Coit's
Message of Man, a splendid anthology of good things. If I
had long to wait for breakfast I read the chapter again, and to
this day I hold a profit from these waiting hours. The first
chapter is " Be not Led into Temptation," and contains a
sequence of thoughts from Thomas à Kempis, Sir Thomas
Browne, Richard Baxter, William Shakespeare and others, all
pieced together to make a barricade against badness.

Then breakfast would come, and after I would get—if I
could—some daily paper. I then read, until the doctor came,
some play of Shakespeare's and marked the passages which I
would re-read.

Lunch over, I slept. It was advised, and I was always
willing, for to me sleep is the great boon of life. I feel I can
never have enough of it. To me very strange is Wordsworth's
" Our birth is but a sleep and a forgetting." I cannot agree.
It is a wakening, but I for one have never forgotten the sleep

from which I awakened and the dear native land of sleep and
nescience to which I—and all men—are happily fated to return.

It may be in the purpose of things that we awake to the
dream of life that we may but sleep more soundly thereafter
and for ever.

That may be, but I rarely awoke much before tea time, and
how much I enjoyed tea in that hospital!

It is one of the things that I remember with thankfulness.

After tea I was always very vigorous. I could tackle anything, and did, in fact, read all Gibbon and all Hume's *History
of Scotland* during my convalescence.

Dinner—light and unappetising I always found it—came
at 7 P.M., and by 9 P.M. I was fast and beautifully asleep.

These bedridden days were happy ones, and were I a poet
I would challenge Shenstone. He found life at its best in an
inn. Had he lived to know the convalescent ward in the modern
hospital, he would have changed his mind!

I cannot pretend, however, that my taste in books would
do for all the bedridden.

Mine was a surgical case which had to have time to heal.
I hadn't much pain after the operations were over. The case
is altered for those who lie in bed and suffer. For such I
cannot think of books—or anything—that would lighten the
weight of incessant, unrelenting pain. Personally, I don't
think I would take it. I have sympathy with those who say,
" I will suffer thus far but no farther." I will silence these
shrieking nerves which enhance every ache and magnify every
pain. I will silence them if I still all this that is me for ever.

But there are lesser states of suffering, and for these I
prescribe the great novel writers. Sir Walter Scott, Thackeray,
George Eliot, Charlotte Brontë, Dickens and Anthony Trollope
—these are the cool, calm, shady spirits.

The good essayists are friends. Hazlitt, Addison and
Stevenson are good companions. The historians can help and
perhaps Macaulay, Green and Trevelyan are best. The
Martyrdom of Man by Winwood Reade, and Buckle's *History
of Civilisation* would be good too. They occur because I have

good editions of both of them and I could sell them with confidence. They are broad and satisfying. If the first is perhaps a little sombre it is good perhaps to temper the rising tide of returning health and vigour.

The bedridden should read reforming books, I think, with profit. M'Dougall's *Character and the Conduct of Life* is excellent and any of us, bedridden or business-worried, would be improved by a short course of *Epictetus* and *Marcus Aurelius.*

My exercise is over. My copy-book pages are full and I have done my task.

When the doctors have done their damnedest, let the good friends of the feeble come to me.

I have the books of life.

I have the guide-books which bring men back to health and happiness, and they can be bought from me for little money and at a strictly low price.

REJECTION

She was radiant. I thought her perfect. I could not believe that a more charming creature ever was. I thought of Mary of Scotland, Madame de Pompadour, Helen of Troy—they did not compare with her in the way the very thoughts of her stirred me.

To-day—it was the forenoon—she asked me about a book —Heaven knows what she can want with it. It is called the *Manners and Tone of .Good Society* by the Honourable Mrs Dowdall. I went to look up the list—I thought it was done by Black—but I wasn't sure.

I was rather a time in finding it and she and her friend came up past the desk behind which I was turning the pages. She mustn't have thought I was in earshot, for she said to her companion, " I wish this pimply-faced prig of a bookseller would hurry. I have to be at Madame Austin's at eleven."

My pimply face reddened as I told her a few seconds later I would get the book for her in two days, but the redness— she could not know—was the setting sun of a foolish regard.

BOOKS WHICH ARE NO BOOKS

Lamb (is it Lamb?) has written about books which are no books, but to-day I think all books are books as sure as eggs are eggs. There are books which men may think are no books— yet they are books profitable to read and profitable to sell. My mind warms to them this day of grace, for I have an order for *Debrett's Peerage and Titles of Courtesy*.

Now this work—which is published by Dean & Son, Ltd., who, by the way, also publish quite a good lot of Rag Books for children—is all " fat " for the bookseller. He is not expected to keep Debrett's *Peerage* in stock any more than he is expected to keep a peer on his premises. He gets it " to order."

The procedure may be imagined. Carriage draws up to his plebeian door—carriage that is—or car—Rolls Royce or Daimler with Mulliner body.

Bookseller emerges expectant.

Peer (or peeress) remains until footman (or chauffeur if slightly decayed or very independent family) removes dust cloth or rug from knees. Peer (or peeress) alights.

Bookseller—anticipatory—greets patron. (" Patron " covers both sexes for the bookseller. " Patroness " is a bazaar term.)

" You can get me Debrett? "

The bookseller doesn't doubt it for a moment. If he is just an ordinary fellow he just acquiesces and gives laud and honour for the order.

If he knows his business he asks, " What binding do you prefer? "

If the patron is buying his first copy of Debrett, a divine

opportunity presents itself. The bookseller can say—if he has had lessons to prevent stammering—Would you have the limp morocco, round corners, gilt edges, printed on thin paper, or would you rather have the levant morocco, gold edges, specially bound? The limp is £6 ; the levant is £5.

The patron might demur and, although this is almost miraculous, yet, if such demurring actually took place, the stammer-proof bookseller would then go on to say—coyly—. " Of course, there is the leather gilt—the same book as the levant—gilt edged—bound specially for £4 : 10s.—and there is the royal octavo cloth gilt, emblazoned cover, for £3 : 15s."

If impressed, the bookseller, to fill up a gap, could say, " These prices are net "—or he might say, " If you would care for your coat of arms, I can have it imprinted in gilt on the back cover for 12s."

These are some of the possibilities which arise out of the demand for Debrett, although my own experience was simpler.

A man servant called and told me to order a Debrett. I delivered it in due course—the 90s. one—and it is still unpaid.

Debrett is an entertaining work. The introductory articles are well worth reading and the often surprising information about the Peerage, Baronetage, Knightage and Companionage is as entertaining as anything I sell.

It has a companion book, *Debrett's House of Commons and the Judicial Bench*, which, if not so lordly in appearance, is less lordly in price. You can choose half bound leather for 25s. or the cloth gilt for 20s.

More popular than Debrett, however, is *Who's Who*, and the stories that those who appear in that work tell about themselves always amuse me. If one can be said to browse in the meadows of literature, I am prepared to admit that I have browsed in the pages of *Who's Who*. One goes from one name to another and wonders if one would recognise the writers from their own descriptions of their origins, their education, their achievements, and, most of all, their recreations. A. & C.

Black publish *Who's Who*, as indeed they also are responsible for *Who was Who*—à sort of book of final entry for the Ferryman—and *Who's Who in the Theatre*. I have a copy—it is not this year's—of *Athena, a Year Book of the Learned World*, which the same publishers do—an odd lot, I think, and fit to stand with its neighbour on my shelf, the *Directory of Directors*.

The *Directory of Directors* has suggested to me the *Politics of Politicians*—the *Divinity of Divines*, and the *Books of the Booksellers*, but these would hardly make books of reference.

My other books of reference, I see, include Whitaker's *Almanack*, Oliver & Boyd's *Edinburgh Almanac*, *The Statesman's Year Book*, *The Railway Year Book*, *The Daily Mail Year Book*, and Brown's *Nautical Almanac*. Heaven knows why I have so many—they are so heavily and so ostentatiously dated too—in this up-to-the-minute universe, I fear they will remain mine if I don't sell them soon.

Atlases and dictionaries are safer stock. Atlases do go out surprisingly too, but I am not so hampered with them as with the books of reference. The pocket road map atlases are a bother. The motorists are so insistent on the new roads. I have told them that a wrong map may show them more than a right one, but they receive this counsel rather coolly. One man had glassy eyes which he turned on me like a basilisk when I said it, and yet, it may be true !

My dictionaries to-day are well to the fore. Nuttall, Chambers, Collins are all good, but I recommend the *Concise Oxford Dictionary* before all others.

Dictionaries of quotations include *Bartlett's Familiar Quotations* which Macmillan publish, and I have a second-hand copy of a little one of Nelson's which can go for 2s.

My best possession among all the books of reference—I would not exchange it for Debrett—is *A Classical Dictionary* of 1809, by J. Lemprière, D.D. Mine is the seventh edition and it has often been for me verily the seventh heaven ! It really is not for sale, but anyone who wants to make reference in it may do so.

There is no book in all my shop I value more.

.   .   .   .

Is a gazetteer a book of reference? I think it must be.
No one would want to *read* the *Ordnance Gazetteer of Scotland*.
It is in six volumes—faded blue cloth—a bulky lot of pictures
of Highland scenery and Border castles introduce the letter-
press. Maps—crease-worn—are at the end.

Scotland is a beautiful country, but my gazetteer does little
to advertise it. These new journalistic writers know their trade
better than those who compiled my set.

I am a good bookseller! Here I am disparaging my wares.
Some books I won't sell because I like them too much—because
I am too fond of them.

Others—and the gazetteer is one—I wouldn't sell because
it would be a shame to take the money!

It is a librarian I ought to be—and not a bookseller. The
sense of profit-making is not in me and, labour as I will, I
cannot create it.

In a neighbouring town (for I must not advertise) there
are two men in my calling. One has above his door the word
BOOKSELLER, with his name. The other, and I know him well,
has only the simple, single word BOOKS.

The gulf which lies between the schoolmen of the Middle
Ages and the modern American super-salesman is not more
effectively expressed than in the difference between him who
puts up the sign " BOOKSELLER " and the other who simply
labels himself " BOOKS."

THE DAUGHTER OF JOY

In the park, boys are playing football and girls are pushing
perambulators with not-too-absurd imitations of themselves in
them. The night is about to fall on us all and lamps are
already lit.

Grimly I sit on a seat alone, aloof, solitary, unsought, unseeking.

A girl of seven pushes her poor perambulator in front of her and glances keenly toward me.

Heaven knows why, but she looked in my direction. Her glance reached me and dropped. She scrambled forward and seized something lying on the asphalt path.

It was a penny.

" It's not yours, Mister? " she queried.

" No," I replied.

I don't know what she did with that penny, but she was transfigured, a Daughter of Joy in a City of Dreadful Sadness and Sin.

BOOKS WITH PICTURES

PLAIN AND COLOURED

It is the offers made by the publishers of the *Studio* which suggest to me some attempt to outline my attitude towards books with pictures. The *Studio* has done a big service to picture lovers and to booksellers, and I personally am indebted to them for some excellent displays of picture books. There is the " Masters of Etching " Series of which it is claimed one hundred and twenty thousand copies have been sold. Each book has twelve reproductions and there is a monograph of the etcher with each book. My taste—which is uneducated and uninformed—approves the Whistler Book, Brangwyn and D. Y. Cameron, but it is de Goya and William Walcot that I have sold best. My best customer for these books of pictures is a man of fading eyesight and he tells me there is more happiness for him in looking at these books of etchings than in a whole week of reading. It is a quiet pleasure but a profound one, he declares, and I am happy in his happiness.

In my window I put the coloured Studio Books at 5s. each

and it was quite a success. Again I have my own choice among these, though where my appreciation was born or how cultivated I cannot tell. For example, there is the reproduction of " The Privileged Three," by Russell Flint. It is a beautiful picture —that much even is apparent to me. The scene is some country bathing pool rudely roofed over with heavy rough-hewn beams. To the edge of the picture comes the water and three nude female figures fill up the background. The composition is gold and brown and red, but all subdued, and, from out the glow, gleams the richest blue colouring of a cloak or dress which the centre figure is putting on. That blue against all the glow of gold and brown and red is poignantly beautiful and that is only one of the series of pictures—only one of many which affects a bookseller as none of his books have ever done.

Pictures in ordinary books I don't like, and I don't think readers like them either. I have a first edition of *Mr Polly*, Wells's book, published by Nelson's before the War, and I think it is spoiled by the pictures. I prefer my own ideas of Mr Polly and of the plump woman (who I don't think is ever named) to those of the artist who is responsible for the coloured frontispiece in that book.

Portraits of authors I don't mind so much, but even these I prefer not to see. To an antique author or a writer of a century ago I do not raise an objection—they are of a piece somehow with the book, but pictures of modern authors— Conrad, Wells, Shaw, Galsworthy—fronting their books is anathema to me.

If we must have employment for the book artists, there is the dust cover. If the reader doesn't like it he can remove it, and if he likes it immensely—well he can clip it out and paste it within. I have done that on rare occasions.

There is a set of Sir Walter Scott on my shelves which has an illustration at the beginning of every volume. The date is 1905 and Thomas Nelson & Sons of London, Edinburgh and New York are the publishers. The books gain little by their pictures : personally for me they would be more acceptable without them. *Old Mortality*, for example, I have reached down from the shelves to look at, and for the life of me I do not fathom the mentality of the publishers who appear to think that the book is improved with a picture entitled " Balfour of Burley in hiding at Milnwood."

Old Mortality requires no such recommendation to me, it being one of the most readable of Sir Walter Scott's novels. The introduction which I have just re-read is an interesting bit of Scottish history. It seems a fine calling, that of Robert Paterson alias *Old Mortality*, and one—had I the art and craft—that I would not be averse to follow. To go from village to village and put churchyards and monuments in order takes my fancy. It is a gypsy life with a plan and purpose. It is a philosopher's calling too—this " daily dalliance with death," as an intellectual and well-read undertaker of my acquaintance called his own profession.

The gypsies with a purpose are few. *Old Mortality*, John Maxwell Senhouse in Maurice Hewlett's *Open Country*, Robert Louis Stevenson's *Travels with a Donkey in the Cevennes*— these are attractive visions ; and there are the moderns, the American Harry A. Franck and the Gordons, works by both of whom I see I have on sale. Theirs are books with pictures, but pictures in a travel book are as important as maps in a guide-book.

It is pictures of people I fancy I dislike. They get out of date : they outrage one's own conception of what the writer had in mind : they are unnecessary : these are the reasons for my dislike of pictures in books.

Picture books, pure and simple (whatever I mean by that), are a different pair of shoes. *London Types*, by William Nicholson, is a regular good thing. It is a large production of rough paper with a splendid picture of a horse busman of the period. With each picture there is some verse by W. E. Henley, but very poor stuff compared with his best. The pictures in this instance are everything. The verse is nothing. I see it is by Heinemann and was produced in 1898. South Africa had not then sailed into the stream of time for London and what a jolly life it seems to have been from this picture book !

Where are these men to-day, whose fathers in their primes were subjects for William Nicholson? The book only cost 5s. in these spacious days, but I want 10s. for it to-day. I observe *The Times* of that time declared that these books would soon come to be prized by collectors and certainly the prophecy is true, for I prize this picture book. I only wish I had a copy of Nicholson's *The Queen.* I saw it years ago in Bond Street, and if I were Chatto & Windus, I would get permission to reprint it with Lytton Strachey's *Queen Victoria.*

That picture and Strachey's books now—*they* would go together! They express—years apart—the same impression of that wonderful, *wonderful* woman—the least royal in a hundred ways of all our royalties, but to me—born in her reign—the royallest of them all. Galsworthy and Strachey and Nicholson, they felt her greatness, and the universality of her appeal touches all who knew her and know their work.

That will do!

Bookseller! You are just scribbling on for scribbling's sake —filling up pages ·in the fond fancy you have something to write about.

You had better go to bed.

NECROMANCY

A very smart lady was my customer a few minutes ago. She almost *castigated* me for not having a better selection of guide-books.

I offered her three or four of Ward Lock's Handbooks—some of Muirhead's Blue Books, but it was Black's *Paris*, an ancient thing in red, that made her cross with me.

I don't know why, yet she was highly finished and polished. I would have called her beautiful if I had not had this experience with her. She quite awed me and I remembered what Sheridan wrote of the awe which beauty awakes.

I have found the quotation in Nelson's *A Dictionary of Quotations*, by Colonel Philip Hugh Dalbiac. What a gallant name for a collector of quotations !

No comments. Write out the quotation.

" Nothing keeps in such awe as perfect beauty ; now there is something consoling and encouraging in ugliness."

And so I have performed the ceremony. I have joined—mated, if you like—in this sheet of scrap paper, my beautiful customer, the gallant Colonel, the awe of perfect beauty and the consolations of ugliness.

I am a necromancer.

IMPROVING BOOKS

The " improving " books *par excellence* are the Home University Library of Modern Knowledge begun by Williams & Norgate and carried on now by Thornton Butterworth. I have several of them, and how grateful the reading public must be to the publishers and the authors.

All Hilaire Belloc's are in my stock and I purr with knowledge of the world when I rise from reading his *Warfare in England* and his *French Revolution*. The whole series is so admirably planned :

Religion and Philosophy,
Literature,
Geography,
Economics,
Politics,
History.

A fine range of reading which bears out Carlyle's truth that " the true university is a good collection of books."

Who wouldn't—I ask my empty and almost echoing shop this afternoon—who wouldn't give a couple of shillings to spend two or three hours with H. A. L. Fisher or A. F. Pollard or H. N. Brailsford or Harold J. Laski?

These books give every man that opportunity and I am glad to be the purveyor of that opportunity. I don't belong to the class of booksellers who put neat black-and-gold labels on their books giving their name and address, but I would be proud to do it on any of this series. H. A. L. Fisher and Gilbert Murray—great educationalists though they are—have done nothing better than they have done in devising and directing this series.

Two shillings—it isn't bookselling—it is exchanging mere silver for solid gold! I owe the series a lot, and any man who buys and reads these books is bankrupt in the noblest sense, for he could never—can never—pay his debt to the producers of them. These are high words but I write them calmly. They are true.

The biggest of my improving books is Cassell's edition of H. G. Wells's *Outline of History*. It is an educational service to our generation. If Alfred Harmsworth is entitled—as I think he is—to the credit of the discovery of the new generation of readers who, taught in the State schools, seek to expand their knowledge in the *Daily* and other *Mails*, Herbert George Wells is entitled to the credit of having taken them one step farther.

His *Outline of History* is stimulating. I am told it is not all history, but is not history a fable upon which wise men are agreed?

I have both his *Outline of History*, 1920, and his *Short History of the World*, 1922. Horrabin's diagrams are most entertaining. He has an openness of line which makes his pictures as fresh and attractive as flowers in the spring. The chapters on the " Making of the World " and the " Making of Man " tell the evolution story as entertainingly as a fairy tale and yet as accurately as modern science knows. They are handbooks to the background of history, and make me glad for the new generation which starts where the ardent debating rationalist Victorians left off their work.

What an attractive story Wells has to tell now that the dust and conflict which Darwin and Huxley raised are now the all-but-proven facts of the beginning of things.

Short of moral homilies, of which I have few, there are no improving books in my stock to compare with these. A dead lot, I think, my set of Carlyle. I am a little weary of this great man, and I am weary of having my twenty volumes by Chapman & Hall on my shelves. I would sell him willingly.

Carlyle's thunder is all in extracts and anthologies nowadays. I doubt if anyone reads him through. *Sartor Resartus* I have sold and the *French Revolution*, but who buys his *Life of Schiller* or his *Critical Essays*?

None of my customers has done so up to date anyway. And yet how good he is—I always like the man and his work —but O! this set of twenty volumes! How I wish I could get rid of them!

All booksellers have *bêtes noires*—and these appear more among the improving books than in any other class—especially improving books in collected editions. Ought there to be collected editions? occurs to me as I look at my Carlyle again and my Kipling and a set of Leonard Merrick. They are the product of the optimism of publishers and the vanity of great men, and they are often the bane of booksellers.

Few of us like *all* a man wrote any more than we could like all a man did or thought. The collected edition tells us we ought to love the writer in twenty manifestations of his genius if we have loved him in one. That may be—has to be —good enough as a basis for marriage—we love her smile— the way she walks—or talks—and we take her altogether for better or for worse. But books—ought we to have to swallow the hook because we like the bait? Are we quite such poor fish?

I place the " Legacy " Series published by the Oxford Press very high in the list of books which are improving without making the reader pompous. *The Legacy of Greece* appeals to me most and *The Legacy of the Middle Ages* appeals to me least of all, but they all appeal. They are good sellers.

F

It is almost impossible to avoid paying 8s. 6d. to know what Greece was and what she has left us as a legacy to live by now that she has gone. The men who come late in life to letters buy this series—the men—I had one to-day—who know how wonderful the life of the past was and how much of it lives in them to-day—these men who had no education after twelve or fourteen—these men know, try and buy the series. I never see and talk to men of that type—my customer this morning was definitely an example—but I remember Gibbon's declaration in his *Memoirs*. " Every man," the historian of the *Decline and Fall* asserts, " who rises above the common level has received two educations : the first from his teachers ; the second—more personal and important—from himself."

It is such second educations we booksellers provide, and this desire lies behind the demand—long may it flourish—for improving books.

ALAS, THE UNRETURNING PAST!

Quite a nice young girl bought one of A. A. Milne's to-day and, as she took it from me, she accidentally upset a rectangular tower of books by the same author which I had set out for display. She was very profuse with her apologies.

I stooped to pick up the fallen books and, as my eyes rested on the floor at her feet, I noticed her shoes.

They were neat and, I suppose, graceful but they did not thrill me as once thrilled me a pair of buttoned boots.

How I adored these buttoned boots of a long lost love ! I would not exchange the memory of them for a caravan of crocodile and snake skins—indeed, not a whole shopful of lizard shoes !

BOOKS FOR OUT-OF-DOORS

" Give to me the life I love," declares the young devotee of Robert Louis Stevenson and I see her *Travels with a Donkey*, *The Inland Voyage* and the neat little *R. L. S. Anthology* which Chatto & Windus publish.

She wears a short tweed skirt and spends her weekdays as a milliner next door, and her week-ends on the moors. I have seen the man in the case, however, and I am not sure that the minx is not just playing up to him. It is enough, however, that she buys books in the present. The future is hers.

After her departure I replaced the out-of-door books which I have. What a lot there are nowadays! Time was when literature was a thing of the study and of the hearth. Now it has left these safe anchorages for the hills.

It is a high test. Any book is readable in a chair by the fireside but few authors can stand being taken out-of-doors. They all of them smell of the lamp and the lamp avails little under the sun or the stars. " Books," it is asserted, " are a mighty poor substitute for life," and it is a bold man who would attempt the exchange.

Still there are some, and I can comment on them as I put them back one by one on their shelf.

First of all in popularity, and I think in place, is E. V. Lucas's *Open Road* published, as all E. V. Lucas's writings are, by Methuen. It cannot be beaten in its way, but if I were looking for an alternative—if I found a customer who already had *The Open Road*—my second string would be the *Week-End Book* published by the Nonesuch Press. It is the brightest product of the Bright Young Things who are so bright just now that even a bookseller must notice them.

Among my second-hand books, dated 1906 and published by T. N. Foulis, is *The Footpath Way*. This book has always puzzled me, because although published in 1906 there is written on the front page " Evie with Eva's love 1905." Perhaps the donor got an advance copy, but the 1905 on the inscription and the publisher's 1906 have always puzzled me. Maybe Evie mistook the year—let us hope there was no mistake about the love.

These waifs of books I specially love and I am fond of *The Footpath Way*. Alfred H. Hyatt compiled the collection and there is a lot of good prose and poetry in it.

Richard Jefferies starts out the way with us and there is little left unobserved or unremarked by one or other of our distinguished companions. The book ends with Stevenson's " Envoy," and I will confess I was glad when the minx (who is also a milliner) bought *The Open Road*, of which I have a second copy, and left me with my *Footpath Way*.

Maps are in many ways the best outdoor companions and I keep a stock. It always happens that I am out of the map that is wanted but I am fairly successful in getting inquirers to wait. The Ordnance Maps are a joy and a boon but curiously enough they have never driven me out-of-doors.

Instead I crease my stomach lying over my counter pouring over unfamiliar names and places a bare ten miles from my door ! I ought to get out and see these places for myself, but the native lethargy of my disposition and, may it not be, the necessity and attraction of my calling keep me to my shop. I recollect the quotation from *Eastward Ho!* by Chapman, Jonson and Marston and I take its words for my comfort, " Keep thy shop and thy shop will keep thee." The same words (I am informed by a reliable source) are to be found in Benjamin Franklin's *Poor Richard*, but I have no copy of either work although I accept the counsel. It is a commandment with promise like the Fifth in the Holy Writ.

It would be better for my health, however, if I had to keep my shop less and see more of the outdoor life. If I were a man and not a cog I would run off—just shut my door—and go. I might take Burrow's *Guide to the Scottish Highlands*, for example (2s.), and refuse to return until I had been to Ballachulish. It is sad to think that I will die and never see even Ballachulish, far less Bombay or Ballarat or the Balearic Islands. Alice in Wonderland-like, I have a fancy to go to all the places that begin with a B.

There is Bradford, and Bradford-on-Avon, and Birmingham

—but this is foolishness. The only B's with which I have concern are the B's that begin BOOKS and BOOKSELLER.

Books for the Open Air? Yes! madam.

" Here is Thomson's *Seasons*. No, not a new book; written by a Scotsman in the first quarter of the eighteenth century. It deals with the four seasons of the year. Out of date? No, the seasons are still spring, summer, autumn and winter just as when James Thomson wrote of them.

Dreadful? Ah! *The City of Dreadful Night*—that is another James Thomson—not the same. You mean " The Seasons " are dreadful. Yes, they do say they are changing. Something with more incident? Yes, of course. Now here is an incident and all out-of-doors. *On the Road with Wellington.* It is—you can see by the cover—a diary of a war commissary on the Peninsular Campaign—published by William Heinemann. A German book—yes—but not like *All Quiet on the Western Front*, not at all. Yes, I would call *All Quiet* an out-door book but it deals with very unpleasant weather.

Scotland—yes—of course, I have *In Search of Scotland* by an Englishman : he seems to have found something—or would you like this one *The Call of the Pentlands*? No, it is not the name of a family. Indeed—of course—it is a name of a family —but this book is about the hills.

Yes, I have a number of other suggestions. Here is a book on the *British Colonies* published by Blackie—certainly an out-of-door book if not also an out-of-date one.

I have *The State as a Farmer, Hills and the Sea, The Path to Rome*—would any of these interest you? I have a great choice of books.

Yes, I believe it is very good. I haven't read it.

Thank you. Thank you. Good afternoon.

Would you believe it, the creature who wanted a book for out-of-door bought *Eat and Grow Thin*—a diet book published by Putnam's !

Anyway it was a sale, and a sale to me these days is about as welcome as a sail would be to the Ancient Mariner.

There are no ideal books for out-of-doors. The answer

that any honest man should give to those who come looking for books for out-of-doors is GET OUT . . .

I remember a book *Get On or Get Out* by Peter B. Keary. The *Daily Express* published it long ago. The lads who read it—I wonder—have they got on or got out?

How I hark on the War! It is a real impediment to me in business and yet how can I go on—and on—and not think of what I have seen and what I have heard.

INSOMNIA

This will not do. I have been awake for hours. I lay on my back in my bed and, though I could not see it in the dark, thought of the ceiling. I thought of the whitewash on it, the streakiness, the hairs left by the painter's brush, the fly dirt and then the plaster—the grittiness of it, mixed as it is with cow's hair. I thought on. I came to the laths and then the rafters on which they are nailed and then the beams. I thought of the space between the beams and the roof tree—a sort of attic where unsaleable books are piled—and I thought on, up to the top of the roof. I passed through the slates and was on the zinc coping. I thought on, freeing myself of things tangible. I was up in the air—on through the atmosphere—I was passing the moon and the stars. I was out beyond the stars. I was in space. I thought on and on. It was endless, timeless. I was hungry with thought, thirsty with thought. I was frozen cold and consumed with fire by turns. I was sick. A vertigo took me. I lost my balance. I fell. I kept on falling. My mind was falling out of my body. I was going mad. I only saved myself by leaping out of bed and holding myself against the wall of my room.

.   .   .   .

I say it is too bad.

Such experiences ought not to come to booksellers.

BOOKS FOR PRIZES

A bachelor book-lover is the most likeable of all the species, and I have one who is a perfect example. Bland, urbane, well-informed, tolerant—he is the kind of man I would wish myself to be were I not what I am. That guarded proviso is due to him as a matter of fact. He it was who told me the story of the most wonderful of earthly trinities—the Scotsman, the Englishman and the Irishman. The Englishman admitted that if he had not been an Englishman he would like to have been born an Irishman. The warm-hearted, generous son of Erin was not to be outdone and he handsomely admitted that if he had not been born an Irishman his preference would be to be born an Englishman.

The Scotsman sagaciously weighed up the merits of the case. He was agreeably disposed, but truth must come before politeness for one brought up on the Psalms, the Shorter Catechism and porridge. He replied that if he had not been born a Scotsman he would have wished to be born one !

I therefore make my proviso and content myself with preferring to be what I am.

My bachelor book-lover tells me that he has two nieces and reminds me of Charles Lamb's opinion that nieces are the nicer—in fact all male children should be drowned at birth. He wants his nieces to like books and he told them that whenever they want a book badly, if they will write a personal letter to him explaining why they want the particular book, he will send it. But the letters must be clear and concise in their whys and wherefores.

The elder Miss demanded a Robert Louis Stevenson. She has *Treasure Island* and *The Travels in the Cevennes* and she wants to have a complete set. Fortunately, I am able to oblige my friend but he has demanded, he tells me, as to the *reasons*. Next time he will want something more than manifestation of the spirit of the collector : he will want the expressed preferences of the critic.

The other niece has asked for *Simple Stories* by Archibald Marshall. She likes the pictures and her girl friend has it, so I have been instructed to procure and post *Simple Stories* illustrated by George Morrow, published by Harrap, 7s. 6d. net.

It will be done.

All that brought me to the problem of prizes for good boys and girls and for clever boys and girls.

For good boys and girls I sell Bibles and Prayer Books. An early drift to piety is not to be discouraged. There is a lot to be said for making these the first books which a child gets, once he or she has got beyond the picture-book stage in life.

My own appreciation began early, and I am inclined to think that those who come to the Bible and the Prayer Book with matured minds miss a lot. The story of the Prodigal Son is a different story to John aged seven and John aged seventeen. The lovely parables of the Good Shepherd should be sown on a young and innocent mind if the full meaning and deep comfort is to come when mature years have informed the intelligence.

The Life of Christ—there are several of them for children— belongs to the same commended catalogue, including those which are illustrated.

The Pilgrim's Progress ought to be a prize for a good boy or girl, but I am not so certain when I come to *Don Quixote* or the *Arabian Nights*. *The Fairy Tales*—Andrew Lang's Series —I always recommend, and with them every year there comes a host of competitors. It is a side of publishing which is well done—these prizes for good boys and girls.

Prizes for clever boys and girls are rather more difficult, but I am never chary of recommending and selling any book no matter how advanced. Thackeray, Dickens, Scott, George Eliot, Jane Austen and the Brontës—every clever boy or girl ought to know that if the reputation of cleverness is to remain with them, they must know something about these really clever people. They should get them early. They will love them late.

Basil Blackwell, Oxford, published in 1927 a very instructive and stimulating book which I sold for a prize and which the donor has told me gave a definite direction in life to the winner. History has marked her for her own, I believe. The book is called *The Curious Years*, and the sub-title is " History, Recent and Remote." The author is Jessie Rathbone. The price is 6s. It never got any good reviews that I saw, but it is a good book for a prize none the less. It begins with the Creation and goes down to 1900. The method is to link a name, a quotation, an event and the date all together. Just at random I take page 125 and learn from it what the seventeenth century was. What a kaleidoscope it is ! Here are some of the names : Guy Fawkes, Marie de Medici, Gustavus Adolphus, Oliver Cromwell, Richelieu and Mazarin, Judge Jeffreys and John Hampden and Fahrenheit. Here are a couple of the quotations :—

" Richelieu and Mazarin made France glorious. Men feared but did not love them."

" Lord Macaulay said of John Hampden . . . ' A great man who never sought nor shunned greatness, who found glory only because glory lay in the path of duty.' "

And here—to complete the picture of what the book is— are a few events :

" First Eddystone Lighthouse built."

" Pilgrim Fathers sail for America."

" First English Newspaper, *The Weekly Times*, printed."

" Peter the Great came in disguise to Holland as a ship-builder."

I think *The Curious Years* a stimulating and original book. It will make an epoch-making prize for a clever young person, and who knows where it may lead?

Last year I sold Napier's *Battles in the Peninsula* as a school prize, and this was very well received. John Murray publishes it and the mention of his name reminds me once again of the Samuel Smiles' books. They are good prizes.

Macmillan's edition of Sir John Seeley's *Expansion of England* is the right kind of book for the donor of a prize. I have, too, Chatto & Windus's edition of Macaulay's *History*— the fine paper edition in five volumes. It awaits on my shelves.

What a fine edition it is—from five to six hundred pages in each volume, all most beautifully printed.

Frankly, it is too much of a prize to sell.

I will keep it.

My cleverness unrewarded at school claims it now.

One may make too much of young people.

A Christmas book is a kind of prize book, but frankly, this Christmas-present business makes me very ill. I am worried by all sorts of inquiries all day long from persons who wish, on the anniversary of the birth of Jesus Christ, to give presents to their friends. They are not the gifts of the Magi ; they are not the gifts of peace and goodwill upon earth, because they seem to be given grudgingly, unwillingly, reluctantly, meanly, and yet I suppose they do represent some slight expansion of good feeling, which the givers only feel at Christmas, which comes but once a year.

I am told by a traveller for one of the less reputable book-selling firms, that my experience is not new. Novice though I am to the bookselling business, I am, however, shocked at this revelation of human nature. The traveller tells me that the classic story in the book trade is the story of the man who approached a bookseller, not as a tradesman, but as a friend. He said to him, " I have got to give a present to my brother-in-law, and I do not know what I can give him. He seems to have everything and is much better off than he ought to be, considering that he is only a blockhead." The bookseller was anxious to be helpful and said—his mind being on his trade— " Why not give him a book." " *A Book*," said the would-be donor,—" A BOOK," he repeated ; " WHY, HE HAS GOT A BOOK." I laughed heartily in spite of all my Christmas troubles at this suggestion, but it is bitterly true. My small shop is packed with books, and my life is full—too full—of books, but I do know how true it is in so many houses there exists as a symbol perhaps, *one single book*, which, having found its way there, remains an orphan to the end of its days.

And so in this muddy, dirty, depressing week which precedes Christmas, I must be careful. I must not push my wares on a reluctant public too enthusiastically. I must remember the other things that the world already possesses ; I must remember, too, that most people already have *A Book*.

THE WHITE FLAG

Some days this bookselling is a very torture of the devil. To-day has been such a day. I have done nothing right.

I burnt myself with my aluminium kettle this morning. Two unpleasant and impatient demands for money were all that my morning post contained. A querulous old man has cancelled an order for a useless book without rhyme or 'reason and I am landed with what will be indubitably more bad stock. A miss—a minx, I might have written—tormented me about some novel she had heard of at a tennis party but she could neither tell me publisher, author, title, or give me an indication as to contents. ." You ought to know if you are a bookseller. Everybody's reading it just now."

Hell !

The world defeats me and my head is both bloody and bowed. My fighting spirit is dead. I wonder what it is really like in the workhouse. Is it so bad after all?

Epictetus was the crippled slave of a brutal master yet from his humiliations he extracted serenity.

Could I?

MADNESS AND BOOKS

It is an unending amazement to me, the subjects to which men and women turn their minds. It is an unending privilege to the bookseller that he may know what men and women are seeking to know.

I have my professor, for example, who is interested in madness—not the madness of the psychologist but madness as it is exemplified in people. It is not his professional subject—he himself is an economist—but it is his hobby.

Nietzsche's life story took him first in that direction as it happened and, also, because a boyhood's friend about the same time developed G.P.I., and after a brilliant career is now shut away from the world in a strange world of his own. He lives in one of the paying parts of a very beautiful asylum near by and I am told is very happy. At first he kicked against the pricks of confinement but time and treatment have now won him to a peaceful acquiescence. He walks about the grounds entirely content with his idea that he is monarch of all he surveys. The great buildings are his. The doctors are his doctors engaged by him. The beautiful gardens are laid out under his direction. The other inmates are poor mentally diseased folk who, but for his generosity, would have neither home nor care. He is completely happy in the possession of that idea of himself and his surroundings, and the hope of my professional friend is that so he will die undisillusioned. I almost envy him his paradise although it challenges my Lord Chesterfield's dictum when he wrote " A fool never has thought, a madman has lost it." Dryden sensed the nearer truth when he wrote—

> " There is a pleasure sure
> In being mad, which none but madmen know."

There are no books on this subject that I can discover, and my friend is writing one, or rather compiling materials for one. Nietzsche is a notable example but there must be many others in the pages of biography. Chatterton, the marvellous boy, would be found to be mad by a modern jury, and there was Nathaniel Lee who was called the Mad Poet, being confined for four years in Bedlam. Cowper in his later days and gentle Mary Lamb are among the company, as too surely also was William Blake. John Clare's story, as told in the *Cyclopaedia of English Literature* (Chambers, two volumes) is a story to which the heart of a poor embarrassed bookseller warms. Born of working-class parents—his father a cripple and a pauper—John Clare began life as a ploughboy. Eight weeks' work gave him eightpence for a month's schooling, and at thirteen he had scraped and saved sufficient to buy a copy of Thomson's *Seasons* for a shilling. His shilling intact, he rose at daybreak and walked six or seven miles to the nearest book-seller's shop. He arrived too early—and think of it, book-buyers and members of Book and other learned Societies—he had to *wait* until the shop was open.

On his return he wrote his first poem, " The Morning Walk." At twenty-four he planned to publish a book and sent out a prospectus at the cost of a laboriously saved pound. His book was not to cost more than 3s. 6d., and although only seven subscribers were secured, this venture led to his collec-tion being published by a London bookseller under the title of *Poems descriptive of Rural Life and Scenery, by John Clare, a Northamptonshire Peasant.*

The book was a success, and noble patrons for a while made his life a happy one, but, like his Scottish prototype Robert Burns, ill-luck with his farm was his lot and he became the prey of melancholy. He was removed to an asylum near London, from which after four sad years he escaped. Liberty, however, was denied him, and he entered Northampton Asylum where twenty tragic years later he died.

His poem " What is Life? " is steeped in melancholy.

> " And what is Life ? an hour-glass on the run,
> A mist retreating from the morning sun,
> A busy bustling still repeated dream.
> Its length ? A minute's pause, a moment's thought.
> And Happiness ? A bubble on the stream,
> That in the act of seizing shrinks to nought."

Turning the pages of the invaluable *Cyclopaedia* I come to the name of Letitia Elizabeth Landon, who wrote under the initials " L. E. L." Hers is no less a tragic story. Born in Chelsea, then more aristocratic than bohemian, she had the felicity of maintaining herself by her pen. At thirty-six she married the Governor of Cape Coast Castle and went with him to Africa. There she continued to write, but who can tell what explained her end? Three months after her arrival in Africa she was found dead with a bottle of prussic acid by her side. Her last poem—the last verse of her last poem—is supremely simple and touching. She writes—

> " O fancy vain, as it is fond,
>   And little needed too,
>   My friends ! I need not look beyond
>   My heart to look for you."

Robert Tannahill, second only to Burns himself and the author of many lovely lyrics, was another ill-starred soul. Following on the rejection of his poems, he fell into a state of morbid despondency. He burned his manuscripts and drowned himself.

De Quincey's name occurs in the same sad category although his miserable existence dragged itself on to threescore and ten years.

Edgar Allan Poe too proved how high is the price the individual pays for what is joy to posterity.

These names are mostly collected from the " Chambers " and I have passed them on to my friend. What good can come of his sombre study if it ever reaches print I cannot imagine, unless it is a satisfaction to some of us similarly affected by that melancholy which has marked us for her own to know of some other wayfarers in the same pilgrimage.

The study of the lives of the writers is for me intensely interesting. Who among my customers knows about Barry Cornwall's luck? His real name was Bryan Waller Procter and he was at Harrow with Peel and Byron. His verse is as readable as any other poets of the second class, but that was not what I call his luck. Mr John Kenyon was a wealthy gentleman who was fond of literary society. He had himself written, but that is not his claim to my regard. When he died he left over £140,000 in legacies, part of the disposition of which was as follows :

Elizabeth Barrett Browning	.	.	.	£4000
Robert Browning	.	.	.	.	6500
Barry Cornwall	.	.	.	.	6500

What a subject for a short play—the evening in Italy when the news came to the Brownings or the morning in the Temple when they heard of Barry Cornwall's luck !

Here is the story of Mrs Elizabeth Inchbald—more remarkable than her tales or plays. Born a Catholic, she ran away from home with a bandbox for her luggage at the age of sweet sixteen. *In extremis*, after many misadventures she asked an actor friend, Mr Inchbald, what would she do. " Why not marry ? " " But who would marry me ? " " I would "— was the dialogue between them and their marriage was the upshot. She wrote plays, she acted and, by prudence, made and saved money. Her biographer in " Chambers " tells how she scoured her bedroom, while a coach with a coronet and a pair of horses awaited her pleasure to take her an airing. She kept her sister at great personal sacrifice, and on her death resided in a boarding-house at Kensington. Unlike this modern generation she declined to write her memoirs although offered a thousand pounds for them, and when she died she bequeathed £6000 to her relatives. She did not forget humble folk either. Her laundress and her hairdresser had £20 each. What a woman ! She needed no vote and did without a husband for years. Some modern woman ought to write her life. I would sell three copies I am sure, but in any case I would order three even if I didn't sell them, out of respect to her memory.

This exercise has not been what it set out to be. I have to find books which deal with madness and I won't make a sale out of what I have written. Still it has been an interesting survey, and I have been happier to-night with the denizens of Bedlam than in the best society this place can offer. . . .

. . . .

" Many a man is mad in certain instances and goes through life without having perceived—for example, a madness has seized a person of supposing himself obliged literally to pray continually ; had the madness turned the opposite way and the person thought it a crime ever to pray, it might not improbably have continued unobserved."

I quote from Dr Johnson and am grateful for the spread of his covering wings. I am not observed. Let that suffice.

" PAYABLE AT DEATH "

The word is the most absolute one in the English language. It is monosyllabic in most languages, I am told, definite, exclusive, complete, curt.

It is a subject upon which every writer has had something to say. In a standard dictionary of quotations there are over two hundred familiar allusions to death, and yet it was none of these, nor even the event itself, that brought my pencil to paper.

A friend (and a customer) has sought long and oft to induce me to insure my life and I am still dwelling on how many annual premiums I must pay to secure two hundred and fifty pounds *at sixty or previous death.*

To my creditors anyway, for me to die would be great gain. And why not?

The merits of dying have been steadily canvassed in this generation. Having been born under pressure of the be-fruitful-and-multiply prophets, we were implored to die for our country by the white-feather Piccadilly patriots.

It is all very confusing for one who is seeking a living in an apparently death-desiring world.

INVOICES, STATEMENTS AND
WHAT FOLLOWS

Firstly they come named.

> 1 Eng. Hymnal
> 1 Conrads Youth.

That is an INVOICE.

Then later they come anonymously.

> To books—£1 : 16s.

That is a STATEMENT.

The next stages are terrible—these slips of paper stuck on the statements.

> " This account is overdue. Your remittance by return will oblige."

There are worse to follow.

How I wish they would begin all over again.

> 1 Eng. Hymnal
> 1 Conrads Youth.

If I could only get back to the INVOICE !

If I could only see books as an invocation again.

How happy I would be.

BILLS—THE BOOKSELLER'S BUGBEAR

" I know a bank whereon the wild thyme blows."

Idiot that I am, that quotation came into my head this morning but I am calmer now. The bank has sent me a serious letter and they are tired of time—they have no more of it for me—and they are wild.

I am not happy. I am damned miserable and I feel I can't go on.

The publishers haven't been bad really. There is no other business, I am sure, where they treat creditors with more consideration, but things are too tangled for any remedy I can see.

I can sell up and close down, but how will that help? A sale of women's drapery may be an attraction for women but whoever heard of a sale of books?

I have ideas.

I will just walk out and leave not a message to anyone. They can discover I have gone when they find the shop hasn't been opened for three days and the milk hasn't been taken in.

The cat—I will put it out—it will find a home although its master missed one. Straying cattle are impounded : there are homes for stray dogs and cats—there are homes for fallen women, but where can fallen booksellers go?

They have fallen too far to go anywhere perhaps.

Of course, I have no heart to blame anyone, least of all the bank. They did all—more—than what was reasonable. I hadn't the capital or not enough of it.

People naturally take credit. I don't blame them either. I buy books I can't pay for—it would be cant to blame my customers for . . . doing the same thing. I could never refuse the man who wanted to take some books and who said, " Send in the bill later."

That young University blood bought too many books and has paid for none.

That frivolous young widow ought to have paid for the solace she declared so often she found in books. " I must read to forget."

All very well, but she should not forget to pay for the means of forgetfulness. The waters of Lethe may be waters bought without money and without price, but my books ought to be paid for in cash.

No matter.

All day I have planned to face up an interview and ask for more. " Ask for more? " Who asked for more? Oliver Twist. I am no twister.

I pull my wandering wits together. I will go to-morrow and see the Bank Manager.

"He is a Good Fellow, and 'twill all be well." He always paid for the books he bought. I think he bought them out of kindness. He wasn't a reader. He used to come in and say he wasn't in a hurry—he would just wait. He was spying out the land for Joseph and his Brethren.

Banks are all Jews. We are in the hands of the Jews. They were against us from the first. They are Antichristian. It is not unreasonable to look among the Antichristians for the Antichrist!

I must get this all clear.

I thought I would go on and come out all right. I have a connection. People do like me. I know they do. They come again and again. They ask my advice on books.

If I go to-morrow and see the bank they will give me time. They must. If they give me a little longer things will improve. The book trade is like everything else, it is passing through a phase of depression. I can bring it round. I will work hard. I won't waste time writing or talk too much. I will be keen. I will change my windows every week and dust the place properly. My personal appearance, I will improve that.

It won't do. It won't do.

They have no more patience for me. They can let my shop to that man next door and he will fill my windows with knickers and hats and God only knows what inconceivable muck.

That's what this letter means.

I wish I had the courage of Mr Polly. He burned his shop and became a hero. He had a new start.

I might do that but I forget the details. There isn't a copy of *The History of Mr Polly* in the place. Fancy Wells being the inspiration of an act of arson!

He wouldn't believe it if I wrote and told him. Did he ever think of burning the Landport Drapery Bazaar? I'm sure he did but he had a lucky escape. His father was a cricketer.

Why do I maunder on like this? Why don't I grapple with my fate and master my destiny?

I could peddle books from door to door if it comes to that. No.

I am not going on. This will do for an end. I have tried enough and will try no more.

" Some die too young : some die too old : still the saying soundeth strange—die thou at the right time."

This is the right time for me. Everything is to my hand. Here in my room, all is set out for the Grand Finale.

There will be no fire. There will be no peddling books from door to door. There will be no seeking for another job. There will be no call on the bank to-morrow morning. I am calm and they can say what they like when they find me.

It is not difficult now. I am quite calm about it. I was going out for a walk but I am not going now. I am . . .

> " I have immortal longings in me . . .
> I am fire and air; my other elements
> I give to baser life. . . .
> The stroke of death is as a lover's pinch,
> Which hurts, and is desired—"

It will not hurt me ; the gas will . . .

> ". . . this knot intrinsicate
> Of life at once untie. . . .
> . . . Peace, Peace ! "

2

THE BANKRUPT BOOKSELLER
SPEAKS AGAIN

INTRODUCTION

Readers who are interested in books may remember that in 1931 Oliver & Boyd of Edinburgh, Scotland, published a book called *The Private Papers of a Bankrupt Bookseller*.

This contained, if I may be permitted to express an opinion, rather an odd preface signed X. Z. E., who, at this stage, I may disclose as the late Mr Xavier Zachariah Evans, a gentleman from Wales who purchased the bookshop as an extension to his drapery business, following the untimely decease of the Bankrupt Bookseller.

Those who are familiar with the preface of the book will remember that the late Mr Evans referred to relatives from America who happened to be in this country at the time of the bookseller's death, and he goes on to state that, at their request, some of the papers were published.

In 1931 I was in England with my father and mother and my recollection of these somewhat hushed-up business affairs, as a lad of eighteen, is naturally not very clear. I only knew that a distant relative of my mother's—in fact she was the younger half-cousin of the bookseller's mother and she came to America in her youth where she had married my father— had died tragically and somewhat mysteriously and that his business affairs were not in a very satisfactory state.

His visit to England at an end, my father, who was about to leave with my mother and me for home, had no time to do other than accept the arrangement which Mr Evans had suggested.

On returning to the United States I took up work on a newspaper and I am now myself engaged in journalism.

It was my good fortune to be handed the many sheets of untidy pencilled paper which were not used by Mr Evans in the first book and the greater part of these—a few incomplete ones still remain in my possession—are now published.

I have chosen the title " The Bankrupt Bookseller Speaks Again " and I hope those readers who felt, as I did, a deep personal sympathy and affection for my relative, the bookseller, will find in these pages further interest in the revelations of his character, of his opinions and his life-history.

I have begun this new collection with a paper " The Shabbiness of a Shopman." It places the bookseller, I think, and then, as will be seen by readers, I have spaced out his own story of his life. It is all very naïf, I know, but, there it is— platitudes, repetitions, inconsistencies, and in these—" The Bankrupt Bookseller Speaks Again."

GEORGE P. J. KLAUS

Offices of the " Detroit Delineator "
60-61 Merrimee Grove Avenue
Detroit, U.S.A.

THE SHABBINESS OF A SHOPMAN

Appearance is all.

It is an external world to which I offer these externalities. I am conscious that my clothes are shabby. It came over me at the bank—bank men—they don't like to be called bank clerks, I learned—are so neatly dressed nowadays. When I was in an office we all had shabby coats, too shabby for anything else but office use. Then the fashion was to have a good suit but to take the good jacket off and wear an old one. Torrens, who had been Head Clerk for years, loved his old counter jacket better than any Regius Professor his gown. It was hoary with fidelity and fringed at the wrists through long and honourable service.

In the best bookshops, Bumpus, Bowes, Blackwell—do they all begin with a B ?—no, there's Hatchards, too—the salesmen have black jackets and waistcoats and striped trousers. I have seen them and have felt a little ashamed of myself, but they don't dust, sweep, dress windows, pack and unpack, keep books (account books, I mean, Day Books, Profit and Loss and all that), clean windows, cook chips, fry fish and sausages, make soup, wash dishes, do up a bed at least once a week, as well as sell books. Theirs are little lives. They sail small boats on safe ponds in public parks—I am Columbus, Vasco da Gama, Tasman, Captain Cook, Louis de Rougemont and Peter Fleming compared to them.

" There is no need for heat," as my Company Commander remarked to me in one of the hottest moments in the March Retreat.

I calm myself and contemplate a new suit.

There is only one modern writer who knows men's clothes and he writes on Spiritualism or something like it now. Dennis Bradley is a Master Tailor but has descended to book-writing.

He might have left it alone and stuck to his trade. That will be forgiven.

(Who said, as he lay dying, when the priest bade him turn his thoughts to the Hereafter—" God will forgive me—it is His trade " ?)

It is a suggestive idea.

There is the " Four Alls "—the old village inn signboard which reads—

> The Soldier—I fight for all
> The Tailor—I sew for all
> The Clergyman—I pray for all
> The Labourer—I pay for all

Is there not a diviner sign for a sinning world?

Each to his trade—to serve and to sin—but over all, God to forgive. It is His trade—perhaps it is all this sad world needs.

A suit—not from Mr Bradley of Bond Street—he is too high and his price is mightier, nay, more golden, than his pen, but if not, to whom?

There are these new people along this street, who travesty man, made in the image of God, with their clothed dummies behind enormous plates of glass—there are these at sixty shillings, and there are these, who, recognising when a man is down and declining to hit him, say, " Pay ten shillings down and we will put up the suit—to be paid, whether worn out or not, in twelve months."

There are a soberer sort who sell clothes ready to wear— and there are real tailors who have no window display worth looking at but who hang half-finished coats over the window rods at the back of their windows.

My taste turns to one of them—only two doors away. He doesn't read now. His favourite was *If Winter Comes* and since then he reads only the papers, he tells me. " My eyes "— tailoring is trying on the eyes—I understand perfectly.

My suit I will certainly, I feel, buy from him but it will be some time yet. I have my style to decide first. Is it to be black coat and striped trousers—or a good tweed—Scotch or Donegal—or a Yorkshire suiting which, he says, wears so well once it is shiny—which is it to be?

I await the moment of inspiration.

And then there is the paying for it—ah, that is another affair!

Let me be practical.

They say the Socialists live in the future because it is easier to do that than exist in the present.

They are right.

My hopes—and with them—my suit lies in the future.

For the moment I must continue to be shabby in the present.

THE EARLIEST BEGINNINGS
OF A BOOKSELLER

Wordsworth must be coming into his own again. A thoughtful youth demanded him to-day. " I have read several anthologies and I want to know the whole man," was what he said.

There are not too many books on William Wordsworth available and in my own stock there are only two—a " Life " and an incomplete collection.

It is a good thing for booksellers, if for no one else, when readers are attracted to know everything about the whole man and all his work, but my young friend will be surprised to learn that the placid William Wordsworth of the Lakes was a very different creature from the young man who pursued strange adventures in France in the hot high tide of youth.

There was storm over Europe before there came the serenity of Grasmere.

For all that, I cannot find any thoughts of disparagement of William. His " Lines Written at Tintern Abbey " and his

" Intimations of Immortality " are too frequently with me for me to be other than profoundly grateful. Somebody told me once that George Eliot read " Intimations " every day and found it at once an inspiration and an invocation.

I would like to think my own intimations of immortality in early childhood were as profound as those of the Lake Poet. How little I remember—indeed how little any of us remember —of those infant days from which we must all travel. I do recollect a lady who remembered her baptism—and she was no Baptist either—she professed to remember quite clearly the water on her face and a sense of being tightly wrapped up and unable to fend off the falling drops with her hands. She did not know, she admitted, the meaning of the words but she professed to have quite a clear photographic mental picture of the benign face of the vicar as he brought her into the Church of her Fathers and gave her her name.

I wonder !

She was a customer who bought religious booklets—tiresome stock for a bookseller—profitable, he hopes, to the soul— but of little profit to him !

My own earliest recollections are smells—the close smell of a wooden perambulator with iron rim wheels in which I was wheeled about. Quite clearly I recollect the cracked American cloth coverlet which buttoned over me, the smell of it, the smell of my own clothes, the capacious, overhanging bosom of my doting mother—these are my earliest, shadowy recollections. There are no manly memories.

Like most children, my life for years was feminine-surrounded. In the boarding-house in which my mother toiled for a living and for me, from time to time, one, whose surname, if I ever heard, I have forgotten, called Liza came and went. She was my mother's maid-of-all-work and all her works were wonderful. She was a benign, a saintly character, though she never thought it. There was no self-righteousness in Liza. She cooked and baked and sewed—her sewing was crude but firm—and moiled and toiled and served early and late the needs of the boarders, but none the less always had a moment or two in which to detach herself from the most urgent of her toils to chuck me under my chin or poke me in my stomach so that I might kick my feet and wave my hands and gurgle for her delight. She was a motherly soul but never granted motherhood, and I think the asthma, the musical wheezy, whistling sort, took her away before her time, to my mother's immense regret.

Her going was probably the first emptiness that I recollect. She went, the genial Liza without a name, the friend of many friendless folk and sinners especially, for she never denied a beggar and, I am certain, that when she passed over, the trumpets which were sounded for her on the other side were those of a brass band, German or Salvationist, to which form of street music and entertainment she was extremely partial and contributed regularly and generously. No harps for Liza —take back your golden fiddlesticks—and give me German Bands—would be her emphatic opinion, I am sure.

My mother's business activities, her determination to pay her way, perhaps kept her from lavishing upon me the fondness that Liza did. I was the thing for which she fought and the battle for me was too strong for her to find time for too much love to be spent upon the body over which the contest was waged.

She fought for victory, my mother did, not for flags.

Less personally interested in making a living, and more interested in Life, Liza filled her place. Between the two of them, these women made my infancy and early childhood what it was.

The belief that a child is happier in a hygienic nursery with a wooden and starched, brisk young woman from a training school is quite a fallacy. Children in such circumstances as my childhood was passed may suffer from disturbances occasionally but they gain immensely by the activity which goes on all round them. Their minds are awakened and appetites evoked, their interests encouraged, and, although perhaps the balance of advantage may fall away in later years, on the whole I think the children of the poor have the better part when they are young.

Wealth—it is a commonplace—is not everything. The rich young man who was sad about his great possessions had more insight than most rich folk. He knew how little they amounted to—how worthless they were. There is a robust heartiness of uncertainty, a sense of adventure, of reality, about the life of the poor and struggling which never enters the experience of the secure.

Stephen Reynolds in his *A Poor Man's House* (3s. 6d., Jonathan Cape) more than any other writer, perhaps, has been the one who emphasised its advantages.

I like the way in which he asserts that the thriftless, even dirty, but frequently well-managed homes of poor people are, from the point of view of the epicure in life, homes the most worth living in, and, although he tells in his writing how he sometimes longed for a good meal or to find again his fingers on the piano, still there was something essentially more vital in his experience in a poor man's house.

This is a long piece of writing, written doggedly over several days, scored and blotted and interrupted by all sorts of business and other disadvantages, but it has been a pleasure to recall again one's origins. Pride of birth may consist in the emptiness of an historic name or the resonance of long lineage. My pride of birth is that I was born as I was among circumstances upon which I never reflect except with the result that I am happier. Such content is rare, but I was taught, and readily believed, I was one of the fortunate ones. I early learned to say four lines from Jane Taylor's " Child's Hymn of Praise " :

> " I thank the goodness and the grace
> Which on my birth have smiled,
> And made me, in these Christian days,
> A happy Christian child."

It was well I learned them early. I cannot find them now.

HOW THE BOOKSELLER FOUND
HIS BOOKSHOP

It was to Lichfield my thoughts first turned.

Dr Johnson was born there—it was a town I had never visited—and for £150, so the Liverpool paper said, all in, including stock and fixtures, I could become the owner of a sweet and tobacco shop with a good trade in Sunday papers.

To Lichfield I went, but I never entered the shop. I beheld it from outside and went away. It was not for this that I had fought in the Somme and suffered in the Salient. There were other worlds, surely, for the happy and surviving warrior.

To the monument to the great Doctor I went. I hope his shade believed me as I tried to persuade myself that I had really come to Lichfield to honour his memory. It would be shocking if his shade thought otherwise. . . .

That night I left Lichfield and went to Liverpool. I had never been there before either.

There was half an idea I might go abroad. . . . West Africa, the Indies, the States, Canada. . . I did not know but I wasn't going back to London yet. I would see something of England before I settled down. One day I went to Blackpool —another I went to Manchester. I saw Picture Galleries and Race Meetings—talked to all sorts—lived in lodgings and hotels and so drew nearer and nearer to my fate.

The New Year came in—I must do something, I thought. I can't go on like this.

It must have been near the end of January when I found on the table of the hotel in which I stayed a copy of *The Bookseller*. How it came there I do not know. Some bookseller's traveller —I wonder—but this issue was to me the chamber of freedom, the gate of hope, the Genesis of all that I may yet be in this staggering world.

The actual advertisement I ought to have kept, but I have lost it.

It was thus—" Second Hand Books : Good Opening : established business : owner leaving for Australia : must sell : £400 or near offer."

It was in February—the first day of February—I came here. Again I looked at the place from the outside—hesitated, walked away, drank beer, ate bread and cheese, came back, looked at it again, took the bus and got away.

A few days longer I stayed in Liverpool. I would go abroad, I thought. I even got particulars at the Liver Building about boats, and then Destiny took me firmly in hand.

I went into a bar—behind the bar was Bella—but I have written about it before. Annabella was the name of the barmaid, but I called her Bella.

Was it still the Goddess of War who guided me into the way of peace? She told me not to mess about—do something —decide—and I decided.

I haven't seen her again to tell her. She was busy the day I called and I haven't been in Liverpool since. Should I go and tell her? I won't now—there was a time, but that is gone. At Judgment Day she will learn what she did with her life and she will be surprised, I imagine. Or shall I be the more surprised? Time—no, Eternity—will tell.

The business wasn't worth Four Hundred Pounds. You can buy a lot of second-hand books for Four Hundred Pounds but I didn't know that then.

It was just as well, perhaps. I would have missed a lot if I hadn't set up as a bookseller.

A lot? Heresy! Sacrilege! I would have missed EVERY-THING.

THE BOOKSELLER ENTERS
ON BUSINESS LIFE

School as a whole I disliked and there came, at length, a time with me when I had a positive repulsion to further study. I wanted to be done with learning lessons. I wanted to try out my talents on life itself. I had confidence. My mother, patient and wise, thought I ought to remain longer at school— had I not won a scholarship?—had I not won prizes?—*Famous Men*—*Tennyson's Poems*—*The Story of Astronomy*—and half a dozen other books—some of them I have still with their gilt labels on the inside covers indicating my pre-eminence in English Literature, my excellence in Latin and French and, first triumph of all, for the punctuality of my attendance!

Still I pled with my mother to let me go.

She busied herself, when she saw my mind was made up, to find some safe water in which she could launch me into life. Since my father's death she had carefully put away all her scanty savings in Insurance Policies. She began with one to bring her in fifty pounds, and had, as opportunity presented itself, raised the insurance on her life to over a thousand pounds in the aggregate. This had given her a ready entrée to the Insurance Office and the Manager had formed of her the highest opinion.

One day, unknown to me, while I was at school she had interviewed him and told him of her desire to place me. The Manager, whom I came to know later as a gentle creature at heart but apparently—on the surface—to the outer world—a man of much thrust and push in business, agreed to see me and promised he would do what he could in the autumn.

(" He did what he could "—there is an epitaph!)

That last summer at school, when I knew that what appeared to be freedom waited for me a few months ahead, was unforgettable. I went more to the playing-fields than I had done ever before. I enjoyed the comradeship of my schoolfellows to the full. I filled them with envy when I told them of my prospect as compared with theirs. I rejoiced in a certain uniqueness, and when the end of the session came I had to interview the Head Master on my decision. He had me in his room and talked to me like a father rather than a schoolmaster—one could not know too much—one should not leave school too early—I was doing well at my lessons—I would be

G

sure to win another scholarship—I might go on to the University —these were his arguments, but they had no avail. Life was opening up to me ; there was no attraction in pedagogics and classrooms. I was soon to be a man and put away childish things.

He asked me to think it over (how can one really do that?), but I told him I had already decided, and his conversation with me made it clear that there was another motive in my mind than merely a desire to get away from school.

My mother's never-ending toil in her boarding-house had touched my sympathy. Could I not do something for her, could I not give her the leisure I imagined she would love to have, could I not make some contribution to lighten the burden of her declining years?

There is in life a Quixotism—a passion to do the right thing —a capacity for self-sacrifice and devotion—which of all the hopeful things in a despairing world is perhaps the most beautiful, and, without knowing it, this motive of mine was the driving one. And so when September came I presented myself before the Manager.

I remember my clothes. I wore a tweed Norfolk jacket, a flat collar of a type boys no longer wear ; I had knickerbockers and boots, plastered hair, a smug face and, for it has always been my weakness, uncared-for, grubby hands. These hands I remember, because the Manager said to me in the course of the interview, " Let me see your hands." I showed them to him reluctantly. He said, " You must look after your hands and especially keep your nails clean." " There are other ways," he told me, " of showing mourning than in the black borders of your nails."

I was given a sheet of paper and he dictated to me a letter. My handwriting apparently pleased him. It was painstaking and careful, although rather unformed. It would do, he said, for my work. He bade me, however, note that the work in an Insurance Office which was valued most was not the clerical work. That was merely a preparation and I should prepare myself, he bade me, for the more important function of going out to secure business. That, however, was not immediately but it was an ambition which he advised me to cherish. My mother was delighted when she heard that I had definitely secured a post and we went to the outfitters to get what she held to be suitable attire for a young clerk.

I went to business with a black jacket and vest, a pair of striped trousers, black shoes and a blue tie. My mother liked blue and she said, I remember, the tie just matched my eyes. I was an odd little figure, I suppose, in bowler hat with stick and gloves, when I entered the marble portico of the Office, and my first few weeks were miserable in the unaccustomed environment.

There must have been a hundred clerks, nearly all men and youths, in the office and it all seemed to me very strange. I acquired, however, early popularity by my willingness to run errands for the clerks. These were of every variety. There was old Bulswul who made me go to Mrs Middleton's public-house every morning at eleven for a roast beef sandwich and half a pint of Burton Beer in a bottle. This repast Mr Bulswul placed in his desk and consumed during the labours of the morning in the policy department. His was a regular order and I had a penny a day from him for my trouble.

The younger clerks were pastry-eaters and less generous in their rewards to me for my purchasings on their behalf. A cake for myself or a penny packet of chocolate now and then was considered adequate by them for the services which I rendered. In an office I suppose there is a lot of hanging around, and this office was certainly no exception if that be the rule.

The favourite place for retirement from the labours of the desks was the basement, and this was as interesting to me and as secure as the Catacombs must have been to the early Christians. Here there was everything, storage of papers, lavatories, convenient and private, coal cellars and—most attractive of all—a very large furnace round which we stood or sat and smoked. I was not a smoker to begin with, but in that dusty, overheated basement I smoked my first cigarette,

The cigarette of those days favoured by the junior-clerk class was known as " Bandit," and whether it was the heat or the unaccustomed experience of smoking which made me sick, I don't know, but sick I certainly was.

Always prone to headaches, this day I brought one to such fruition that, grey and drawn, pale and wan, one of the senior clerks noticed me and told me I had better go home. The fresh air did me good as I walked home and my mother's solicitude and concern for me are still things which I remember. She put me to bed ; she physicked me and, in the morning, after sound sleep I was fit to resume, if not my experience of " Bandit," certainly the more legitimate, though less daring, calling of the day.

Most of the youths in the office had girls, but I never took well to the sex. On a few occasions I attended dances. If I was not exactly a wallflower I rarely ever took the floor. I had not had any experience of women except my mother and her succession of maids, and, somehow, to touch a creature, as the intricacies of the dance demanded, was beyond me. I shrank from it and the girls quickly recognised that there was not much fun in a fellow like me.

They were right ! there never was ; there is not now.

These social activities being unattractive to me I tried to find interest in my work, but it was dull and mechanical. I could not inject romance into the correspondence and other duties which were my care, but I now know that that was lack of imagination, for romance I know is everywhere. These insurance policies were charters of hope, had I only known— these letters which I filed and sealed and stamped were harbingers of happiness to those prudent folk who had provided against the wrath which inevitably must come.

Books, then, took me.

I became a regular frequenter of the Public Library and I borrowed from any who would lend. I read, I understand the word is, with avidity and, seeing my studiousness was deeply ingrained, my mother turned my mind to something more practical. She was always concerned with the means of earning a living, of being independent and not needing to beg or to ask, of being in a position to demand, without fear or favour, a livelihood from the world. She sent me to night classes and I took writing—they called it calligraphy—shorthand and typing—these were the proper qualifications for a competent clerk—and although my writing is now hardly legible to my own eyes and my shorthand and typing have fallen into desuetude, I believe the discipline was good for me. The class I liked, however, was English Literature. I took English Literature and Language and did well in these, especially in the essays which were set from time to time.

These years passed. I became more and more a solitary, but not unpopular, member of the staff. The Manager was always helpful, always encouraging. He tried to make the most of any qualities he found in his staff, and he stimulated me to consider taking up what was called " outside work." This was the business of calling upon people with a view to securing their insurance.

It meant more money. It meant freedom out of doors. It meant fewer of the restraints which inevitably fell upon those who were the regular office staff and I determined to try it.

My salary now enabled me to dress better, and my reading and contact with the world had given me confidence.

Equipped with the Rate Book of the Company I set forth with the Manager's plan well impressed upon my mind. He believed in the law of averages. He said, " If you will make twelve purposeful calls every day, that is sixty a week excluding Saturday and Sunday, you are bound to find business. Insurance is what all the world is needing in this uncertain world ; nothing is sure except insurance." And with that text I went out to preach the gospel.

My success was really surprising, once I had overcome my reluctance to approach people without introduction. There was an advantage that the Company was a good Company, and I suppose there was a certain plaintive persuasiveness about my approach that compelled clients.

These gay Insurance men whom I met, although they were

apparently happier than I, were, it seemed to me, the wrong people. Insurance was a solemn matter because Insurance dealt with life. I had the necessary solemnity. - I spoke and looked like one having authority.

Some days I was sent to the country, and although business was sparse I enjoyed the long distances. I had often to walk or cycle to see my prospective clients and much hospitality was given me in farm-houses and in the parlours of the country gentry. It benefited my health, it increased my self-confidence, and I believe that I gave satisfaction. They looked upon me in the Office as a steady, reliable young man, as one who would never touch the high-lights of the profession, not one destined for Manager or Superintendent, but one who could put the case for Insurance with simple acceptability.

It was quite a business. First, the call, the leaving of the necessary literature, the call again, then the argument with the wife who, if she were consulted, oddly enough was generally against her husband's proposal. Then there was the arranging of the Medical Examination, the producing of one's man at the Surgery, the days of delay before confirmation could be granted by the Head Office, then the glad moment when I was able to say, " Everything is in order. Let me congratulate you and take from you your first premium."

It was not always so simple, but now that the mists of years intervene I recollect these Insurance days, certainly with satisfaction and something like pleasure.

In all these days, however, at the back of my mind was my mother's health. I pled with her to take a smaller house and exert herself less than she was doing. The kind of idea I had was to move to a small house with just mother and me. She had, however, worked so long, worked so hard and worked so continuously that the prospect of leisure and idleness really appalled her. She would be up and doing as long as there was . work to do, and work seemed to come to her hands.

Less urgent now was the making of a livelihood, but she found on every hand opportunities for doing something for others. She was everybody's neighbour, not only to those who fell among thieves, but to all who came. I see her now as one of those people who make life worth while. She asked nothing from it except to give and give and give. She sought no more than to work, to help and to serve, and I am hopeful that I am not wrong in believing that some day all shall realise that of such indeed are the Kingdom of Heaven.

HEART STORIES

Reading Richard Jefferies' *Story of My Heart* makes me think how true it is that every life can tell a story. My edition is the old " Silver Library " Edition by Longmans—a good series, that was. I had an inquiry a few days ago and this was the drift of our talk.

" Yes, very good—A Victorian Barbellion," I said.

" Is it still in print? "

" Oh yes, it is still in print—has been in many editions since Mr C. J. Longman got it in 1883."

" You have a copy? "

" Well, yes—but not one you'd like. It's dirty, you know, and besides I couldn't put my hand on it here in the shop." (True, it is lying on the kitchen table in the back shop.)

" It was reprinted several times during the War—I can get you a copy in a couple of days."

" Well, thank you, I'll let you know."

Away he went.

I lost a sale, but I went to *The Story of My Heart* with a new earnestness. I had sacrificed profit for love of a book—a proper thing—of which, as a bookseller, I am not ashamed.

Hear him—this Richard Jefferies.

" It is in myself that I desire increase, profit and exaltation to-day, mind and soul. The surroundings are to me utterly indifferent. . . .

" Let me be in myself, myself fully. . . ."

I read on.

I am glad I kept my book. It is a Story of the Heart—alas ! there are too few of them.

A REJECTED BOOK

This feeling about books in me is a mania. A mania is something which possesses one to an abnormal degree. Books do possess me that way and they don't possess others.

Mr Mailer makes me write this. He comes two or three times a week either on his way to, or his way from, the office. He is a produce broker (I imagine), although I never have had the curiosity to ask.

" Anything new ? " he asks sometimes, but that is when he is in a lively mood. Usually when I am in the back shop I hear someone and it is Mr Mailer moving about picking up a book here and there—once he dropped one—I hate people who drop books. They nearly always let them fall on their corners and bruise them shamefully. My John Buchan's *Montrose* (Nelson, 7s. 6d.) was dropped by some wanton and its two lower corners are broken. I mind it more than Montrose, perhaps—he climbed high and fell far, " so fine a man—the foremost Scottish man of action "—he deserved a better fate. I feel I have added to his misfortunes—to have permitted his book to become dog-eared and broken in the cover—Montrose—but it's not Montrose—it is Mailer—I must keep to my muttons. It is a new resolution with me, to keep my wandering wits under control. The bank manager says I lack concentration.

" Remember St Paul, ' this one thing I do,' " he said.

It was over Lowes Dickinson's book, *A Modern Symposium*, I was vexed with Mailer. He was on politics, and said all the best books were written by Socialists—that, though Johnson had as far as he could done his best to see that the Whig dogs didn't get the best of it—they usually did in literature. Writers were rarely Conservative—they were nearly all delineators of discontent—glorifiers of grumbling, prophets of perdition. There were no balanced views in books.

I got him out my own *Symposium*—an early edition, Brimley, Johnson & Ince, 1905—and begged him to take it and read it. There, I told him, he would see life steadily and whole through thirteen minds each expressed in exquisite English, speaking the truth that was in them—Tory, Liberal, Conservative, Socialist, Anarchist—up to the Poet and the Man of Affairs.

He took it from me, and to encourage me perhaps, for he is a good soul at bottom, he bought Andrew Carnegie's book, *The Empire of Business.*

That was weeks ago.

I thought he would come back glowing, but he hasn't. He returned me my book to-day, and told me he wasn't impressed much.

Heavens, I bow my head beneath the marvels which you cover!

Not impressed—very well—I have a mania for books—the words which Lowes Dickinson wrote on his title-page are truer than I thought—wider in their application than I imagined. Life, like a dome of many-coloured glass, does stain the white radiance of eternity.

A GOOD LONG BOOK

He wants a good long book. . . .

" I'm tired of these short stories and collections of snippets. Give me something I can get my teeth into, something sustained, something as long and interesting as life itself."

" Quite so, I shall give the matter my attention."

He is going for a cruise, he tells me, so bulk is important as he has to think of the book in the terms of luggage.

G 2

My own choice, and I hope he takes it, is *The Forsyte Saga*, which has 1104 pages—it surely is a good long book! Then there is the copy of Holbrook Jackson's *Anatomy of Bibliomania*, which has 854 pages. A fellow bookseller, one at any rate who hangs on the more ragged fringes of the trade, has written a book called *Hunger and Love*, published by Putnam. It has 705 pages.

But if my customer wants serious reading and sustained interest I think I shall sell him my Longmans' edition of John Stuart Mill's *Principles of Political Economy*—1013 pages—as this is an extremely sensible book. Handling Holbrook Jackson's book, I think of a copy of Burton's *The Anatomy of Melancholy* which I ought to have. . . . After searching I recover it.

I think of Gibbon. Personally I never liked the World's Classics edition, and on that account might more easily persuade myself to sell it.

It is not so long as some, however. Chatto & Windus's edition of the *Anatomy* has 747 pages with an index, but, of course, it would be a triumph to me as a bookseller if I could sell him my twelve-volume edition of Gibbon. It is done in excellent leather, dated 1832, printed by H. & J. Pillans, and published by Thomas Nelson and Peter Brown. Each volume is from 450 to 500 pages and, quite apart from its hundred other virtues, it would be an excellent guide-book for the proposed Mediterranean cruise.

I am determined to make a sale and am fortifying myself against all argument. I am prepared to go to great lengths indeed, and if he tells me that Gibbon in twelve volumes is too big to pack in his valise to take for the cruise, I shall be quite frank about it and say that he had better give up his cruise and stay at home and read Gibbon.

THE EXTERNALS OF A BOOKSELLER

This question of externals is quite important. I return to the subject. It impresses me. I don't need to read *Sartor Resartus* to know that man has bought authority in his clothes. But the subject with which I am concerning myself is my own attire.

My neighbour is resplendent in morning coat, striped trousers, silk hat—I think, personally, rather an absurd figure, but he appears to evoke, if I am to believe him, considerable admiration. As a matter of fact he wears this silk hat because he is ashamed of his baldness, and wears a morning coat because if he wore a jacket suit the distension of his paunch would be more noticeable. The morning coat, with its sweeping line from collar to tail, is designed for such successful figures as his, and there is no doubt that this fashion is a gift to the cartoonists. Max Beerbohm has done splendidly with it, but Will Dyson and Low have made a triumph of it. The capitalist class could not ever appear as odious as they are made to appear without the silk hat and the morning coat.

I approach the problem of the externals of a bookseller in a simpler way, but I am not oblivious of their importance.

Out of doors I have little difficulty. I wear tweeds, rather coarse and shapeless, though I like to fancy they suit rather than fit my hardly athletic figure.

My inclination would be to go to the best tailor I could afford, but my most recent tailoring extravagance drove me instead to a gentleman's tailor whose claim if nothing else it is, at any rate, to be a " tailor of taste." Taste is such an indefinable thing that it would be difficult for me to decide whether he made good his claim as regards myself or not. Apart from tweeds, I wear my old brown hat—the newer ones have a stiffness in texture for which I do not care—at holiday times, and with my most comfortable shoes, socks disengaged from sock suspenders and falling in loose folds over my ankles, I enjoy my leisure.

For wet days—if they are really seriously wet—I have my war-time waterproof—or, to be quite accurate, the waterproof which I won in the War through the untimely decease of a very gallant young subaltern of the Company in which I served. Its belted back and faded fawn colour—as I look at it hanging on the nail outside the door—take me back to the figure that once wore it so jauntily, I remember, with no thought of his own early grave and the remote future of his waterproof. I must not forget that I always carry an umbrella, even when I have a waterproof, and mine has a crook handle because I find that handiest. These are my out-of-doors presentation.

But indoors is my problem. Out of doors I am free, belonging to nobody, but here within this shop I am a somebody, a person of distinction, and clothes are all-important.

Fortunately, for the present I am equipped.

I wear a brown alpaca jacket—very suitable it is for the summer weather—brown is such a pleasing colour for a bookseller, for all booksellers live almost continuously in a brown study—or is it more appropriate to establish the parallel between being done-brown and the bookselling profession?

I don't know, but I plan for the autumn the purchase of a brown velvet coat for the colder weather. Cord or plain? I have not yet decided. Brown, though, is going to be my colour, and my indoor attire will not be the least distinctive part of this important business which I am giving my life to establish.

BOOKSELLER AFTER THE RETREAT GOES ON WITH THE WAR

Really I suppose the War ended for me when we said good-bye to the Australians who took over from us in front of Morlancourt.

I was indeed through because of experience. I had endured

too much.   Like a water-logged sponge, I could absorb no more.

On the road, by rail and in buses they got us up to the Salient, but I remember nothing but sleep.   I moved and then slept and moved again, then fell asleep.   There must have been a week in which I lived comatose.

From what I have read I now know what happened.   The Fifth Army fought the delaying battle of the Somme, and when the troops who had fought the battle were reduced to impotence by more than half their numbers being either killed, wounded or taken prisoner, they were moved to what was believed to be a quiet sector upon which no attack was expected.   The quiet sector was Ypres, and sure enough it was quiet as it never had been in its three years of bloody history.   The Australians had held that front while we had taken our punishment in the Somme, and now they were being withdrawn and the Fifth Army units were to be sent into the line to replace them.   It apparently was inevitable, but it was unfortunate that these hammered divisions—the Ninth, Twenty-first, Twenty-fourth and their companions who had been linked together in the Somme Retreat—should be placed side by side in the same part in the Salient and adjoining sectors.

Perhaps it did not matter.

We were men who had known the worst of the worst and for whom, I imagine, death offered no novel terrors, although its terrors were never less horrible because they were now abundantly familiar from association.   Man, horse or mule . . . all knew every kind of military offensiveness from rifle, machine-gun bullets to the heaviest of artillery and gas.   We were shock troops in a peculiar sense of the term, because nothing could shock us with its unfamiliarity.

It is in the Salient, then, that I find myself this morning as I scribble away, almost as confident to-day that I will have no customers as I was confident then that the Germans were too busy in the Somme ever to think of attacking us.

I hope I see as many customers this April day as I saw Germans in 1918 on the day of which this is the anniversary.

They say the Portuguese began it.

The Germans raided to see what troops were in front of them and they discovered the Portuguese. They attacked the Portuguese, who did not stand up to it very long, and I for one am not going to blame them. Their appearance in the War, I think, was a gesture that we might as well have done without. It was, I imagine, a sentimental association. . . . Did not Wellington introduce the British soldier to the Peninsula and the Peninsula introduce Port to the British soldier?

That began the attack anyway, and the hole that was made in the Portuguese front was extended indefinitely until Ludendorff apparently decided that it would be a greater achievement to drive the British into the sea and seize the Channel ports than attack Amiens and divide the British from the French.

Perhaps if he had chosen what was his second offensive for his first the result might have been different and I would have been engaged to-day in learning German. (The Germans keep good bookshops—I might have had my place.)

In a few hours after the Portuguese retirement my Division was involved. We remained involved for ten days while, I suppose, as far as we were concerned, the end of the world hung in the balance. Never were representatives of more units in any battle, nor did any battle ever seem to last so long, or seem so incapable of coming to a conclusion. The Commander-in-Chief, for the first time in his relations with his troops, descended from Olympus and sent a message to each one of us. We who had been in the War since the beginning remembered the earlier message we had from Kitchener. It was that we be good boys, remember that we were British soldiers, and behave like gentlemen in an Allied country. None of us had kept the little message—none of my comrades had done so anyway—but I was able to remind some of them of it.

The new message was from another Commander-in-Chief, the great Haig. He put it plainly to us that the day was far spent, that there was no hope left in England, that the higher command had no strategy wherewith to support us, that under the Belgian sky each of us held in his own person the destiny of his country and that, standing where he was without hope, he must give his life for the highest price he could exact. The great collective experiment of the British Empire was abandoned, and in this last resort it left all to private enterprise, private courage, private character, private determination to save it.

It was the apotheosis of individualism. The system had collapsed, but the men remained.

Haig, they say, was something of a metaphysician but I doubt if he was as metaphysical these days as Brother Drummond, Father Oddy, Hathorn Hall, the deliberate unshaven imperturbable Duke and the ever-ready Norman, to mention only a few. We were realists and individualists, typical as we must have been of thousands. Unlike the army of mercenaries who saved the sum of things for pay—we saved it because none could help us and we could do no other.

It is all vague and uncertain. Day was fused into night, minutes into hours and hours into days and weeks, but there came a day when we emerged.

The jangle and tangle was resolved.

The fronts were at length stabilised. Reliefs came. Trench warfare for a time was renewed and the first symbol of hope, the dove upon the waters, was a message from Divisional Headquarters that Educational Officers were to be appointed. The Teuton was beaten. Laying aside for a moment the bayonet, the British soldier would take up his book—there was a day coming when bayonets would be less useful than books, we would need to prepare ourselves for the peace which none of us thought at all imminent unless it was the peace of death. Still, it was an omen, an omen that the vitality of Britain and her Armies was not dead.

They got us into the back country in May and June, and combed us and dressed us—groomed us, as they say in the film world nowadays—preparing us for the next attack.

It is to Haig's eternal credit that while the rest of the world, including the French, thought the War would go on at least to 1919, by May he had made up his mind that if it were possible he would finish it that year. His analysis was right. The last desperate throw of the armies of the United Empires

had been made. It had nearly been successful but it had
failed. They had no resources, no reserves. The War, if it
were to be won by those who had borne the main burden of it,
must be won this year. The War won by the armies of the
United Empires would be intolerable to be borne by the
military leaders of France and Britain . . . therefore, this year
. . . not next year, sometime or never, but this year. Those
of us who had fought through the Retreats took the line again
and it was almost with feelings of sadness that we found that the
hard fighting was over. It hurt me to hear lads who had just
joined the War a month or two before speaking disparagingly
of the German opposition. It was a libel on the lads who had
died in the Somme in July in 1916, an implied criticism on the
courage of the men who fought through the winter of '17 and
the spring of '18. Attacks were better mounted, resistance
seemed less continuous, gains were larger and more spectacular.
We crossed from Armentières to Ypres to the Zonnebeke
Ridge in four hours when many a time it had taken all the
available might of the British Armies to carry a hundred yards
the year before.

One must not blame the young soldiers.

They did not know.

How could they know? What could they know of fighting
who only this time knew?

It was in Courtrai that peace descended upon us. The talk
then was that the Bosches were going to dig in on the line of
the Scheldt and hold it for the winter. We were to go into
winter quarters and to wait for the Americans. These were
views that were current in our Division, and I for one was quite
indifferent. The War could go on if it liked or stop if it liked,
I would go on, I supposed, until I was no more use for it.

And then out of all these gloomy prognostications came an
exchange of telegrams and messages. The Turks had sur-
rendered. The Balkans had thrown in their hand. Austria
was suing for a separate peace. Germany was exchanging
messages with the President of the United States—hints of this
reached the soldiers in the line but no certainty until the night

of the 10th of November. A message was sent round the line to the effect that troops should stand fast at the point reached at eleven hours. No further advance was to take place after that time, no offensive action to be taken, but defence measures to be maintained.

The long arm of coincidence has no more unique achievement in its long record than that the Great War should be concluded at the eleventh hour on the eleventh day of the eleventh month.

It was a squalid night but some of the R.A.S.C. made a fire with much-needed petrol in the street. There was not much to drink and supplies were short. The men found their satisfactions not in festivity but in recollection. None of us believed that it could have ended like this. Was it for this that we had lost home and home ties? Was it for this that we came so far and endured so much? Was it for this—to stand in the cobbled streets of a Flemish town with no drink in us nor yet food to encourage us, nor yet music nor words of thanksgiving? It was badly arranged—but who could have arranged it better? My Padre told us that we should pray, and perhaps it would have been a suitable ending that all of us along that long front line on both sides should then have got down on our knees and offered a prayer of thanksgiving to Almighty God, a prayer for our enemies and a prayer for ourselves—a prayer that those things, in that they hurt the spirit of man, should not be again, and that those things which raise, refine and glorify men should be again if it were God's will, in different and nobler circumstances. The long, long trail began for us a few days later. We were the Army of Pursuit. We had to follow at forty-eight hours' distance the retiring enemy. The rest of us were less fortunate ; they remained behind to clear up the battle areas, became disappointed, and right through the winter saw a distant ignoble demobilisation in the spring.

We in the Scotch Division went forward into Germany and, alien though I was among them, to see the King's Own Scottish Borderers march over the bridge across the Rhine into Cologne to the tune of " The Blue Bonnets are Over the

Border " was an unforgettable experience. It sent a shiver down one's spine and a lump to one's throat. It was to me the finish of the War and possibly better than the universal attitude of prayer which the Padre had suggested as fit for the troops who were laying down their arms and would fight no more.

The discovery of life in Cologne and the area round about it was that the Germans were like ourselves. " We've been fechtin' the wrang folk," said Sergeant Murray to me. The Scotch found the Germans rather like themselves, similar in speech, given to hospitality, and for a while we settled down to great comfort among them.

But I was sick of it all and when demobilisation began I wanted to get away. If I had been wise I would have stayed and got a good job. Things became gay, I believe, in Germany in the summer of 1919.

My heart wasn't in it. Having come through great tribulation I knew it was not for me to stay enjoying the fruits of conquerors. I had other things to do ; it was not for that that I had been saved, and with no more than a vague uncertainty I put myself forward for early demobilisation. It came even quicker than I expected. Perhaps I was troublesome and not wanted. Anyway, they let me go, and down the Rhine in a boat I went to Rotterdam, across to England, reported at the Demobilisation Centre and found myself with my War Bounty in my hand, a free and, what was most astonishing, a living man.

THE LAWYER AS A BOOK BUYER

Lawyers are among my best customers and I am grateful for it.

They are a little aloof and forbidding, the one or two of them I know. They do not read legal books much, as far as I can discover, for the few such books which I have they apparently desire me to retain, as no serious attempt has been made by them to unload my shelves. They read detective fiction quite a lot, however, and I am a little surprised by the lightness of their minds. But the semi-educated like me are always like that, I imagine, thinking that persons who have had a better education than they must necessarily have had an infinitely better one.

Education up to a point—a fine point—makes a great difference, but beyond that there is little to choose between one man and another.

This present demand for detective fiction, I think, must wane. It relies for its interest on something really essentially trivial. A dead man is no more important in the eyes of literature than a dead cat. It is an inconvenient thing, a mere dead body, in modern society, inconvenient to dispose of, inconvenient to account for, and must, of course, be the subject of police and legal action, but dead men in literature literally tell no tales, and detectives, whether private or official—they are peers' sons or doctors—are for me, after one has met one or two, the kind of persons that one no more wants to meet too frequently in fiction than in real life.

The "Famous Trial Series" with the full documentation of trials generally, by writers such as William Roughhead and Filson Young, are in a different category. There you have the whole story, background and foreground, speeches and all. There, there is something worth while—the real, actual human concordance—the thing that might have happened to me—I can accept that but not the corpse of Lord Richard found in the pantry.

I prefer to find pickles in my pantry.

Lawyers are, however, no more exclusive in their taste than other men.

The question is asked, " Should a Doctor tell? " but whatever the answer may be, they, no more than the lawyers, don't tell me very clearly what they want to read—they want something and generally take away anything.

Books for them, as for most, are a recreation and, the truth must be told, the more educated they are the more they want books for recreation.

It is the ardent inquiring youth, the aspiring and perspiring plodder, who feels there must be something in books.

These are they who think they will find in literature a tool to raise them in life. They are, of course, mistaken. Literature is not a tool. It is a recreation—a happy delusion—a spent illusion—a lovely dupe—a doorway to a fairy land—an escape from reality—colour in the embroidery of time—an aider and abetter of sloth—the foe of sleep—these things—all these things —is literature, but never the tool, never the weapon, never the means to an end.

It is forbidden that you harness butterflies to bodies or that you make traps to catch moonbeams.

HOW SHALL I ADVERTISE ?

These booming gentlemen come in from time to time to see me but I am quite equal to them.

One came to-day, with a navy-blue suit with a double-breasted jacket (my mind dwells on the possibilities of a new suit), a sort of " Admiral Beatty " angle to his hat and a blue tie with white spots—he hectored me, he cajoled me, he persuaded me, he jollied me—he was quite breezy in all the ways the breezes blow—and his idea was that I should advertise a selection of books for the country in his bus time-table.

It was with difficulty that I persuaded him to desist.

I had to imagine the kind of people who sit, rubber-necked, in these terrible buses which speed along what once were pleasant country roads. I thought in a flash of rural solitudes ruthlessly raped of what was peaceful and idyllic ; I thought of country cottages by the hundred with illiterate notices indicating that teas were provided ; I thought of the ice-cream ; I thought of wayside meadows ; I thought of saharas of waste paper and litter and societies for the prevention of them ; and hikers and all the disorder that had fallen across our once orderly countryside, and there solemnly surged up in me an irresistible English force, like that perhaps which stood up at the battle of Hastings or under the leadership of Boadicea—a feeling like that—like the sea—like something which belonged to Nature and not to that mere simulacrum of Nature, Man.

I felt all these things with an intensity which I cannot now explain, but I felt with sufficient intensity to tell to the salesman of space in the Bus Guide that I would have none of it.

I do not want to announce to the public through any printed medium the books I have to sell. I do not intend to offer those who desire a country life a selection of books appropriate to their mood.

I am a bookseller.

I have a shop in which I have collected many attractive volumes which contain allusions to, descriptions of, and admonitions regarding life in the country, but I will not stoop nor, for that matter, will I ascend to the heights of addressing the public through the Bus Guide as to the character of the volumes which I have for sale.

Of course, this is all very well and elevated. I have not forgotten that when I made these observations in these pages I had taken over twenty-two pounds, which is almost a fabulous amount for a retail bookseller, with no assistants, to take in one day.

I conceal from myself that the sales are inflated by the fact that I sold one copy of *Who's Who*, one copy of Oliver & Boyd's *Edinburgh Almanac*—shortly I hear to be out of print—and *The Memoirs of Casanova* translated by Arthur Machen—two volumes done for 25s. the set—which, with the various odds and ends and sundries, including, further, a very much overdue and unexpectedly paid account, made up this amount.

The elevatedness (is the word not elevation?) which comes to a tradesman when he has had such a successful day enables him to take in the evening a detached view of the whole problem of advertising, but—there are other days. Always the sun does not shine, as one is reminded by the music-hall song. And in the more mellow mood which " Amount of account rendered " engenders in one, I am prepared to consider more seriously the whole problem of advertising.

One feels, of course, that books should not need to be advertised. They are things of merit and require none of the puffs which are customary to less meritorious merchandise.

One feels that ; but while one feels it one feels it is an opinion which it is not likely will be shared by others.

I abandoned later that point of view, and while I feel that books should not be advertised, I am driven to the second line of defence, for after all in this self-advertising world I must do a share.

The next natural step is that the publishers should advertise, and here I feel for a moment or two I can rest with satisfaction.

The unfortunate thing, however, is that publishers advertise only books which I have either sold out in advance or have just sold out, or have, most unwisely, omitted to purchase.

The publishers' list in the *Sunday Times*, in the *Observer* and *The Times Literary Supplement*, and the *Spectator* and the *New Statesman*, and *Time and Tide* and so on and so forth . . . these publishers' lists are a perfect bugbear to booksellers like me.

I buy three on journey and by ardent introduction sell them before the reviews begin to appear. I am then irritated and annoyed beyond words to learn that other people besides the three chosen ones desire them.

But that is only one case ; the opposite occurs just as often.

I reject the opportunity of buying three from the publisher and then come the advertisements, and then come the reviews, and I am left trying to persuade someone to buy *Robinson Crusoe* or *San Michele* or some other book which I have over-bought, rather than the book which he is ardently desiring because of what So-and-so has said in the reviews and what the publisher has said in the advertisement. The situation is a very defeating one and I admit defeat.

" How shall I advertise ? "

I ask myself again and again and briefly I drive myself to these conclusions.

My advertisement is my shop, first and foremost my shop, its position—its windows, and what they display.

My second advertisement is myself—untidy, unhealthy, to the casual, an uninteresting human figure but still, when roused, one who can mouth things about books as eloquently as any.

That is my second advertisement.

And what else can I do?

I write postcards : " Dear Mr A.B.C., You will be delighted to learn, I am sure, that another book has just been published by X. written by Y. You will remember how much you enjoyed his last book and I feel that I should not miss the opportunity of telling you of his new one. May I hear from you? Yours sincerely, ——."

I write lots of these postcards at a penny each, laboriously by hand.

They bring little response. I fancy some of them say : " What a bore ! I'll buy my books at the bookstall or by post from the Book Society, or go to The Times Book Club when I am in London, or go to Foyles or to Hatchards or to Bumpus, or anywhere rather than go back and see that fellow again. Why is he so enthusiastic? How can he possibly tell that books can be so interesting as he imagines? "

Oh dear ! Oh dear ! Oh dear !

Advertising is not for me.

Large space in the newspapers, catalogues with the assistance of the publishers, specially typewritten or printed lists for selected customers—these are not for me.

I must stand at the receipt of custom, humbly, modestly, I hope honestly, prepared to receive what comes.

Frankly I cannot sell books.

If people want books I have them. They are good books and, taking them all in all, thank God we will not look upon their like again.

That is my advertisement, and if sweet are the uses of advertisement, doubtless, in contrast to many other users of advertisement—I have tried to be sweet.

BELLA, THE BOOKSELLER'S INSPIRATION

She liked to be called Anabella—in fact she called herself that
—but I called her Bella.

We were straight with one another if it was only for a
week.

How old would she be then?—she must have been forty
and I thirty.

On this dull February day—the sleet sliding down like sheet
ice—uninterruptedly—I recall it all. The shop hasn't seen a
customer except a man at nine—a stranger—he wanted the
Daily Express—or he would take a *Times*.

" I don't keep newspapers," I said, " I keep books."

" You can keep your books," he said.

Then I went back to Bella. Bella was a barmaid.

There used to be a song

> " Bella was a barmaid,
>   Bar,—bar,—bar."

It went on :

> " She had a breach of promise case,
>   Just to increase the trade,
>   Bella was a bar—bar—maid."

She was.

It was in my Year of Grace—that happy interregnum—
inter-bellum—or is it inter-bellos?—my Latin isn't—in the
year that I spent recklessly between the Real War and the
Peace which I now—in my best moments only—think I enjoy.

It was a February day just like this. I was in Liverpool
and at the opening hour went into the bar where Bella was. I
had had no breakfast and had an appetite. I had a good bottle
of beer—a bottle of good beer—and prawns on toast. It was a
wet day and Bella was communicative. She hated Liverpool
and loved Marie Corelli, and we went to a music-hall that
evening, it being very fortunately her night off.

That's how it began.

She had lost at least one man who would have married her—down in a " Q " ship—and was now sadly serene. The Bar—her memories—Marie Corelli—these filled her mind as she filled the pint pots and glasses.

I saw her often but she let me go.

She did not send me empty away, though. She said : " Make something of it ; you have survived when better men died : you have an idea of a bookshop : visualise it : don't take a pub : buy a bookshop : find one somewhere : don't drift into drink and futility : one deed of noble note before the end. . . ."

All that.

I never said good-bye to Bella. I attempted it but the Bar was busy that time and I just had—my appetite was not so good—a bottle of good beer and prawns on toast, and went away.

" So long," she said—and added " Cheerio."

It was classic in its simplicity.

I went away and in a week I was a bookseller.

To-day, this dull February day, the sleet sliding down like sheet ice, uninterruptedly, I recall it all.

ORATORY

James Maxton is a man I have never seen. I owe what knowledge I have of his appearance to the cartoons. There is, however, a follower of his in this city and he seeks to become an orator. He has black hair which I think he oils, so shiny, almost slimy, it appears, and the blackness of his hair is repeated quite artistically in the blackness of the tips of his finger-nails.

I keep my finger-nails filed short—to save the trouble of using the nail-cleaner—but my young friend has no use for any of these things. His colour scheme in black shiny hair and black nail-tips is not a studied one ; both are incidental gifts of a divine, I am sure, but inexcusable Providence.

He desires to become an orator. He wants to stand on the tribune and move the hearts and actions of men by his eloquence, and it is, to me at any rate, a notable and a worthy aim because he believes that it is through books he can acquire knowledge.

I want young men and women to believe that books are the way to wider living. Those people who know by instinct are no use to a bookseller. He does not sell instinct. He sells the printed word. I, therefore, sell him books, and Dent came to my help to-day and enabled me to sell him four. I have sold him *The Speeches of Charles James Fox, The Speeches of Lord Macaulay, The Speeches of Abraham Lincoln, The Speeches of John Bright*, and more, I have received an order from him for *An Anthology of Historical Speeches* produced also in the Everyman's Library.

It is good business.

I wish I were able to follow up this line of activity. I might call on hotel-keepers with a list of books on hotel-keeping, with perhaps John Fothergill's *Innkeeper's Diary* as the first and most important. I shall visit the Bankers and tell them about Walter Bagehot's *Lombard Street*. I shall visit . . . I shall visit them all in turn. . . . I shall be a big business man— if that is possible for a bookseller.

A DEJECTED DIARIST

Byron wrote, " One lies more to oneself than one dares lie to others."

It is true.

These sheets and sheets are a proof.

I daren't talk to others as I write about myself. I know of

no other listener so comprehending, so silent. " Of all my wife's relations I like myself the best."

It is too fine to be tolerable.

I am unmasked.

I am a vain man, covering my vanity with a bogus humility. I know that I have no tale to tell, no story worth while. I know I can command no audience nor could I find, if I were courageous enough to seek, a publisher.

And yet I think my little life so important and valuable. They ought not to pass me by—my misshapen, shabby self—on the other side.

I cry out in these pages.

Take notice of me—see me, a man with a history, a man, not born a bookseller, who has made himself one. I won't be a forgotten man. Am I not, too, made in the image of perfection?

It is true.

We are all made in the image. We are all alike. I am just another of the Vanities. Of vanity in a vain and foolish world . . .

To business—let me dispel this mood with sound practical affairs. What diaries have I in stock? *John Evelyn*—" Everyman's Library." *Memoirs of Baron de Marbot*—Longmans. *Journal of a Disappointed Man*—Chatto & Windus. *A Last Diary*—Ditto. *Sir Walter Scott's Journal*—David Douglas. *The Private Papers of Henry Ryecroft*—Constable. *Journal of Arthur Stirling*—Heinemann. *Amiel's Journal*—Macmillan. *Memoirs of the Foreign Legion*—Secker.

It will do.

I will put them all in the window to-morrow with a card. I am good at writing window cards.

It might be

> DIARIES OF YESTERDAY
> AND   TO-DAY

or

> " CREEPS IN THIS PETTY PACE "
>
> DIARIES
>
> FROM DAY TO DAY

.   .   .   .

It was not a success, my window show. I had only one inquiry. " You keep diaries? "

" Yes, I have a special collection of them."

" Can you give me one, a page at an opening? I want it for my Gardening Notes."

It was a dejected diarist who had to admit he had no diary of that kind.

PRAISE

The note of praise which seems a natural one to some of us is one which leaves me unstirred.

Why should I praise?

The devout may choose to praise the Lord for His goodness and His wonderful works to the children of men ; the snob may feel that he wants to praise those in high places ; the sycophant may want to praise his master : but who that is sincere and honest with himself wants to praise anyone?

I am not forgetting the Apocrypha with its " Let us now praise famous men, and their fathers that begat them."

After all, the famous have their fame, the rich have their riches, those in high places have their high places—each has his reward.

Men get what they ask for, and if it doesn't turn out to be what they expected it is none the less what they wanted.

There are two disappointments in life, asserts George
Bernard Shaw : one to get what one wants and the other not
to get it.

If it comes to praising, I would like a new Laus Ad Hominem.
It might begin :

" Let us now praise the poorest men and their fathers who
recklessly begat them.

" Let them be praised in that they find themselves not praise-
worthy.

" Let us praise the poorest men in that having nothing they may
find that they have all.

" Let us praise the poorest men. . . ."

Stephen Reynolds' book *The Poor Man's House* has been
republished after twenty years in a new edition by Jonathan
Cape. It was worth it.

Books about the poor are the books the great mass of people
might want to read. I don't believe that it is more difficult
for a man to conduct himself wisely with wealth than adequately
with poverty. Writing with full knowledge and from a wide
range of observations, I would assert in the face of those who
say that money does not matter that money does matter immensely—that no happiness occurs but can be benefited by the
possession of more—that there is no misery but may be
alleviated at least to some extent by the possession of some.

There is a lot of good about money.

They who say that money is the root of all evil know little
about the tree of life or its roots.

DEMOBBED AND NOTHING TO DO

Of all the books written about the War none tells of that
extraordinary period when hundreds of thousands of us sud-

denly laid down the job of soldiering and turned to face the new world which we had been told our fighting was to bring into being. Do not blame us if we did not recognise our offspring, the child of the War.

Anyone who knew London, for example, in the days of demobilisation will remember the crowds of tired, vacant-faced men hectically spending money with a view to recapturing contact with what they thought was a world well lost. Theatres were full, a woman or two escorted every man, shops enjoyed an unparalleled boom of extravagant spending, and the fever of peace was scarcely less than the fever of war. There was not only the demobilisation of the soldiers but the return to normal life of hundreds of thousands of men and women who had given up their usual and accustomed callings and now, with more money in their pockets than they had ever had before, they thought they would make all things new. Possibly one in a thousand realised that ambition, but as the months moved on towards 1919, increasingly, the more intelligent among us saw it was a broken world to which we had returned. Familiar landmarks and familiar friends had been effaced, accustomed economic activities had disappeared and new ones had not yet taken their place. All the Air Force men wanted to keep on flying and most of the Infantry subalterns wanted to go into the motoring business. Women who had lost their lovers in the calamity redoubled their energies to secure someone else to solace them, and the merry widows were restrained not in their merriment but only by the knowledge that they would lose their widow's pension if they married again.

That perhaps, is an unfair picture, but part of it is true. It was that aspect of it—the hectic aspect—which presented itself to me as I walked about at a loose end in London when my demobilisation had been completed.

I did not see, because they did not show themselves, the broken lives and ruined careers, the debris which was all too soon to rise to the surface of the waters of life.

London streets did not seem to lead to Heartbreak House, but Heartbreak House there was, no doubt, in every street in every town in this Kingdom and those other lands which had shared in the burden of the War.

I had a lodging in Brixton with the widow of a man who had been in the Royal Engineers. How I got these rooms I never very clearly remember. I think it was in some public-house in the Strand where I heard of them. I had been living in an hotel for some weeks and had fallen in with a crowd of Scotsmen, Englishmen, Welshmen, Australians, Canadians, South Africans and Americans, and it must have been one of them who told me they were going back home and I would do well to establish myself in Catterick Mansions.

She was a woman of appetite. Her husband had been one of those men—and there were a good many of them—who had never taken his leave from the Front. He had been away for over a year before she got the news that she would see him no more. He went out in that miserable time which followed the Retreat—those weeks between the days of " backs to the wall " and the time when reorganisation made an advance possible again.

The Historians, I am glad, now give Haig fuller credit than they did at the time. Foch thought of a War finishing in 1919, but it was Haig, disappointed in the Somme, overwhelmed in the Passchendaele, defeated in the Great Retreat, it was this Haig who, drawing upon some deep-seated fountain of deter-mination and resource, planned that the war should finish, God willing, in 1918.

It was a triumph of the dourness of the Scot over the divination of the Frenchman, and all the more paradoxical in that it was from the Scots one might have expected caution after so many untoward experiences, and from the Frenchmen one would have expected *élan* and dash and a rapid recoil from the hammer-blows of the opening months of the year—but fate worked otherwise. The Scotsman, determined that the War would last no longer than was necessary (did he count the cost?), announced to the surprise of the world that his armies were ready again for the fight and, in these marvellous months of war which began with the attack on Meteren in May and finished in November, Haig proved his claim to be considered one of the great commanders of history.

No such thoughts, however, filled my head as I walked idly from street to theatre or from picture-house to restaurant. I was determined that I would not return to a desk and my mind played with many possibilities. Henry David Thoreau and his *Walden* was one of the many books upon which I hung my thoughts. I would repair to some solitary place and there in a hut would watch Nature, learning the art of living well on little, and cultivate my soul. Quite a number appear to have done something of this kind—I read of them living in improvised shelters on rubbish-heaps, or caves which were not unlike the dugouts they once knew in the War days. Such souls had had enough of living companionship, they wanted to be alone with their thoughts ; they had been too deeply immersed in life and death to want any more contact with their fellows.

The hermit spirit, however, is not native to my countrymen and it was only a temporary phase with me. I wanted a life of freedom and irresponsibility, I wanted to be no one's servant ; I wanted to live largely and I was not greatly concerned whether I could live usefully or not.

My contacts with the Colonials made me for a time think of the wide-open spaces, but I had sufficient sense to know that these were not necessarily as wide and as open as my imagination encouraged me to believe. Some of the narrowest of men came out of these same Colonies, and that carried its warning for me. I couldn't see myself a bushman in West Australia, nor a pioneer farmer in New Zealand, nor a grower of oranges in South Africa, nor yet seeking my fortune in the gold-fields of Victoria or the woods of Vancouver. England, my own, now that the bugles had blown, England, my own, would be the country for me.

It was Charing Cross Road perhaps that helped to crystallise my mind in the direction which I went at last. I spent hours in that most fascinating street of London, lifting book after book and buying book after book, until in my room, against every wall, there were piles of them, for my landlady provided no bookcase. Twelve volumes of *Cassell's Popular Educator* was one, *Great Thoughts from Many Lands* was another, a " Gibbon " in many volumes, a series in buckram and red cloth done by Blackwood called *Ancient Classics for English Readers*—these were some of the purchases which I made and carried home to turn the pages and to read.

If I could have heard of a shop in Charing Cross Road within my means I would have taken it, but the hour was not ripe for decision. It was Bella, entrenched behind her bar counter, who sowed the idea in my mind which finally fruited forth into this shop in which I now sit to-day. Where she is now I do not know, who lies beneath her spell I cannot imagine . . . it was her wayward words perhaps that most definitely set me on the road that led me here.

There were many days to intervene before the day when I read the advertisement in *The Bookseller*. I had much disillusionment to achieve before I signed the documents that made me a bookseller on my own—much I have forgotten, but some things I remember still.

I kick myself and know that I am here. . . . The stock I took over was as poor a collection of books as I have ever seen. Those I brought with me from London were a hundred times better, but I was right to take the shop.

I like the place. It is a bookshop.

It has shelves with books on them—two counters facing each other—two windows to the street—a door in the centre—steps up—these are proper—one rises in the world when one enters a bookshop—and a good back shop behind.

Where would I have done better? Where would this lost dog have gone? I was right to come here.

This is my trade. This is my calling—keeping a bookshop.

The only fly in my ointment is that I keep the shop and keep the books.

I can only keep the shop by selling the books.

I will not be a book keeper. That is a poor business.

I will—I must—be a book seller.

H

THE RIGHT TIME

Who knows the right time?

Was I born at the right time? I wonder.

It was an inconvenient business. It was an embarrassment. It was an unwelcome event. It was a surprise. I know it only too well. .

My lot was no different from other men. We don't come out of the everywhere into here with a gladness and a clapping of hands. Our life is an irruption—an excursion—an intrusion, and no christening robes can make a better of it.

Man is born in trouble and to trouble.

I would plan my departure better.

That is my will, and my will shall be done.

" Some die too young," says Frederick Nietzsche, " some die too old ! "

" Still the saying soundeth strange—die thou at the right time."

I would it were possible after long grief and pain, but it looks as if I am to fade away—dribble out in the muddied delta of life, through the flat sands, into the open sea. I would it were different. I wanted to pass from hot blood and high pulsing endeavour into quiet stillness. I would choose to go like one I knew who, riddled with machine-gun bullets, fell forward on the wire of the enemy's front line—or like another with frantic, too late and now unavailing, effort sinking into the muddy, turbulent waters of the Thames one night by the Waterloo Bridge—or yet another, after a few hours of delirium, descending into oblivion through the furnace heats of pneumonia. These—or something like these—would be my choice, but the choice is not mine unless I make it.

Could I make it—could I have the courage to choose—am I brave enough to be called the coward who quitted?

No. I am not.

I am bound to breath.

I am bound to business.

I am a distributor of books.

God will forgive me—it is my trade.

SHALL PEACE PREVAIL?

The pacifists are a thoughtful folk, and I have—as clients—quite a number of them. There are those who saw the War—saw too much of it for their stomachs, and say, " It is enough. I went, but my sons will not go. It was a war to end war, and I insist as far as I am concerned that peace shall prevail."

And there are those who did not go to the War. War settled nothing, they tell me, although they do not know, as I know, the settling effect that the big stuff had on a lively and living trenchful of men ! Peace, I suspect, for them meant arrival at an unexpected peak of prosperity.

I hope I do them no injustice when I think that they want to stay put.

These are the pre-War vintage in the main as I see it in my shop. They buy Wells and Huxley and John Strachey—the publications of Gollancz—anything that the Oxford Group father, and similar books. Good customers, interesting people, I mustn't write a word against them.

Then there are the Post-Warriors. They are not the Happy Warriors of whom Sir Henry Wotton wrote—they have other gods than the household ones.

They are too proud to fight. They see no object in it. Why should I fight a German or a Russian? It is not suggested, not for a moment, that a German or a Russian might want to fight with them and insist that two make a quarrel. They have nothing to fight about, they say. They are civilised, urbane, sensible. Feebly I have tried to tell one of them that we do not hold our position in the world, with the privileges which go with it, by consent. We hold it by conquest. We cannot hold it this generation by any other means.

Do we want to hold it . . . this form of liberty of being an Englishman? . . . Do we want to hold it . . . this right to speak the English tongue, follow the English way, maintain this English tradition?

He thinks we do—he doesn't want, anyway, to be *forced* to change.

So peace may not prevail.

Perhaps Christ may be believed by Christians when He brought, not peace, but a sword—perhaps the path of progress is by God's will, intent and purpose—the way of War.

I am not ashamed.

I find that Uncle Toby is with me, and to *Tristram Shandy* I turn. What a pity my edition is not a better one! Yet it has George Cruikshank's illustrations. My price—weak in the spine—green cloth—Hutchinson, 1906—is two shillings, but the quotation . . . here it is :

". . . For what is War, what is it . . . when fought as ours has been on principles of liberty and upon principles of honour ? What is it but the getting together of quiet and harmless people, with their swords in their hands to keep the ambitious and the turbulent within bounds ! "

Shall peace prevail?

I, the disbanded soldier become bookseller, declare that the matter does not lie with me or those like me. It lies with the ambitious and turbulent. Let them take heed of their responsibilities and let sleeping dogs lie.

The dogs of war are not a wholly extinct species.

TOUJOURS LE CHANGE

Why don't I change my windows, they ask me. They say, " Your windows have been the same for weeks and there are bluebottles and flies and, indeed, spiders' webs to be seen in the frame. I am tired of looking at a few copies of ' Every-man's Library ' set on white paper crosswise, and as for the backs of the other books with which you pack the shelves, they have faded almost to invisibility."

This is all too true. I accept the indictment of my progressive customers.

I ought to be like other shopkeepers, always dressing my windows, always adding something new, always finding something to tempt the passer-by, but that is not my disposition.

Frankly, I think I am lazy, but am loath to admit it. I prefer to think that I have a deeply ingrained conservative instinct, that I am not one of those who are continually chasing the latest or the newest. I think of myself as sober-brained, restrained, deeply conscious of how long the world has been in being—how long this City has been sitting upon its hills—how long may yet be the story of my bookselling—and because of this deep consciousness of the permanence of things I don't feel inclined to keep changing my windows.

Besides, one book may be just as good as another. Who am I to say that the books which I am now offering to the public in my windows are better than those which lie on my shelves inside?

One book may be as good as another for the man who needs it.

The great Dr Arnold, it would hardly be believed, is one, however, who holds that such a conservative view as mine is positively a social danger. He says :

" There is nothing so revolutionary because there is nothing so unnatural or convulsive to society as the strain to keep things fixed, when all the world is, by the very nature of its creation, in eternal progress ; and the cause of all the evils in the world may be traced to that natural, but most deadly error of human indolence and corruption—that our business is to preserve and not improve. It is the ruin of all alike—individuals, schools, and nations."

It is observed that he says " individuals, schools, and nations," but he does not say shops.

I would like mine to be an old-established shop—established

for over a hundred years—what solidity there is in that sentence
—and one of the ways to give the impression, assuredly, of
solidity is leaving one's windows unchanged.

It is odd that I should be charged by the Doctor with being
revolutionary because I want to keep things standing still.
Charles Lamb wanted that in his *New Year's Eve*. Doesn't he
own that here he wants to stand still, no older—no younger, in
love with the green earth? I remember that, but I cannot put
my hand on it just now. It is in *New Year's Eve*, I'm sure.

One of my competitors runs what he calls " The Workers'
Bookshop "—an amusing fellow—he thinks himself a revolutionary. I feel I ought to·go round and tell him what Dr
Arnold tells me—that I, the conservative, the do-nothing, the
changeless one, am really he who stands for the inevitable
upward and onward sweep of time, and in that sense I am a
revolutionary more daring than he dreams of in his modern
pamphlets and his foolish reprints of obscure and decayed
economists.

But old Lord Melbourne, I frankly remind myself, was
accounted a great Prime Minister, and Queen Victoria entrusted
her realm to his wise and prudent guidance. He did not favour
frequent meetings of his Cabinet, but when they did meet it
is told that he used to read the agenda or list of business
placed before it and, having read it, would sigh and say, " Well,
gentlemen, here it all is. What does it all amount to? Must
we really *do* anything? Can we not leave things as they are? "

Whether, then, it is any justification for my indolence, my
preference to lie or sprawl on this counter and write this
pencilled rubbish, or whether it is because I—a deeply and
profoundly convinced social failure—am not going to bother
myself to take out my window to-day . . .

To-morrow—and to-morrow—and to-morrow—there may
be time—but not to-day.

After all the world may end to-night, and it would be a pity
if I had wasted my last hours in dusting books, cleaning windows
and redressing them when I could be as I am—doing what is,
in the sum of things at any rate, nothing at all worth while.

"I KNEW SAINTSBURY"

" Personally, I knew Saintsbury. I was in his class at Edinburgh."

I was astonished, as I had never seen a student of Saintsbury's before, although there must be thousands of them. My Saintsbury was *Notes on a Cellar Book*, and for the rest I knew little about him.

It was disappointing for me to learn that he who knew Saintsbury did not know the *Notes on a Cellar Book*, and although I let him turn the pages of both editions—the de luxe one with his signature and the ordinary one—he felt he knew sufficient, apparently, about Saintsbury without adding to his knowledge by buying his book.

It is a pity, for although I have poor unhappy brains for drinking—there's something in Shakespeare about that—I none the less count Saintsbury's book on wine among the treasures of my shop. The dedication is good, and the bold assertion that no money he ever spent was spent better than on good drink—that is good too. He lives at Bath, they tell me; and I like to think of him as a sturdy, fiery soul, looking upon the earth and finding, at any rate, something that has good in it, and taking hold upon what he finds good and holding it fast. These milk-and-water people, how they blaspheme the universe with their passion for wrath, or indeed revolution !

I have little patience with them nowadays. The fire that once burned in me has died out. My pocket is no better lined, but my blood perhaps is cooler, my sense of reverence greater.

This strange complex world, with what infinite strife and struggle and difficulty it has come into being, with its patient endurance of men for generation after generation ! How, when one looks on it, can one do other than look on it with awe, with respect, with reverence and with affection?

The world is so full of wonderful things that at this stage in its history there would seem to be no justification for aught else than that we should just wonder and give thanks.

Is life so intolerable to the men in this island? Are things so unendurable?

Does one require to be a stoic nowadays? What is the worst that we endure—ill-health—poverty—death—trial—pain? . . . Man has endured these things.

We too can endure.

That is what I like about Saintsbury, although I never was a student in his class.

Here is what he writes about the death of Molière. I transcribe it from the *Oxford Book of English Prose*. These are brave, heartening words :

". . . Molière was not old ; he was almost exactly the age of Shakespeare when he, too, ' died less tragically ', as they say. . . .

" As for ' tragedy ' (I miss bits) there was little for tears here, little to wail, except in so far as ' the end ' is always sad."

Now here is the rub :

". . . If God has given you brains, and courage, and the upward countenance ; if you have loved : if you have had your day and lived your life, what more do you want ? "

Who cares if they refuse me a further overdraft?

" FOR SHORTNESS CALLED NOLL "

There is to me something attractive about the spacious days when booksellers were publishers and sometimes writers, and when men of intelligence spent their evenings in pubs.

They probably were the great days of literature when Johnson ruled the roost in the Cheshire Cheese. It is a disappointing thing, however, to go to the Cheshire Cheese, for me at any rate. Its flavour has gone. I cannot find the Great Cham. I cannot any more find him there than I can Cleopatra in the Egyptian Rooms of the British Museum. He is gone, the authentic Johnson, and holds his court of literature beside some other river than the Thames.

Still, I don't readily give up Dr Johnson and his circle, although it is impossible for me to recreate them in the place which they frequented.

There are on the shelves of this shop quite a good collection of Johnsoniana. The valuable set (which I don't intend to sell) is a 1794 edition of *The Lives of the Poets*. It is in four volumes, and in Volume One there is a steel engraving of Samuel Johnson, LL.D., himself, "Published as the Act Directs, August 14th 1794, by T. Cadell, Strand . . .," four volumes bound in leather, a little weak at the joints, but, I reassure myself, not purchasable by anyone who is likely to walk in at this shop door.

I have no millionaires as customers.

There is a copy of the Oxford Boswell, and also *Our Tour to the Hebrides*, the latter edited by R. W. Chapman, the refreshing introduction or preface written in Salonica. I have always liked that preface, and Mr Chapman is right in supposing, I am convinced, that Boswell and Johnson would have liked it too.

There is a book by O. F. Christie called *Johnson the Essayist*, published by Grant Richards, but I have never taken to it, nor have my public.

The rest of my collection, I see, is made up of "*Sir*," *said Dr Johnson*—Duckworth ; *The Conversations of Dr Johnson*—Knopf ; *Samuel Johnson*, Hugh Kingsmill—author-banker—an excellent piece of writing which also may be in the non-purchasable class ; *Dr Johnson*, S. C. Roberts, M.A.—Cambridge University Press ; *Dr Johnson and his Circle*, John Bailey—Home University Library ; and, lastly, another book of S. C. Roberts, called *Samuel Johnson, Writer*, Herbert Jenkins, at 5s. . . .

That, I thought, was my stock, but I have found pushed into the back of the shelves Macaulay's *Life of Johnson*—the original is in the *Encyclopædia Britannica*—a somewhat soiled-looking book which really is a school reader. How I came to possess it I don't know, but it is a book which at one time has been loved, for it is marked and annotated and contains a

H 2

number of paper cuttings from various journals dealing with the great lexicographer.

These words, I see, are merely a ramble—a sort of Johnsonian journey—there is a good title for a book—" A Johnsonian Journey "—but I will not be the author of it !

It was Oliver Goldsmith who drew me to paper this evening when perhaps I would have been better employed taking a little brisk exercise as recently ordered by the doctor.

To-day, among an obsolete collection of books the average price of which did not exceed sixpence, I have secured an Oliver Goldsmith, rebound apparently in part and edged with red leather, dated 1822. It was printed by J. Robbins & Company, Albion Press, Ivy Lane, Paternoster Row, London. The full title is " Selected Works of Oliver Goldsmith, Comprising the Vicar of Wakefield, The Toll of Years and Poems with memoirs of the Author, including original anecdotes collected by the Rev. J. Evans, LL.D., author of ' The Juvenile Diarist,' ' Geographical Walks and Talks,' et cetera, et cetera." This, with all its shabby binding and shabby origins, is an interesting book and my heart warms again to that most lovable —almost only lovable—native of Ireland, Oliver Goldsmith, " for shortness called Noll, who wrote like an angel and talked like poor Poll."

So they wrote, but it is a bald understatement to say there is no more lovable figure in literature.

Macaulay's Essay does no more justice to him than the same writer does for Johnson himself. Macaulay did not like either Johnson or Goldsmith and did not hesitate to say so.

It is some weeks now, but I have not forgotten the meanness of Macaulay in this.

The Deserted Village, which is a delightful poem, is dissected and condemned because Goldsmith combined in one poem some recollections of the scenes of his boyhood with something which had come within the range of his experience some twenty years after.

This, says the great Lord Macaulay, provides an absurdity in that the poem described something " which never was and never will be seen in any part of the world." Heavens that wait for us, what a condemnation by one poet of another! Surely if poetry is anything—even narrative poetry—it is something that never was seen in any part of the world—in fact that never was on sea or land!

How dare the author of the *Lays of Ancient Rome*, of *Ivry* or the *Armada* attempt to apply such a standard to the author of *The Traveller* or *The Deserted Village*!

HAPPINESS COMES EASIEST TO BOOKSELLERS

" The secret of happiness is to put your business out of your mind."

So declares Mrs Walters, a good, kind creature, a widow who mourns a son missing in the War and a husband who did not long survive his disappearance.

There are no secrets of happiness. Everyone learns that happiness is indefinable, incalculable, elusive. It is the uncaught bird, the glance of a sunbeam on the water, the smile on the face of a child, the low sympathetic voice of a woman, a pressure of the hand on the arm from a man (a comradely thing), a note of distant music, the smell of trees and grass after rain, a bit of work reluctantly approached and done well at last—these things are happiness.

It is not manufactured, it is a by-product.

None can give and none can take it away—blessed be the Lord of Life.

The secret of happiness then, Mrs Walters, is not to put business out of one's mind. One may find it in business. One may find it equally out of business. It is a real BONUS—how debased has that word become! BONUS, good—the absolute thing—has become an extra—something with a packet of tea or a box of soap. The pure, the immaterial, the classic perfection has become a thing of coupons. Mrs Walters reads uplift books—books which are a little sad—as life is—and sentimental —as she takes it to be.

She reads *The Road Mender* by Michael Fairless, and *The Journal of a Disappointed Man* by H. M. Barbellion, and *The Friendly Road* by David Grayson. These are her country— a country for those who are blind to Nietzsche and Carlyle. They are these writers—those who despair of the garland which is only for them who will run the race and endure the dust and heat. They are of the wayside—over the ditch—down the bank—beside the hedgerow, where amid the undisturbed grass there are violets and buttercups and yellow bedstraw. They sit with their backs to the road. They look through the gap in the hedge to the calm meadows and green pastures beyond. They hear the traffic but they heed it not, and the dust that falls on their shoulders is light because it is only a symbol of unhappy, harping, unnecessary things that pass quickly away.

It may be necessary for soap manufacturers and silk mercers to put business out of mind to find happiness. It is not so for booksellers. The faery world is too much with them. Even in getting and spending they find happy hours.

I acknowledge one such happy hour and it is not yet ten this morning.

IDIOTIC VERSES

This is a day when the bland mildness of the spring drives me to certain inconsequent idiocy. It is not an unpleasant frame of mind. I feel tolerably well and yet not vigorous. I feel deeply happy and yet not ecstatically joyful.

In this mood I have received a request for books of nonsense verse, and I have an idea that there is an anthology, and I cannot put my hand on it.

Edward Lear's *Book of Nonsense* I have and, of course, there are the " Alice in Wonderland " books, but these my inquirer has already acquired.

He asks me if I can trace the following :

> " The sunset occurs in the west,
> A bubble will burst if it's pressed—
> And water is wet
> And escapes from a net,
> And everything's all for the best."

This, he says, is a " Didactic Limerick "—whatever that means—but I don't know where I can find it. He himself is rather proud of his gifts in this direction, and has left me one which looks like a parody on W. E. Henley's " Invictus " :

> " Out of the glass that covers it
> He pricks it with a barber's pole,
> And he cares not for lover's wit
> As he swallows the sandwich whole."

It seems to me not nonsense but sheer rubbish, but I did not tell him so. I set myself instead the task of seeing if I could do any better and I am quite pleased with the result.

I feel I have achieved absolute nonsense :

> " My neck my collar presses,
> They say the book is Bessie's—
> The future is just guesses,
> And yet they say time presses."

I might send that to the *New Statesman.*

THE BOOKSELLER REMEMBERS
GALLIPOLI

On the magic Peninsula I saw dawn and sunset as never I saw them before—a discovery of the War was that there is a dawn, a daily miracle which we are so foolish, so ignorant and so stupid as not to get out of bed and see for ourselves every day.

And not only the dawn.

There is the night of stars, incredibly, indescribably lovely, which no one who has lived in towns with their distracting city lamps can ever really know.

There may be many ways to the stars, but I know one.

As soon as darkness had fallen the sergeant had named the party. We were destined for funerals—for several funerals— being held without benefit of clergy in no-man's-land . . . no drum was heard, no funeral note for this expedition.

Certain of my fellow-countrymen and certain of those who had fought and died under the Crescent lay unburied, and, for sanitary as well as aesthetic reasons, it was desirable that they should be seen no more. We emerged, so many with picks, so many with shovels, some with entrenching tools. The surface of the earth in front of our line was hard and rocky and they were not buried deep, these comrades of ours. The occasional tat-tat of machine-guns, snipers' bullets, Very lights away on the flank rising in ghost-like green—these were the only interruptions in our task. Two of us went to each corpse ; the sergeant moved from group to group, and in two hours we had done our job without a casualty.

Hearne and I had the furthest area to deal with, and when we had finished, having been told by the sergeant that we should return to our front line by the correct route when our task was done, Hearne said to me : " It is too soon to go back. There will be a fatigue on that back latrine which they are making, and there is revetting material coming up from the beach to-night, and we may as well be here."

I agreed, and in a large shell-hole we lay down. There is serenity in no-man's-land and a view of the stars which is intensely satisfying.

It is a refreshment, an unbelievable peace to lie with one's hands clasped behind one's head and gaze up into the black purple-blueness which was the Mediterranean night.

The phase of the Gallipoli operations which I saw differed entirely from my previous experience in France and Belgium and my subsequent experience there when I was fated to return to the Western Front.

There was no back country on Gallipoli. The whole of that little area could be machine-gunned and almost any artillery could fire well over it into the sea, so limited was it in expanse. Security by distance from the enemy simply did not exist, all of us were under sentence of immediate death and the enemy held us in the hollow of his hand.

There was no feeling of dread, however, animating the troops and there was more gaiety on Gallipoli than any other area of war in which I served. The 29th Division and the Australian and New Zealand troops seemed endowed with a quality of defiant gallantry which, because they were a limited force, never seemed to settle on any other of the Armies. It was, on reflection, a pleasant time I had on the Peninsula. I made friends ; casualties were only occasional, and, at this distance as far as I remember, none of them was horrible. Dysentery took a number of us away.

One settled down ; one became a new creature adapted to one's environment like the lizards or the flies. There was bathing too, once or twice for me, and it was a real pleasure to be out on the Ration Party and go down to the beach below the protecting cliffs. War is not horrible all the time, as pacifists seem to believe. There are compensations for everything, and there is compensation in comradeship, intimacy, freedom from economic anxiety, the knowledge that once one's mind is adjusted to the worst that can happen—and that is a pretty bad and bloody wound or swift and sudden death—one settled down to existence as an Infantryman.

Man is an adaptable animal—I acknowledge that myself.

I adapted myself more easily to the environment of the trenches with its lice, filth, heat, stench, flies, dysentery, danger —I adapted myself to these more successfully, I repeat, than I have been able to adapt myself to this life as a shopkeeper.

To-day I have difficulty in recognising myself as one who took a man's share in historical events—and yet it is a fact. I kick my left ankle with my right foot to reassure myself that this seedy shopman played a not unheroic part. I took part in a couple of raids, I remember, and came to hand-to-hand fighting with a Turk. I am not sure that I was not glad when he fled from me up the sap where we had met without intention or appointment.

One morning—Sunday morning it was—when an Artillery Bombardment descended on our trench system with unusual accuracy, I was pretty good, standing up to my job with the best of them. Two badly wounded men I helped along to the Aid Post in intervals and all the time felt great exaltation. I was pleased I had cleaned my rifle that morning. There was no grit in my breech and I did the rapid with great satisfaction, but, it must be admitted, at no immediately recognisable target.

At first we were at Suvla and then there came the preliminary evacuation. Off we went, the whole of us, from that section of the Peninsula and, after standing out to sea for a night and being thoroughly sickened by the choppy waters of the Ægean, we were decanted on Cape Helles for another go at the War. It had been our hope that we were bound for Egypt at least, if not Blighty, but the early eastern dawn disclosed that the dogs were returning to their vomit.

Up the line we went and received a leaflet from high Staff officials stating that no further evacuations were contemplated on the Peninsula, which information, with its unusual candour, left us wondering why we should be told the intentions of the Higher Command.

Whether it was weeks or days I never remember, but the second phase came soon enough.

There was no more fighting. We did it like Sir John Moore's Burial Party, silently and at dead of night, down these long communication trenches. " Step short in front," " Close up in the rear," until we found ourselves on the beach beside the *River Clyde*. We stood out to sea and got to Mudros. At Mudros I collapsed with dysentery. As long as I was in the War I was all right, but this sailing about the Ægean in a boat registered for river traffic on the Bristol Channel between Bristol and Ilfracombe was not for me. They told me I was pretty bad, but I didn't care. There comes a condition when one has no desire to live and has no desire to die—that was my condition when they lifted me into the hospital ship at Mudros—my destination, I being told, was England, Home and Beauty, and a hospital.

BUYING HISTORIES

There is no concealing it.

I buy these histories for myself. There is no sale for them.

I have bought to-day the *Historian's History of the World* in twenty-odd volumes. I paid one shilling a volume but that is too much. Still, I couldn't resist him—a nice lad—finished with his studies—Father consents at last that he is a duffer and may give up the Law—and its profits—and go off to Australia or the Argentine.

" I am sorry for the old man—he thought I would follow him in the practice—but I can't. He had the War, you know, and getting through it he was jolly glad to settle down. . . . But I've had no War—nothing—my only thrill is a girl—a sports car—a bit of flying. I want to go abroad . . . the big spaces, you know."

And so I bought his books—a pathetic lot his kind of books —short cuts to knowledge a man who has no taste for learning would buy—just rubbish. But why do I buy them? I can make nothing out of them. They are paper, pulp, piffle, not books !

It has to be faced. I am book mad. I have the bibliomania. I would buy any printed thing. The only thing that doesn't interest me on paper is the blankety blank. " Is it printed? " seems to be my criterion and will be my passport to bankruptcy !

History books, even when I buy them for myself, are the least profitable of purchases. History is a fable—a fairy tale—

on which men are agreed—who wrote that?—it is not original but it is true. Who can tell the truth, the story, the history of the Fall of Man or the Crucifixion, or the Death of Socrates, or the Fall of Carthage, or the Entry into Jerusalem by Allenby—who can tell these things?

There are no reliable reporters.

There are no accurate historians.

History is a fable upon which men are agreed. Anyway, what does it matter! What do we want to know?

They were born, they lived, endured, suffered and died—that's all human history.

The background changes, the costumes are modified, there are divers tongues but the story—the history—is the same.

Who wrote—the business of life is to be, to become, to do, to do without and to depart? It is an epitaph on the whole duty of man. It ought to be a warning to me in buying histories.

They are bad stock.

ORPHANS AND LARGE FAMILIES

Looking along my shelves I look at some books which I think of as orphans.

There is Richard Jefferies' *Story of My Heart*. There was an orphan! And in the same category Gilbert White's *Selborne*. I call them orphans because they are single books by celebrated writers. They may have written other books, Jefferies and White, but they are remembered by these books only.

And there are other orphans. I have Winwood Reade's *Martyrdom of Man*—as far as I remember the only thing he wrote.

There must be many more single efforts of great minds, although as I run my eye along my shelves I can see none other just at the moment. There is something sad about these only children, but if there is sadness in them there is sadness too in what are called the Sets.

There is a splendid set in twenty-four volumes by Bulwer Lytton. I will be lucky if I get a shilling a volume for it, and I have also sets of Sir Walter Scott, Dickens and Carlyle. Then there is my Temple Shakespeare—a set in many volumes —and a very nice edition of the *Adventures of Gil Blas* in four.

These are large families and gave their parents doubtless much joy, but the sets which are heaviest of all on my shelves and on my stock books are the bound volumes of magazines and periodicals. I have *Good Words*, it appears, for almost a century. I have a set of *The Quiver* and, I fear, an unsaleable set of *Punch*, as well as the eighteen eighty-four edition of the *Encyclopædia Britannica*.

My heart is sore for these orphans but my shelves are heavy with the sets.

WHY DON'T THEY ?

" You have palmed on me all sorts of books but they're no use. Galsworthy, Wells, your ideas that I should know Shakespeare and Shelley are just nothing. I want a book about the Meaning of Life."

Thus young Denis Clayton Tacchi, a good fellow with whom I fear all will not be well.

The Future is dark for Denis.

His parentage is mixed, I learn ; an Italian father and an English mother—now under guardians attending this University. He has been a good customer—has bought largely— and paid well, but now I am to lose him.

He threatens to take Holy Orders—he may—terrible thing in this city—embrace the Catholic Faith. He has deep anxieties — profound uncertainties, appalling hopelessness. He is floundering in life, and none in Heaven above or earth beneath seems to be able to help him find his feet.

And so he comes to the bookseller.

He wants a book about the Meaning of Life—the wherefore and the whither—the old desire of bewildered youth to know the purpose of it. I could have quoted :

> " Up from Earth's centre through the Seventh Gate
> I rose, and on the Throne of Saturn sate,
> And many Knots unravelled by the Road
> But not the Knot of Human Death and Fate."

There is a door to which neither Bishop nor Bookseller has a key, and I sent him away sadly for all my great possessions of books.

The learned and the wise, the Universities and the Colleges, the professors and the preachers ought to get together and produce a Book of Books telling the world, as far as they can decipher it, the plain meaning of life. Why don't they? Is there a reason?

This business of providing a book on the Meaning of Life keeps recurring to me. Sleepless, for what seemed a century and probably was only an hour, last night, I kept turning it over and over in my mind. Why are we born? Why are we condemned to struggle? Why are we condemned to die? Is there a purpose?

Tommy Marriott, now gone back to Australia, told me a story which made a lasting impression on my memory.

It converted my dull, dusty and depressing little shop as he told me into an arena in which great drama found a place.

He told me how in his calling as a timber buyer he found himself in the big timber country in the southern part of Western Australia. On the edge of a vast clearing stood the shack of a sleeper-cutter, a great, big-boned Slovak who had found his way there to earn a living, hewing and sawing the jarrah. As Tommy Marriott drew near the sleeper-cutter's house he thought the place unusually still for that stillest of all countries, where no birds sing and where Nature seems always to be holding her breath as if in suspense. He dismounted and hitched his horse to a bush. He called aloud, for he knew the man. There was no answer. He pulled aside the sacking curtain which overhung the entrance to the shack. He looked inside ; for a moment his eyes did not adjust themselves to what they saw, but quickly enough he recognised what lay before him. The Slovak was dead—had been dead for at least a day—died, he discovered later, of what not infrequently causes death among such toiling men—heart failure brought on by overstrain with the axe. But that was not the significant thing. Marriott's next impression, he told me, was the clock on a box opposite the bed—a seven-day clock apparently— which ticked with a noise as loud as the reiterated stroke of a hammer on a plate of iron.

It was that that moved him.

The Slovak who had wound the clock was dead but the clock went on, and from that experience the Timber Merchant founded a theory of the Universe. He held and expounded often one aspect or another of the idea that the universe, as we know it, had been started by a hand which was now, if not dead, palsied, and the world, like the clock in the shack in the big timber country in West Australia, went on spinning on its axis although the hand that gave it its impetus was no longer able to control it.

Recollecting all that, I have wished to see Marriott again and hear what more he had made of his theory, what facts he had got to bind up with it, but Marriott is beyond my call.

And so I sprawl on this counter writing when I should be dusting.

I consider again the necessity of a book on the Meaning of Life. It seems the one problem.

Should we not give up all argument, all talk of war, of armaments, all talk of everything except working for the bare needs of existence until we have found out the great Wherefore and the greater Why? It is surely man's supremest need, and if, when the pundits have examined the whole question and reported to the world at large, their conclusion is that life has no meaning, or, if it has a meaning, it is beyond our power to discover it, let us then join hands together and invent a meaning.

Let us invent not only a meaning but a great purpose, and having done so, let us live our lives in an endeavour to serve it.

BIRKENHEAD

When I read the word " Birkenhead " I seem to think of Bolingbroke. There is a full-mouthed, dynamic quality in the name and I must confess for a weakling, a man of peace, afraid of the War as I was, terrified of the world, disgusted with the flesh and likely to be overcome by the devil—in spite of all this I have an admiration for the Noble Lord.

It seems a pity that he has turned from the life abundant to literature, even if he does connect his name with *Fifty Famous Fights in Fact and Fiction*. It is a book, however, which I will sell quickly. There must be some full-blooded gentlemen who want their sons, nephews and grandsons brought up in the Roast Beef of Old England tradition—able to take your part in the world, my boy, use your fists if necessary and give a good account of yourself—that sort of tradition must not be discarded by debased booksellers who have lost their nerve in the horrors of the peace.

Birkenhead, of course, is entirely right in spite of what they may say to the contrary. This world has not yet reached the condition when the lion lies down with the lamb. Even if one does not seek glittering prizes the sharp sword must sometimes be taken in the hand.

Although I take it there are no new worlds that this island people seeks to conquer, there are places in the sun which we seek to defend, and who are we to say that we will now lay down the burden of imperial responsibility? What about those who have relied upon the strong arm of Britain and who, although they may, like unruly sons and daughters, sometimes kick against the pricks, know not what they would do if the parental protection were withdrawn?

These are high policies for a bookseller before breakfast, but Birkenhead has provoked many another besides me to mental alertness.

And so this morning I fell from grace.

For months now I have made it a rule not to read until I have swept the shop, taken the covers off, dusted and cleaned the windows.

To-day I broke my rule.

Not that *Fifty Famous Fights in Fact and Fiction* is a justification for the breaking of the law ; but justification or not, it is the cause, and here I am now unbreakfasted, unshaven, windows steaming and greasy, babbling about Birkenhead when I ought to be attending to my business.

I will carefully insert my over-used pink blotting-paper as a book-mark and close this book. I will add a resolution. I will not fiddle away my time any more to-day until all the proper routine of the shop is done and I have sold twelve books.

WHAT YOU HAVE MISSED

Fate—which made me feel I wanted to be a bookseller even if bookselling bids fair to introduce me to bankruptcy—fate, I repeat, denied me many other things less desirable.

I sometimes reflect on what I have missed.

I might have been a specialist in fashions, and it is a queue of women stretched across the front of my shop waiting for the opening at nine o'clock of my neighbour next door which provokes these observations.

I have been out twice to tell them to make a space in case somebody does want to buy a book, but the queue joins up again almost before I have got to the back of the shop. They began to arrive before eight. When I collected my milk I thought it was odd that women should be looking at my windows at that time of the morning, but they were merely amusing themselves idly while they waited for the greater bargains of the shop next door.

And what is it that they find attractive? I have seen the things. There are blouses and handkerchiefs and something called " Nearly-Silk " at 10½d. a yard. There is a statuesque display of truncated female figures which directs public attention to corsets and, of course, everything is offered at extraordinary reductions. Large pieces of cardboard on which the price figure is produced in red letters create a nerve-jangling spectacle as one glances at the displays in these windows.

It has really disheartened me because I have things to sell which, if women only would buy, they would find therein they had more lasting pleasure. Why should not I sell a beautiful set of Jane Austen? I have several George Eliots second-hand but almost in mint condition, and if they do want something modern, what is wrong with Vicki Baum? I would sooner sell *Grand Hotel* than see them waste their money so uselessly.

And when all is said and done, what do they make of it? They are not well dressed, their clothes display little taste—in fact I don't think women dress as well as they used to. What it is they spend their money on, heaven knows, but it is not books. What they spend on clothes they seem to spend to little advantage.

This hubbub round the door, which has lasted most of the day, has kept me inside. There lingered most of the morning an idea that I might get a few customers from my neighbour's enterprise. Nothing has come my way, and the only sweets of life that have been mine to-day are two meringues and a glass of milk, and that is hardly an inspiring diet.

After closing time I am going to have a good meal and, perhaps, fortify myself with strong drink and go and see my neighbour. He may tell me how he does it, for I must get more business if I am to live.

BOOKSELLER AS SOLDIER

Becoming a soldier, even when soldiers were wanted to serve their country, was no such simple business in September 1914.

The improvised Recruiting Offices were crowded and it was almost a favour to secure service.

I quitted the town, however, and made for a small country place where I knew I would have less difficulty. There, through the good graces of a retired Captain of the Regular Army, a policy-holder with my Office, I found myself in the local County Regiment. He put me up for the night at his own house until he could arrange for my transfer to the depot. It was a day or so before the transfer could be arranged, however, and it all seems a dream to me, these days that I spent— the last for years in England—in the quiet of an English country home . . . the order of the place, the quietness of it, the excellence of the meals, the decorum of the household, their restrained acceptance and absorption of the exciting news of the day . . . all these remained with me, a heartening, stabilising memory in the days of confusion which lay ahead.

In due course the letter came which was to find me a road into the regiment, and the Captain bade me good-bye, wishing me the best of luck and telling me to keep the honour of the regiment high. He had been with it in South Africa and was steeped in its lore. It was to him The Regiment. He gave me to understand that to have been a private soldier in that regiment was higher honour than to have been a Colonel in any other.

With this inspiring encouragement I made my way to the depot and eventually with much difficulty got myself enlisted.

The Medical Examination always remains with me as a most interesting memory. About forty of us there must have been. We were told to strip at the back end of one of the barrack walls, and this we did, standing quite naked except that we had our hats on—and they were a varied collection of headgear —each of us holding his boots in his right hand and the rest of his clothing in his left. We waited for some ten minutes before the Doctor appeared. As for me, he was never nearer than twenty feet. He must have had good eyesight. All of us were passed without a single doubt or challenge.

As I was dressing myself with the rest I saw that there had been spectators—soldiers' wives, I fancy—from an adjoining tenement. But who were we to care for a little exposure? were we not destined to expose ourselves to much else before we were much older? We were given a couple of hours' leave and told not to get drunk. At nine we were to report again to the depot and proceed to Aldershot that night.

This looked as if we were going to be in the War after all, for, quite frankly, most of us felt we would be too late to take part in anything.

Some of us did get drunk, but I was of the sober, reflective kind and spent part of the time in a hotel writing to the Manager of the Office, apologising for having left so incontinently and thanking him for all he had done for my mother and for me. I felt that it was due to him and it seemed in a way as I sealed the letter that I had written my last will and testament for the life that was ended.

When I got back to barracks it was a gay and unusual mob which I joined. We were quickly hammered into shape, all of us in plain clothes, and placed under the command of three or four ex-Army men who knew how to look after a bunch of men such as we were. We marched to the station. We were cheered by the crowds. We cheered them in reply. We were an odd lot—every kind of headgear—every kind of clothes—clerks — shopmen — countrymen — engineers — carpenters — gentlemen out of work—workmen out of elbows—tramps—tailors—thieves—a hand-picked sample, representative of our country. After infinite delay, standing about, sitting down and getting up, we got into a train. Eight or ten of us were in each carriage. One man in my carriage got on the rack and slept there quite satisfactorily ; another got under the seat.

They sang, they laughed, they told stories, they waved dirty handkerchiefs about out of the window, and they lost their hats ; they emptied their bottles ; they ate their food ; some became very sober ; some became drunk ; some became sick—and in that atmosphere we all moved on to Aldershot.

The delays the train encountered made one wonder if our offer of service to our country was really appreciated at all—did our country need us ? did our country want us ? I wondered several times during that long night.

It was dawn when we got to Aldershot—a clear, grey dawn—and when I stepped out I remember still the freshness with which I inhaled the air. The atmosphere of the railway carriage was worse than suffocating, it was more overwhelming.

I was one of the more sober ones—I was always that—less dishevelled than my comrades, and was told off to take care of the baggage—the parcels and boxes and packages which we had been carrying were dumped together—and the parade marched off, leaving me with Gillespie (who became my bosom friend), a clerk in the bank in the town in which I enlisted . . . leaving us in charge of them. An hour later an army lorry came to relieve us of our responsibility and we then piled our packages on the lorry and made our way to the barracks. There we found our crowd had been washed and cleaned and scraped and shaved, and those of them who had any kind of thirst left were having tea served out of a bucket. The barrack-room, I noticed at once, was built to contain eighteen men and one non-commissioned officer. There must have been two hundred of us in it. Tables had been removed and beds, and, with these out of the way, it was possible for us by lying very close together, when night came, to find room.

I distributed the kits.

Some of the wiser ones made a selective choice which caused no small embarrassment next day.

Two or three days must have passed before some sort of order was restored. I bought a pair of boots for one of my comrades who was really walking on his socks—these were the days : but though I do not remember much about the days, I remember the nights.

Our barrack-room content had been made up from different

parts of the country ; the English were most silent. As night drew on, the Welsh with " Land of my Fathers " competed with the Scots, who sang " Scots Wha Hae." As always, the English had to mediate in the end. At about ten o'clock, the respective singing sides tended to become exhausted and silence was enforced by the least vocal of the United Kingdom. The Englishmen would hammer for silence with the barrack-room shovel, and after half a dozen appeals the English formed an alliance with the Welsh and drowned and downed the Scots. One or two of the Sweet Singers had to be removed as incorrigible and these passed the night in the Guard Room. At length silence reigned and the soldiers dreamed the soldier's dream.

It is difficult to remember this phase now and there must be comparatively few left who remember it at all—the phase of barracks and plain clothes and no discipline and high spirits and uncertainty.

I remember it. It is a treasured memory : the English civilians going to war.

There came a day when the sorting out began. Some were given railway warrants and sent home as physically unfit or socially undesirable, or not likely to become good soldiers, and the rest of us were placed in platoons and companies. This tremendous task was made possible by the influx of half a dozen more old Army men, men who had come down from pension and rejoined for the national emergency.

They called them " Old Sweats," and certainly they earned their money as well as justified the adjective which described their appearance. They had the uniforms of their regiments but we had no uniform for many weeks until we were given a navy one, surely the plainest, least distinguished uniform that ever soldier served in.

(A Band passed along the street—it is ten years and more since the War finished and yet a Band stirs me as nothing else does in heaven or earth. God knows, Bands must have their place in the divine mind. Even Paul knew that, as I never allow myself to forget. Does he not say emphatically that the trumpets *shall* sound? I left my task to go out and watch it pass by. I stand to attention while the careless onlookers stand at ease. I take off my hat to the Colours. I am proud to say that whoever else may be ignorant, I know what the Colours mean. I know what the soldiers stand for . . . what a silly snob you are, you know quite well that you are only proud of the soldiers because you yourself were a soldier . . . you were not a very good soldier . . . you really hated soldiering . . . you were always afraid when you were in danger and always uncomfortable when you were out of it. . . . Faugh!)

I resume my writing.

What can one do these days when nobody seems to want books and this shop is an empty, echoing place filled with the silent voices of the past and no voices of the living present to disturb it? . . . I take up my story again and my mind is aligned with what I write. I see myself in my mean blue uniform.

After the Old Sweats, there came the Officers. They too were from Reserve Regiments, or had come back from the Front, or returned from overseas. They were not a very competent lot, but " in the country of the blind the one-eyed man is king " and we were all blind in comparison with their comparative knowledge. Training began. We trained early morning—after breakfast—after dinner—after tea—and lectures at night. We had only an hour in the Canteen before dinner-time and an hour at night. Fortunately we did not require much longer as our pay was slow in forthcoming, and incredibly small in amount when it did come. It must not be forgotten that these early soldiers, if they were married with three children, only drew threepence a day. A shilling a day was their payment but sixpence was deducted for the wife and a penny for each child up to three ; the minimum wage was threepence a day and the maximum was one shilling. There was a good deal of unpleasantness when this fact was discovered, but it adjusted itself, although I remember one or two desertions by realist Welshmen and Scotsmen, all miners, who had an ingrained belief that the British soldier must receive one shilling a day.

The period of training continued in its intensity until, oddly enough, the Fall of Antwerp, when, I do not know if by intention, the authorities abandoned Sunday training. Sunday for the remainder of our stay on this side consisted in Church Parade only, unless one was on special duties.

All that winter we toiled and moiled with drill, parades, rifles, manœuvres and training, until our souls were sick, our feet were hard and our muscles were keyed up to the job we had assumed. Every day we asked when we were to go ; we believed that we were fit to grapple with any enemy, and then, for some, there came a complete lassitude . . . we were never going to the War—we were merely up to be trained in physical jerks and rifle exercises. These two schools—the eager, longing and waiting on one hand, the pessimistic, despairing school on the other—divided not only the soldiers of the line but the officers as well.

You could see it in their attitudes.

And when spring came there seemed even less hope for us. The news we had from overseas was that the Line had stabilised, people had settled down to permanent trench quarters, and that was that. No one visualised what the outcome of the War would be. The Germans had sprung at us and we with the French had sprung at them, and now, like two wild cats, we faced each other waiting for the next move and neither knowing what it was going to be. There was a great change came over us, however, when we were issued with khaki and complete field equipment. We were put out on Salisbury Plain and inspected in a blizzard by the French Minister of War and our own Lord Kitchener. . . . Inspected is an overstatement.

In this overwhelming blizzard these renowned leaders walked in front of their motor cars at a distance of two hundred yards from the formed bodies of troops, entered their cars again, apparently entirely satisfied with our fortitude and our steadiness on parade. Some of us got pneumonia and some died of it, but the rest of us felt that the worst had now come and the future held nothing which might cause us fear or trembling.

At length the day came—we were for overseas. It was June, and when darkness came we entrained and found ourselves at Southampton.

It was the first time I ever crossed the water and I felt the dream of all England was—and had been—crowding on my mind and imagination as I scrambled up the gangway on to the troop-ship.

There we were, laden like Christmas-trees—packs, haversacks, gas helmets, pouches and bandolier of ammunition, rifle, bayonet, the clumsiest of boots, the most ungainly of putties, the most unspeakable trousers, wearing surely the worst designed tunic and hat of any troops that ever took the field. Yet we felt, or I did, that la belle France and brave little Belgium were there in the romantic foreground. . . . I had to be inspired to fight before I was willing to die.

In close darkness we crossed the water.

My farewell to England was a farewell to some ineffectual lights that I could not name on the southern coast, and early in the morning we saw the coast at Havre and soon found ourselves being disembarked there.

This was good. Somewhere over here we were on the very edge of things. Would the battle be to-morrow or the next day? This was the purpose for which we were intended ; for this we had enlisted, suffered, strained, trained, endured ; here we would prepare to do and die for our country.

None of the war books that I read does justice to these generous, half-felt, inexpressible influences ; the commonest of us, the most ordinary among us, were touched with the feeling that we were embarking upon something tremendous, something bigger than ourselves, something for which it was worth while to make sacrifices—even the supreme sacrifice of all. No, there isn't a book in my stock that tells that. Could any book tell it? I would like to—I have tried to—but I can't. Most of those who felt these things are dead. Dead men don't keep bookshops or write diaries.

Dead men tell no tales.

BOOKSELLER AS A SOLDIER
OF THE KING

There must be few who recollect now the details of these days when the young armies arrived in France, few of the soldiers and fewer still of the French folk among whom we lived—we must have been a surprise to them, invading the privacy of their homes, billeted on their farms, consuming their omelettes, drinking their watered beer and the strangely different coffee. I loved it all—the freedom, the change of scenery, the entirely new environment—there was no great merit in that, if I did not love it all, who should? I was carefree; no anxious, worrying relatives lay behind me, no pale hands had waved me an anguished farewell. . . . I was free to go and free to do as I wanted.

Very few of my comrades in arms had a like freedom. They were entangled in endless anxieties. . . . Evans's wife was expecting ; Mackay—he had seven and his wife was not getting the proper separation allowance ; Gillespie had a girl and her disappointment was that he would not marry her before he went ; Jackson had just set up business as an architect and the rent was due ; his clients were disappointed because he had thrown up his profession and he did not know what was to be the end of it all . . . they all had their troubles. I was carefree. None laid his head on his pack and slept in the straw with easier conscience than I did. I had said good-bye to all that and England was over the seas and far away.

Every day was a new revelation.

We drew nearer, we knew, to the inevitable hour, but I was buttressed against it and feared no foe. At length we left these billets at Hesdin and were sent forward to the front line in front of the Brick Works to learn our job. Our tutor was one of the London Regiments.

We thought they were a happy-go-lucky, carefree lot compared with ourselves, principally because they wore, through the indulgence of their commanding officer, khaki shorts while we still fugged along in trousers and putties. They showed us what trench life was like, patrols, wiring, trench digging and maintenance, repairs, revetments and parados, rations to be eaten, no cooking during the day, sleep, lice, rats, interest, fear, boredom, sleep . . . we went through it all under their benign guidance—a fortnight of it and we had only one casualty, old Gilchrist, a runner, and he only slightly wounded—and then orders were that we should go back for training.

We went back, but not for long.

The hour approached and we were due for something big. It was the Battle of Loos, still lying unnamed, unborn in the womb of time. I suppose I was fortunate. They attached me to the care of two ammunition mules which I led up to a spot behind a hedge in the rear of the battle.

These were the days.

I asked my Company Commander where we went when the attack began. He said, " Berlin, I believe," and I have often laughed at this simple answer. He went to heaven, I hope, and within the next year the theory of the Limited Objective was born, but too late for him. That was the morning of all mornings, following as it did a night of nights.

I can see myself stroking the long ears of these two mules and getting word to go forward with ammunition for the front line. One of the mules, Herbert, was eager, and Wilfred, the other, was reluctant. It was a comedy, but I saw little of the humour of it then, holding one back and dragging one forward. I made little progress—sufficient in time to reach some with the S.A.A., and then counter-shelling began and I was soon like the rest of the separated troops, in the thick of it.

I was crossing the *pavé* road when a shell exploded quite near me and killed or wounded my mules, I never knew which. I seem to have been thrown in the air and when I picked myself up found I had been hit on the back of the head. What had happened apparently was that I had been thrown down violently on the *pavé*, my head hitting the causeway, and my forehead had been grazed by a piece of shell. My face was covered

I

with my own blood, my hands and my uniform splashed with the blood of the mules. Somebody took charge of me—I do not know who now. My first clear thoughts came to me as I lay in a hospital at Étaples. Weeks later I learned what had happened in this first venture of Kitchener's Army. They had talked of Berlin as their objective and had got as far as Lille. The counter-attack had mopped them up and forty-eight hours later we were as we were, two days before.

I do not know what the Higher Command learned but I, like another Paul on another road to Damascus, had seen a great light and fear now no longer was with me. I had been roughly handled and knew the worst. My idea was to get well and get well quickly and be back with the boys. England, home and beauty offered me nothing, and I had a rendezvous with my Company, and death only would dissever me from my love.

These seemed impossible ideas, but none the less they animated me in sober truth—they animated thousands of others, the best men of the country in these days. You won't find me disparaging the soldier if he can satisfy me that he served in the Infantry of the Line. I think there should be a questionnaire which should be answered by every aspiring politician, every man who seeks to offer himself for public office or public honour. He should be able to answer at least the following questions :

1. State briefly what the following are :
   Parados.
   A cushy one.
   A pineapple.
   A woolly bear.
2. What is a bangalore-torpedo? Explain its origin, place of manufacture and use.
3. Name six uses for sandbags.
4. Give the names of the following :
   (a) Manufacturer of tinned jam.
   (b) Brand of popular cigarettes.
   (c) Describe the difference between the report caused by (1) a 4.5 dud and (2) a gas shell.

The answers to these questions would indicate the standing of a man, and if he couldn't pass 60 per cent I would refuse him all promotion in civil life and deny him any public honour to which he might aspire. The examination itself should be set by three ex-privates, one ex-corporal who has been reduced to the ranks and secured promotion, one sergeant three years unwounded in the infantry, one Second Lieutenant who has not obtained the Military Cross.

Committees with this personnel should be set up in all centres and be the advisory committee for the conduct of public affairs.

Is this bitterness? I ask myself the question.

Perhaps it is, but if I am bitter there are those who have more cause for bitterness than I, although they have not lived to say their little piece or tell their tale. . . . .

BOOKSELLER — AFTER HOSPITAL — VISITS THE MEDITERRANEAN

If there was heaven to the soldier it was the hospital. There was peace and quiet and regular meals ; pyjamas, beds, contentment and devoted women. It was a veritable heaven and I was fortunate because no one came to see me in hospital and I did not grieve because others had bunches of daffodils and boxes of sweets. I was content enough to lie in my bed and see others have their friends around them. They came to an end, however, these hospital days, but not before I had come to the conclusion that in a hospital ward was the highest comfort and serenity that I had known.

There came a time when I found myself with fourteen days' leave prior to rejoining my Unit, and these fourteen days I spent in London in hotels which had too many Canadians and Australians for me to recognise them as old-time places. There was an unreality about the streets and in public places, theatres and bars—the kind of places I went to—there was hysteria, I suppose, which so much matched my own.

Something went wrong or grew up and flowered in the girls of these days, and sticking out of the empty morass of memory there is Clara Hocking. What her nationality was I never knew but it was not English, and yet she was to me astonishingly attractive. She danced in Broodie's, which was behind Wardour Street somewhere . . . surely she was the brightest of butterflies in that St Martin's summer of my days. She lived, apparently, on the top of a form for which she had had no prior training; she was a creature of gaiety and must have known hundreds of us. She matched our minds and our outlook on life. An adventuress normally would have been a creature to be avoided, but to us who knew we were adventurers she seemed to align herself in a way which all of us understood.

I don't think I met her more than half a dozen times, and two years later when I sought her she was gone, a casualty, as so many whom she had known must have become. She just disappeared. Edwards told me that she had joined the W.A.A.C.s, but I cannot believe that. She floated like thistledown into my life and into the lives of others, but like thistledown as untraceable, as unimpressible, as fantastic and unreal she disappeared. And yet she was much to many of us and I have no doubt in the Larger Charity she will be understood and forgiven because she did what she could.

It was at the end of 1915 I got to the Reserve Camp and found myself strange and unwelcome.

" We have had people like you here before," said the Adjutant, " and we know what to do with you, late for parade, unshaven, dirty rifle; you are posted to the Active Service Company." So said the bright young man who had not yet seen what soldiering was.

The Active Service Company was a sort of chain-gang. We were looked upon as brutalised old hands. We had already, all too young, been and seen the war. The other units of the training camp were refined. They had regular hours, strictly limited activities. We had irregular hours, night marching, fatigues, hard-bitten officers, mostly Regular Army non-commissioned officers, but we had the consolation that we had seen and we had done.

All drafts were taken from the Active Service Company, and the fact that I had become a nuisance made it seem eminently desirable that I should be passed overseas as soon as possible.

I achieved my ambition. I insulted the Assistant Adjutant because I could not find the Adjutant to insult, and they had me parade on a draft for the Mediterranean Expeditionary Force.

I was given three days' leave and remember these three days particularly because I spent them in Southampton. There I bought and read for the first time John Law's *Serious Call to a Devout and Holy Life*—splendid book for one in my frame of mind. ˙ I gave it to a Corporal of the Military Police as we marched aboard the troop-ship in the dark.

It astonished me to think that anybody could have considered being sent back to the War punishment. I thought it a real escape, an opening of the doors of existence, the abandonment of the limitations of life.

The Mediterranean Expeditionary Force meant nothing to me, or Ceuta, Malta, Cyprus, Salonica, Gallipoli, Gaza, Mesopotamia. I did not care that Fortunato's purse was opened and all the things in it were gold for me.

Across the Bay of Biscay, tossed, sick, overcrowded in bunks, filled with fantastic stories of torpedoes, submarines, frightened by horrors of how, when a torpedo strikes the side of the ship, you are like mincemeat between two plates of steel, —with these as companions we made our way through the Pillars of Hercules and saw Gib. dawn, grand and grey. Hooper, an intelligent Second Lieutenant of Wadham, recited, looking from my porthole, a piece of Browning. He did it so well that, a year later, in Cairo I got a Browning and learned it as a testament to his memory, he being dead with the Hampshire Regiment on Gallipoli six months before. I never read it now but I remember Hooper, too intelligent, too young, too good if you like, to die.

" ' Here and here did England help me: how can I help England?'—say,
    Whoso turns as I, this evening, turn to God to praise and pray,
    While Jove's planet rises yonder, silent over Africa."

This magic of the printed word, this linking-up the living
with dead men's lives—this is a modern text and their permanent blessedness.

I cannot write this stuff any longer.

What would Hooper have been?—a teacher?—a priest?—
a professor?—a man with a wife and three children?—a happy
poet?—a writer?—what would Hooper have been? I don't
know. He lies in Hampshire Valley on that deserted Peninsula that once saw the heroism of a hundred thousand of this
country's best.

At Gibraltar we entered with a convoy, and night and day
some of us were posted with rifles to shoot at any submarines
which showed their periscopes above the water's surface. I
saw no periscopes or submarines, but saw the coast of northern
Africa, the southern part of Italy, numberless islands and small
fishing villages and steamers and activities, and at length came
to Valetta. An hour or two ashore and we were on again. We
saw the dawn and sunset on windy isles and were all, the
plainest of us, touched with the southern beauty of earth and
sky and sea.

They took us, common soldiers all, through the magic of
the Mediterranean and landed us at Salonica. I was attached
to the Essex Regiment, but apparently the Essex didn't want
me because, after a few days in this camp at Salonica, I found
myself transferred to another draft and landed on the Isle of
Mudros. There for a few days we stayed scratching for
rations, sheltering ourselves beneath inadequate tents against
tropical rains, until one dark night, in a vessel the shape or
contour of which I never saw, we were ferried over to Suvla
Bay.

There I landed and in a nullah discovered that I was a soldier
of the line, unheralded yet carrying on all the traditions of the

1st Royal Munster Fusiliers in the incomparable 29th Division.

I demand an answer from the silent and inscrutable fates—
how can I sell copies of Jack London and P. G. Wodehouse
when I have written the story of my Odyssey?
" I want a book for holiday reading."
I can tell him that the great opportunity for Continental
holiday-making is over, that no trip to the Mediterranean is as
well conducted as one by His Majesty's Navy in the autumn
of the year 1915 ; I can tell him that there is no place worth
seeing compared with the Mediterranean as I saw it . . . but
I shall not tell him.
"*Burning Daylight* by Jack London . . . here is a cheap
edition ; Heinemann, 7d. Good afternoon."

PRAYING SOLDIER

Poor old Crawford stumbled into my recollection this morning
as I kicked my window bucket half full of water and upset it.
He was the Cook's fatigue-man.
He fell to that almost lowest level in the military world
through untidiness—he was dirty and untidy and incompetent
—and yet he was a student of Oxford University. He told me
once his story—how he had with crowds of others joined the
Lancers and in some three or four months had been sent to
some Bicycle Corps ; in turn, however, to be degraded to the
common Infantry and arrive as a recruit in a Line Regiment.
His father wanted him to take a Commission but he would
not. He was by disposition a poet, and an idler. When I
knew him he had been five times wounded, and this was the
third time of asking at the War. He told me he had written
a couplet of which he was very proud. I remember it :

"" Between his bullet and my brain,
Lord give me time to say ' Amen.' ""

Crawford was going to be some kind of professor, I imagine. His father was a successful manufacturer in the North but he himself had a mild, sentimental, simple, poetic view of life. Thrust into the Army he became accustomed to things. He had more money than some of us, and used to pay a comrade to clean his rifle. The story was told that an Inspecting Officer, looking down the barrel of his rifle, found it atrociously dirty and reprimanded Crawford. Crawford said in a gentle voice, " I am very sorry, sir, my batman is no good." The Officer stared at this untidy private soldier incredulously and passed on without finding the appropriate word.

Crawford was one of those chaps who never could avoid a fatigue, who was aligned for every carrying party, who was the willing donkey for anything the sergeant required. Out of the line he was on the cooker, in the line he was available for anything that was wanted—not through inclination but because he never learned the art of dodging the orderly sergeant.

Crawford became deeply religious in this way of life. He took a great interest in prayers and his couplet poem was the passing expression of his hope.

He must have had some conception of the death he was to die, for he did take a sniper's bullet through the head.

Why I should write about Crawford I don't know, but he pushed himself into my recollection when I saw my upturned pail and the dirty water—so reminiscent of one of the latest, perhaps most important, services Crawford rendered to his country before he rendered up his life.

GIVE US EACH DAY OUR
DAILY WORK . . .

Bad business makes me wonder what is to become of me.

Every hour to-day it has recurred to me. Marcus Aurelius does not help me. I worry and can't stop worrying.

Work, employment, occupation are necessary for man. Time was when, during the long, warm tropical ages of man's forgotten history, he could luxuriate in years of uncountable idleness, contemplating the green world around him and happily ignorant that one day it would be black coal in the unimaginable fireplaces of his descendants.

We have been too long prisoners in towns to enjoy freedom —we have been too long slaves of routine work to recover the once familiar habit of endless idleness. I wish I could. I wish I could take my ease ; loaf and invite my soul ; do nothing the livelong day.

W. H. Davies is right when he demands " time to stand and stare." It isn't so easy, however, to do that. Heaven knows how many pounds' worth of books are on my shelves which no one seems to want, and yet when I bought them what gems of literature they seemed, what prudent purchases, how likely I thought they were to catch the eye of the seeker after knowledge or entertainment or joy in literature.

I read their titles : *Magnolia Street* by Louis Golding— why was that written? ; *The Wondrous Year* by William J. Locke—that splendid story ; *Agricola's Road into Scotland*— there is something worth reading ; and my small editions of Jack London—*The Game* and *Burning Daylight* by the same author—what a diversity of pleasure I offer on these deal shelves of mine, and yet I have to cry idle in the market-place, for no men desire them.

I must get something to do.

I have not the temperament to stand idly by.

I must be up and doing something to stop the endless wheels of worry in my brain.

Reading is not enough. Talking to customers is not enough. I must have activity.

And yet, as I say that, I know I scamped the sweeping of the shop only this morning—the back of the counter I thought would do for a day or two, as it had done for a day or two. A few ends of string and bits of paper—what are they?

When did I dust my Everyman's Library series?—weeks

and weeks ago, I fear; and as for my windows, they have an oily smear which I have not been able to remove. Hot water won't do it, and my chamois is greasy. I tried flinging buckets of water at them—a very exhilarating experience it was—but it did little to improve the window-glass. On sunny days it is almost a mirror into which the customers from my neighbour next door look, preening themselves with their new purchases. I provide for Alice an alternative looking-glass!

I must find something to do.

"Give us each day our daily bread," if you like, but we must work for it, even if Thou givest it to us. "Give us each day our daily work" is perhaps more important than daily bread. Occupied is what we poor mortals must be, or we go mad like mice in this whirling, revolving cage which we call the world.

LADIES IN CHURCH

The forenoon has been spent in seeking through the "Nelson One-and-Six Burns" for a poem called "To a Louse, on seeing one on a Lady's Bonnet, at Church." I cannot find it.

Perhaps Nelson has excluded it from this edition. What my customer wants with the poem, heaven only knows. He can surely deliver his Burns Lecture without reference to this most obscure piece of the poet's writing.

Still, the search has not been without profit, because I found in my "Queen Elizabeth" book, which stood next the Burns, an assertion made by that great Queen which has pleased me.

The Bishop preached against images in the Cathedral, but Elizabeth at length lost her patience, and called out: "Keep to your text, Master Bishop, we have heard enough on that subject."

Women perhaps are prone to be too quiet in Church. There was a Scottish woman who threw her chair at an Archbishop. She was, the Scotch recognised, a real pioneer, although, as Chesterton reminds me, Christ threw furniture down the steps of the Temple.

Few audiences have the moral courage to assert strongly their opinions. Perhaps it is a pity.

Back to my Bible-reading, Burns and Elizabeth lying down together, I search for Paul's injunction to his Church at Corinth —his question, " Is it comely that a woman pray unto God uncovered? "

These were my complexity of diversions for the morning : Queen Elizabeth, the Scotch harridan and St Paul, with his aversion to women, fighting his beasts at Ephesus.

A pleasant interlude, but my foolish face will look more foolish than usual when I admit to my customer this evening that I have not found Burns's poem " To a Louse, on seeing one on a Lady's Bonnet, at Church."

SYDNEY SMITH

Sydney Smith, for whom I confess a regard, writes in his review of the *Memoirs of Madame d'Épinay* a few hard words about the French bookseller :

" It is a lovely book, relating the habits of many remarkable men, mingled with some very improper passages which degrade the whole work. But [and here is Sydney putting it across] if all the decencies and delicacies of life were in one scale and five francs in the other, what French bookseller would feel a single moment of doubt in making his selection ? "

There may be a justification for his feeling about French booksellers and the French generally.

The book which he reviewed was published in Paris in 1818 and was reviewed in the *Edinburgh Review* in the same year. Waterloo was 1815. Since five this morning I have been turning the pages of *The Works of the Rev. Sydney Smith*

—four volumes, printed for Longman, Orme, Brown, Green & Longmans, Paternoster Row, 1840.

One hears of syndicates nowadays but there was a publishing house with five partners in the Hungry Forties.

(Perhaps I should have a partner. I reflect—a business partner, or one in marriage? Ah! there is a thought early in the morning.)

Sydney Smith, I aver, was one of the best minds of his day —a great Englishman—a man of wit and wisdom—a humorist and a humanist.

He ought to be re-read.

His life ought to be written again. He should appear anew upon the stage of life, he who so brilliantly filled it a hundred years ago. He was as great a character as Doctor Johnson himself—and no less worthy and wise.

SHAKESPEARE FOR SHOPKEEPERS

They come into my shop from all the ends of the earth—so I imagine extravagantly. I am a focal point. I am the centre of things. I am a nucleus around which Knowledge—and the search for Knowledge—clusters.

But that is my grand manner. There are other times when life does not ride so high with me.

There are my shabby moments when I do out these very dusty lower shelves under the counter. Where the dust comes from I sometimes wonder! Is it the dust of all the ages stirring, circling, accumulating in layers all over the shelves and mantel-pieces and furniture of the world? Is it the dust of all the dead men . . .

" Dust and ashes ! So you creak it, and I want the heart to scold.
  Dear dead women, with such hair, too—what's become of all the gold
  Used to hang and brush their bosoms ? I feel chilly and grown old."

I feel chilly right enough, and I must not scold. I must get on with my business.

"What is your name and business?" said the Mad Hatter in *Alice in Wonderland*.

"My name is Alice!"

There I go again.

These shopkeepers—of course—but this time it is a store-keeper from Java—retired to opulent and oppressive leisure. He has made a fortune and, to put it in his own words, "I have more money than I will ever spend." His story—like anyone's story—is briefly told. A farmer's son—apprenticed to an iron-monger in a country town—an offer of a job as a storekeeper in the East on a plantation—acceptance and farewells—twenty-five years—rubber booms—impaired health—retirement before fifty—bored with less fortunate friends—bored with travel—bored with hotels and hydropathics—back to books, and in that last extremity I came in, or rather he comes into, my shop.

"I want to do a bit of reading."

"Good." ·

"I want to read Shakespeare."

"Great."

"How do I begin?"

And so I told him.

The book which contains the whole of Shakespeare is *The Man Shakespeare* by Frank Harris. Keats, on reading Chapman's *Homer*, I am sure had no greater kingdom presented to his eyes than I had when I first read Frank Harris. Shakespeare, who had been one of the dullest textbooks of my dull school-days, became at once a living man who wrote about his own life, his own feelings, his sufferings and his achievements in his marvellous plays. Shakespeare to me had hitherto been only a man who had written some rather moving speeches in the mouths of Roman senators or Scotch chieftains.

He had been that and no more.

I feel it impossible to express at this length of time what Frank Harris did for me.

A long way behind Frank Harris came many writers.

W. Carew Hazlitt is one—*Shakespeare, The Man and His Work*; Hazlitt and Coleridge are others; and then there are the moderns—the great Masson, Logan Pearsall Smith and Dover Wilson—they all have their place in the mosaic which is my impression of " The Man Shakespeare "—it is heterodoxy to write it—but it was Frank Harris who opened the way.

From customers I have learned something about this Frank Harris—an extraordinary character. Wells, I see, in his *Attempt at Autobiography* gives a vivid picture of him, and I have among my second-hand books a volume of short stories written by him called *The Yellow Ticket*. The first story, from which the book takes its name, is the best, but Frank Harris was inspired when he wrote the book which I have recommended most enthusiastically to the retired storekeeper from Java.

As I write " Java " I remember Joseph Hergesheimer's book *Java Head*. How stupid of me to have forgotten to mention it! I might have persuaded him to buy it, but then it might not have anything to do with Java, and I would lose a good customer if I pretended I knew something about a book which, when he got it, he would not like.

" Shakespeare for Shopkeepers " is the heading I wrote for these pages.

Alas! Shakespeare has not much to say about us. He was most likely a snobbish sort of fellow, and if he had any feelings for shopmen at all they were sympathetic and pitying.

I feel he wanted to be a country gentleman, slaving hard and saving hard for that lively ambition, and then, as he might have known with his ripe, mature wisdom and observation of men, when the thing came his way it was not much to him after all. The discarding of second aims, like discarding second beds, is to what life brings us all, Shakespeare as well as shopkeepers, at the end.

NO BOOKS ABOUT GARDENS

It hurts me when people speak ill of Francis Bacon. He took bribes, they tell us. He was exonerated by his country, he suffered no disgrace. I know little about him except what I have read (who knows any more?), and that is little enough, but I like him.

I visualise him towards the end of his life on his road from London, stopping at St Albans to die from a cold which he contracted because of this passion for scientific experiment. He wondered what the effect would be of extreme cold upon animal tissue—would it arrest decay?—and leaping from his carriage procured a fowl, had its neck drawn—poor martyr for science—plucked and cleaned it and stuffed it with snow. This experiment in the open air began the illness from which the great Chancellor died.

I remember Francis Bacon with gratitude to-day.

I sold Bacon's Essays in the " Everyman's." I sometimes wish there were no " Everyman's " because it reduced my sales to a few shillings in place of many shillings. Still, don't let me complain of a series which has given so much delight to so many. I sold it because of the *Essay on Gardens.*

" God Almighty first planted a garden ; and, indeed, it is the purest of human pleasures. It is the greatest refreshment of the spirits of man ; without which buildings and palaces are but gross handyworks."

So he says, the great Lord Chancellor who took bribes and who stuffed the fowl, and so I hope he found gardens in his lifetime, and so I hope he finds them to-day.

This piece of writing, like all that I write, confused and inconsequent, arises out of the request for garden books. Fool that I am—what a poor selection—but who am I to buy books on gardening illustrated on their covers with monstrous tomatoes, giant gooseberries and overwhelming onions and walloping sweet-williams?

I think I was right to tell him that he would do better to study the philosophy of gardens rather than the practical art of growing fruits and flowers in them. I am afraid the interview was unprofitable to me.

He bought, but grudged buying, all Bacon for all his *Essay on Gardens.*

From Bacon I come to Lord Tennyson — though irrelevantly—

> " Come into the garden, Maud,
>   I am here at the gate alone."

And throughout a long, dull forenoon, while I seek for customers and do not find them, my mind runs on gardens everywhere from the Garden of Eden to the garden beyond the dawn of the next world . . . and the garden of sleep which lies for certain at journey's end.

T. E. Brown wrote on gardens. . . . I turn it up :

> " A garden is a lovesome thing, God wot ! . . .
>   The veriest school of peace ; and yet the fool
> Contends that God is not—
>   Not God ! in gardens ! when the eve is cool ?
> Nay, but I have a sign ;
>   'Tis very sure God walks in mine ! "

The afternoon ends and a waste of streets is in front of me.

I feel tired—I wish I had stocked garden books—I have sold no books to-day. I have merely ruminated, reflected.

I remember the first murderer . . . gardens have made me devilish. . . . " Cain made the City but God made the first garden."

After a long walk when I am too tired to walk longer I come again to these scattered sheets, lying so untidily on the back counter, and bring them to my table in the back shop.

I try my hand at verse once more.

Here it is : .

> Sleep will not come,
>   There are all these books on shelves,
> Thoughts of dead men so still and quiet,
>   Set out in ink on paper

Bound with crackling cloth.
    Sleep will not come
Because these dead men's thoughts
    Keep me awake who lie so close,
A bookseller sleepless in his room behind his
        shop ;
    Sleep will not come.

Sleep will not come,
    Yet those books in shelves
Filled with dead men's thoughts
    Tell too of gardens.
Gardens gay and lovely in long summer days.
    Gardens in spring. . . .
Gardens in grim autumn
    When dead earth decays, dead flowers and
        leaves. . . .
Sleep comes to gardens,
    Sleep will not come to me.

All things have end
    And these dark hours will pass.
Slumber will seize me in this room.
    I will dream of gardens,
Surely sleep will come. . . .

LAMENT FOR A DEPARTED BOOKSELLER

He was a slovenly fellow—my predecessor.

He never washed the kitchen table as I have done. It was ink-stained and food-stained when I got it and I have scrubbed it and stoned it. These patent soaps are no good. The sailors know that water and sandstone make wood white and clean. When I took over this shop—I'll never forgive him—the cups and plates were on the table next the sink unwashed. It gave me a turn.

I am as slovenly as he, but if I sell this shop I will wash the cups.

Will I ever sell out? Is there another such as I who would want to buy a bookshop for £400 including fittings? Where is he now, my predecessor?

I only know—I came : he went.

They are as classic, these four words, as VENI, VIDI, VICI, but my commentaries are not as Caesar's. I render to him the things that are his. He had the purple ; victory ; fame ; death. Only one of these I am to share with him, but one other I will have which he never had.

I have my bookshop.

Have I conquered?

He has left us his commentaries. What wrack will be left behind of me? I will go as my predecessor here went. It is a fond hope, but surely not too much to expect. Anyway I will wash the cups. I will not let the cups pass.

ELEVATING BOOKS

He tells me he is tired of modern fiction and he is surfeited with Scott and Thackeray and Trollope. He is not interested in Jane Austen any longer. He has seen through all the plots and all the devices. He wants a book—he wants to read books —to elevate him.

I sent him to Lowes Dickinson . . . *A Modern Symposium* has always been a favourite with me. There is a range in the book which helps one to preserve one's balance. The Conservative could have justification for his views, and even the Anarchist finds something which can warm his somewhat cold blood. I recommended *A Modern Symposium* and he bought it. It is rather a delight for a bookseller, when he has recommended a particular book to a customer, to learn that his recommendation was appreciated, and my advice was sought again.

" I want all the books this man has written," I was told, and I fortunately was able to supply him with *Justice and*

Liberty and, slightly soiled it is true, *The Meaning of Good*, and I got an order from him to procure *The Letters of John Chinaman*. It was that last book which sent him into rhapsody, and he valued it so highly that he was able to recite to me what is one of my favourite passages in English Literature.

Drivelling away here as I do on these sheets of paper, detailing customers whom I have served and whom it seems I will not serve again if this depression continues, I am better employed in writing the thoughts of a great man than trying to conjure out of my scanty wits and limited experience thoughts of my own.

I will write, therefore, these lines from Lowes Dickinson and, having written them, will draw this day of dull business to a fitting close.

It is worth copying out—it is an invocation to a bookseller. It deals with his stock-in-trade. I will be a better seller of books when I have transcribed these words :

" . . . In China letters are respected not merely to a degree but in a sense which must seem, I think, to you unintelligible and over-strained. But there is a reason for it. Our poets and literary men have taught their successors, for long generations, to look for good not in wealth, not in power, not in miscellaneous activity, but in a trained, a choice, an exquisite appreciation of the most simple and universal relations of life. To feel, and in order to feel, to express, or at least to understand the expression of all that is lovely in Nature, of all that is poignant and sensitive in man, is to us in itself a sufficient end. A rose in a moonlit garden, the shadow of trees on the turf, almond bloom, scent of pine, the wine-cup and the guitar ; these and the pathos of life and death, the long embrace, the hand stretched out in vain, the moment that glides for ever away, with its freight of music and light, into the shadow and hush of the haunted past, all that we have, all that eludes us, a bird on the wing, a perfume escaped on the gale—to all these things we are trained to respond, and the response is what we call literature."

BOOKSELLER'S LIFE GOES ON—BEREAVE-MENT—BUSINESS—AND THE WAY TO WAR

It was F. E. Smith who, speaking only a few months ago, said that those who had not lived before the War did not know what life really was. Things were cheap, taxes were negligible, and what little we had to pay we grumbled about paying.

No such Elysian days were mine, but in retrospect these few years before the glorious summer of August 1914 seem wonderful.

The dark red curtain of war seems to have blotted everything of the light from the human retina and nothing is quite the same again.

My mother toiled away at her boarding-house, worrying if she lost a boarder, but greatly consoling herself with those that remained. She literally slaved for them. She had the capacity of devotion. She toiled for them early and late. If they demanded less cooking, there she was, wanting to know what washing and mending she could do for them.

To work was, for her, to be, and merely to sit with folded hands was a quiescence in which she could not acquiesce.

I was more happily minded.

I loved idleness and got too little of it to satisfy me.

About eight in the morning I left my house, fortified always with a good breakfast. My mother believed in a good breakfast. "The Church's one foundation" had as its counterpart the one foundation of man—a breakfast in which porridge and milk prepared an unsubstantial enough base for bacon and eggs and toast and butter to rest upon. She ate little herself but the man should be well fed—had he not to wrestle with the world of principalities and powers which she knew not nor understood but yet feared?

They took it, these lodgers of hers—they paid for it—and I took it for granted. We preened ourselves with the conviction that we were men, doing men's work in a manly way, when as a matter of fact this little creature worked harder and did more for the world's happiness than all of us put together.

I used to like to get to the office early because even then I was a diligent student of the newspapers. The *Clarion* was all-important in these days and its resounding note had not got lost in the faint echo of the modern Labour Party. Robert Blatchford thundered like a veritable Jove ; A. M. Thomson, " the immortal Dangle," and R. B. Suthers made up the best paper of its kind that ever saw the light of print.

Our souls burned for the better day and we would have been prepared to challenge God Himself on His throne rather than let slip any of our duties to our neighbour. Of course, there was the *Daily News* too and Gilbert K. Chesterton and A. G. Gardiner, C. F. G. Masterman and L. G. C. Money— these were Rulers in Judah in these days. My daily paper was less inspiring. It told the news ; it did not scan the horizon with such high hope. I used to feel in these days that the Revolution might be to-morrow, we saw the glory dawning . . . even that afternoon I might find myself at the barricades. Wishart, one of my special friends in the Office, used to talk about " the sure and certain hope of a glorious revolution." What kind of revolution we wanted we never very much defined, except to quote William Morris who declared that

> " These shall be ours and all men's,
> And none shall lack their share
> Of the toil and the gain of living,
> In the days when the world grows fair."

The cleaners in the Office used to go about half-past eight and I always saw them before they went. I remember the counter by the front door. It was like a wave of the sea, ridged in the centre, rising, from where the Cashier stood, in a graceful crest and falling away to be received at the proper line of the abdomen of the customer. On this counter I spread my papers and digested my breakfast and the news of the day.

So I love to read to-day—but the counter is my own now. About half-past nine I had got any correspondence to which it was my duty to attend—inquiries for a rate or information wanted about a policy, or someone in straits desiring to surrender what they had accumulated so laboriously. Then came my certain direct calls which I had to make, but, for the rest, I was free to find in the population of the town people to whom I could tell the story of Life Insurance.

I worked on the law of averages and sedulously cultivated the instructions of the Agency Manager, making a certain number of purposeful calls every day. Often I was tired of it ; other things seemed more interesting and it required an almost stoic sense of duty to keep everlastingly at it. It was with pleasure in a way that I came to the end of each difficult day, although I must admit that my duty ought really to have taken me, more often than I made it, out in the evenings in order to interview people at their homes.

The Company, possibly because of the high opinion my mother had bespoken for me, treated me extremely well, but it was not the life I liked. My only trouble was I did not know what life I would like.

I could not see myself making a great place for myself in the Insurance World. Frankly, I was fond of reading and idling and again more reading and idling, and, in my hazy, obscure way I had a fondness for food. I cultivated, as every young man has to do, a liking for beer, ultimately overcame my disinclination for whisky and got into the way of finding pleasure in company, debating societies, walks, in the summer-time futile games of cricket . . . these in a way filled up my leisure, but there was no salt in life—there was no substance in these days. I hung, so I felt, on the edge of things waiting for something to happen, and I was right. Two events were on my horizon and they came with unmistakable emphasis to emancipate me. My life would have petered out into nothingness, disillusionment, but for these two events . . . the death of my mother—and the outbreak of war in August 1914.

.   .   .   .

She died in 1913.

It was as I expected. I knew I would not have her with me always, even to the end of what was then my world.

I knew that I had to lose her. I knew that those who take for better or for worse were paralleled by those who lose for better or for worse, and for me it was worse, immeasurably. The end came quite suddenly, and although I had fortified myself against its inevitability, as always, I was unready when it came. She dropped out of my life and left something which could not, has not, never could be filled.

Writing away here this afternoon, when I should be doing something more profitable, I try and recollect all about it.

It must have been four or five when she was taken badly and they hesitated to let me know at the Office, and when they did get a message through I was not available. And so when I came home it was rather unexpected. She had only an hour to live, to spend with me, she who had spent all her life in order that I might be and continue to be when she was gone. Things were too uneasy for her to speak much but she wanted to have an assurance from me that she had done what she could, and very overwhelmingly I felt that no woman had ever done more. I was dumb as the disciples were when their Master said of her who had brought an alabaster box of ointment and anointed His feet, " She hath done what she could," and I could not say that she had done anything, I could not say she had done nothing . . . she had been everything to me in all ways.

But I gave her, haltingly, inadequately but, I am profoundly convinced, an entirely satisfactory assurance, and if gratitude was a human quality at all she had evoked it in me to the uttermost of the uttermost . . . she was satisfied when I gave her that assurance. With her fine sense of the fitness of things she knew that her time was far spent, her hour was come ; she had only one other question, one other assurance to receive from me.

She said " You will be a good boy ? " and she knew, although my voice would not say it, she knew that she had pledged me for ever and a day.

Then she died.

Quite simply she ceased to live and her tired, worn body seemed like a thing which had fulfilled its purpose and now no longer had any cause to be.

It is years ago and the bodies of many dead lie between, and yet I remember quite sharply how completely I felt she had run her race and finished her course.

There was no knocking of the breast, there was no protest against fate or fortune. Here I had profited so much, here I had received so much and the giver had no more to give and now was gone . . . that is how I recollect it . . . a supreme finality, an end, a finis. There was the funeral and the searching for relatives whom we could not find and who did not come.

The Manager of the Office, I thought rather finely, put aside his burden for an hour or two and attended. The Vicar, too, came and one or two old friends of my mother's who had been her tradesmen—the Grocer who had stood by her in difficult months and always trusted her, the Chemist too, and her Doctor—and that seemed to make up all the party that stood round her graveside.

There was a finality about it and when I dragged myself back to the house I felt, as every mortal must feel on such occasions, how empty the place was—no new or unusual sensation, just a commonplace which comes down through the centuries to all of us faced with an irrevocable, final bereavement.

The maid then was Elspeth, a wannish, fay-like creature who came from Wales, and she decided at first to remain with me as Housekeeper. If she had resisted the attractions of Blednog Lewis Jones, I am not sure that I would ever have sold the house or given up bachelordom with a Housekeeper or, for that matter, gone to the War.

Elspeth, however, was Welsh and sang, and she was in the Choir and passionate, and Blednog had black, untidy hair and challenging eyes and a determined way with him, and a good business as a travelling draper somewhere in the Welsh valleys.

And so Elspeth left me and I was left lamenting.

That must have been in February 1914. I only recollect by guess ; I never retained any papers—there are no receipts or documents by me, and so I must just remember it by reckoning—what an odd phrase that is, " by reckoning." Is the only reckoning we know which can be relied upon the reckoning of the dead? Is the compass nowhere true on earth? Is the magnetic north itself invariable and is the only thing true and final to be found in death? Is that why we talk so confidently of " dead reckoning "?

The house fetched almost a thousand pounds—and the furniture—it very nearly broke my heart to see things go—the linoleum off the floors, " five shillings for the lot," the auctioneer said . . . and the next month I found myself comfortably situated with a front parlour and a window looking on to the river and a small back bedroom.

What my mother had left through her insurances and what I got for the house made me feel positively affluent. I lived comfortably. I moved in my few personal belongings, and through the spring until early summer plodded along at the Insurance business, but life was a disembellished, disembodied, disconsolate thing.

On Sundays I used to go to my mother's grave—but that was only for a few weeks. I soon came to the conclusion that she is not here, but if anywhere she is risen. I went walks, I attended classes, I began to buy books, I was extravagant in food, tasted drink, sought and bought companionship, but found nothing much in the scheme of things. It was the end of an epoch for me as it was approaching the end of an epoch for the world around me.

It was May and a lovely May. It was June and the beginning of summer. It was July and down somewhere in the south-east of Europe men were quarrelling, a bomb was thrown, a train of events was being laid which was to lead to an explosion. The explosion came in August—what a lovely August that was! —and by the end of it I had made up my mind that whatever entanglements enmeshed me, whatever responsibilities seemed to hold me, I was keen to get done with Insurance . . . the depressing limitations of an inadequate existence . . . and seek what there was—if there was anything—behind the resounding drums of war.

It was in the second week of September, after being given

a week " to think over it and don't be foolish, it will only last a few weeks," that I finally resigned from my job as Insurance Clerk and became a Soldier of the King.

SEEING GHOSTS

James Etchells is one of those odd people who seem to have no visible means of subsistence, yet seem to live very well.

There is a background of Malay and engineering and money made out of rubber and lost in the same elastic circumstances, and now retirement, apparently impecuniously, here.

He wears tweeds of a durable character—always worn, never new. He shaves badly and his hair is thin, from, he tells me, the tropical suns, the topee, and the ensuing excessive perspiration. A maundering, doddering sort of ineffectual character—a book buyer and book lover of sorts, and, therefore, I profess a fondness for him.

For a week or two now he has been after books on the Occult. He has a theory that the dead get leave of absence from time to time and are allowed for an hour or so to visit any place they have a fancy to see again, or present themselves to some individual with whom they were familiar or fond in the days before death took them.

James Etchells is sure that he saw John Morrison Murray who died of black-water fever thirty years ago, a red-haired Orcadian who came out to the part in which he lived, did well and then departed. He is sure that his friend has twice visited him, once in his sitting-room and once passed him on the street.

The street business was indeed a mystery. It was a fine summer day, almost a tropical day, for James Etchells felt the sun on his head and thought of his topee, musing on how people in England sometimes got sunstroke. And as he mused there passed him, with the same lively, lilting movement that he had known years ago, John Morrison Murray.

It took him some minutes before he collected himself, so taken aback was he with surprise. Twice he looked over his shoulder and twice was half convinced. The third time he stopped and stared. By this time Murray, or what looked like Murray, was yards away from him, still walking briskly in the opposite direction. Etchells turned, walked quickly, saw Murray for a moment, lost him, saw him again, saw him stop at a crowded street crossing, saw him turn up to the left into a side street, saw him turn into the first lane on the left, overtook him at the corner and found the street was empty except for a grocer's boy with a bicycle from which he was delivering a small box of eggs. James Etchells wandered mournfully about for hours. He never saw where he had gone, although he climbed stairs and looked into doorways, visited shops all round the neighbourhood. There was not a sign of his friend.

It was some nights later, near midnight James Etchells tells me, that Murray came to see him again. He was sure it was Murray, he wasn't asleep, he wasn't dreaming,—he saw him at the door of his sitting-room, although the door was closed. He sat up in his chair and he was going to say " Hello, Murray, I'm glad to see you," or something like that, and just then outside his house some jollifying nocturnal revellers hooted and shouted on their homeward way and what was Murray faded into the door and was gone !

And now James Etchells wants books upon the Occult.

It is little help I can give him.

The books on the Occult are as occult as the subject of which they treat. He gets them from me and returns them telling me they are not worth buying.

It has spoiled his taste for ordinary books. He lives for the moment when he will see Murray again and I am really deeply concerned as to what the end will be.

There is the story, said to be from the Chinese, that the dead come to life again when those who loved them remember them, even if it is only for a moment. When they die first of all, they are always being remembered by those they knew and loved, and so their spirits live in the reflected memory of those who remember them. But time comes when few remember and some remember less often and they revive less frequently. Time comes at last when on earth no one at all remembers them and they are dead.

I wonder if I can tell this fable to James Etchells?

Perhaps I had better not.

Helping a customer to see ghosts is not the business of a bookseller.

A NEW USE FOR OLD BOOKSELLERS

For a long time I was puzzled by the kind of questions which I have been asked by would-be buyers of books. The most profitable of them buy dictionaries.

I sell them *Chambers* most freely, but others have taken the fancy of some as well.

They do not usually want to buy a book, these curious customers of mine, they want to ask me a question and hope that I will give them a verbal answer. Some of them are quite crude about it.

To-day's best example is the one who wanted to know if I could tell her a word of four letters which spells the same way backwards and forwards. I told her I only knew one which was a good word and another which might pass for a word. The good word was " poop " and the second-rate word, at which she scoffed, was " toot." I wish I had thought of the other one which came to me before I sat down to write. It is the word " boob," but I see that the *Shorter Oxford English Dictionary* will not allow me to use the word; they give me " booby " but they do not admit the abbreviation.

It is a pity.

I had another one who wanted information about the rivers of Kent beginning with the letter " m "; but I have no book, as far as I recollect, which would be any use to him for his purpose.

I know now that they are Crossword Puzzle solvers, a despicable race—at least in so much as they seek to get their information from harried booksellers.

The Crossword is not the only general knowledge competition apparently which afflicts the just. There are others.

I have now before me two questions which an obliging young man wrote out for me, handing them to me when I was trying to sell my second-hand set of Dickens and telling me that he would come back for an answer. There is a short question and a long question. The short question is : " ' Pan American '—is it a dish, a place or a man? "

The longer question is written as follows : " ' Bowdler '— a hunting dog, the name for a bandy-legged man, a Court functionary, a riverside tree, a term in archery, a literary refiner, or a part of a boat—which of these is a ' Bowdler '? "

Oh dear! Oh dear! Oh dear!

I should have remained in the Insurance business.

This bookselling is beyond me.

DO OUR SINS FIND US OUT?

It is held that our sins find us out, that there is a nemesis which ruthlessly exacts the consequence of wrongdoing.

It may be so, but a case ought to be made out for the use of evil in the world.

I feel that it is an omission that no book that I have or have seen deals with this major problem. Dimly I think that life means a whole—that good and ill are merely light and shadow and in themselves reality. And so it may be that our sins find us out in quite a different sense than is generally implied.

Our sins find us out in that they enlarge our nature, widen our experience. One of my rarer sins is the sin of envy.

There are some men who, for a time at any rate, I wish that I were. How long I would live in their shoes I do not know, but envy often holds me.

Perhaps I am too hard on myself—perhaps it is only disgust at my present circumstances, the limitations and hopelessness of them, that makes me feel I would be happier if I were someone else. Envy, of course, may be merely a mild disease. Usually there is the envy I feel when I read a book which greatly attracts me—in judging I have two standards of literary criticism—I find one is slightly contemptuous—one which makes me say " I could have written this book myself."

There is the other which has a touch of awe—a suggestion of humility mixed with the burning envy which inspires it. I am envious when I say of some books, " I wish to God I could write like this."

The wrongdoer in this sense is not so black as he is painted. What harm is there in my wishing myself a Member of Parliament, running about rabbit-like with a portfolio under my arm in that warren of corridors which surrounds the House of Commons?—what harm does it do for me to see myself a mayor in purple and ermine presiding at the Town's meeting for the society for the extension of knowledge among aborigines? —what harm does it do me to feel but there, for the grace of God, might I go up in purple and ermine?

And when the curtain rises and falls on the leading actor and he advances and retires and at length comes into the centre and bows, what harm is there in me if I should sometimes feel that I would like to be as he is, the centre of acclamation and applause? While he goes to his dressing-room happy and breathless, excited and gratified, I make my way down the worn stone stairs from the gallery, across the road, and thread my way about the back streets and so home to my bed from a night at the theatre.

No, I am satisfied that there is no great harm in envy. It is not a cardinal sin. It is really the grown-up equivalent to dressing up ; it is just taking our clothes off and hanging them on other pegs and seeing how they look to our imaginations.

The seven deadly sins—I forget what they are—but I am sure envy is for me at any rate not one of them. .

THE ART OF LIVING

Those happy married men who come in and out these days buying books for themselves and books for their wives and books for their families don't know how fortunate they are.

I live a withdrawn, secluded—almost monastic—existence. My life is bare.

They go home to their comfortable houses and sit in their buoyant chairs in front of agreeable fires reading books after a substantial evening meal.

How different is my fate.

The crowds, thronging the street, begin to diminish about five ; about six they are gone, and about seven the street sees no one who is interested in books. Youths and girls pass by on their way to the Palais de Danse or the Parthenon Picture Theatre, but they have little interest in me or my wares.

It is then that I lift up the mat by one of its drier corners, give it a shake and beat it once or twice against the side of the door.

I then pull it over the threshold and let it flop. The door I close and lock. The shop is then my own.

The stale, heavy smell of someone's cigar or the sharper and more acrid odour of cigarettes lingers and there is a stuffiness, dampness over all, the indescribable smell of books—a smell that is unanalysable—it is made up of ink and glue, paper, and the binding of these together. I cannot see myself from behind, but as I turn my back to the door and walk towards the back shop I must be a somewhat melancholy figure. The fringe of hair which falls over my thickening neck, the collar of two or three days' wear, the white dandruff which, regrettably, is too frequently present on my shoulders, the general hang of my trousers, the fact that my boots are worn rather down over the right heel—there, I suppose, is my back view.

I come straight into my back shop and quite a different odour greets me. These smells of cooking still remain— sometimes coffee—sometimes it may be a piece of cheese which I have cherished too long on the dish covered with the airtight glass lid—or it may be the fine smell of apples or oranges.

I don't often observe that I have kept my resolution to clear away the dishes from the previous meal so that everything is set for the next one. I see I should keep this resolution. It would bring me a better appetite, and now I wearily clear away the soup bowl and the spoon, crumbs of bread and the butter and cheese which, with the apple parings, are the remains of my luncheon, and I set myself to prepare my evening meal.

Recently I have been taking note of what my weekly costs are. It is possible for a man of my age to live, I can see, on a shilling a day as far as food is concerned. This astonishing figure, of course, refers to the occasions when I abstain from strong drink and content myself with tea.

Here is a little budget :

	s.	d.
4 whole-meal loaves at 4d. .	1	4
1 lb. butter	0	10
1 piece of cheese . . .	0	7
Onions	0	3
Apples 6d.—Oranges 6d. . .	1	0
Tea, sugar and tin milk . .	1	0
3 eggs at 1d. each . . .	0	3
Potatoes	0	2
2 lemons (for tea) . . .	0	$1\frac{1}{2}$
Watercress	0	3
Carrot	0	2
	5	$11\frac{1}{2}$

The balance, I imagine, I spent on other things that were bought in pennyworths.

It is a Spartan week, of course, to do without beer or wine or meat, but I don't remember that I suffered any discomfort. It is not a diet that I would recommend for anyone who finds it necessary to have their appetite and imagination stimulated with food and drink, but it is a suitable diet for one who, as a shopkeeper, is approaching the day when he has to face his Landlord, the City Rate Collector and the Keeper of his over-draft,—it fortifies his courage without unduly stimulating his body.

They tell me—some Civil Servant customers of mine to whom I showed this diet sheet—that I would do better on Public Assistance—that in the Workhouse the cost of living is much higher for the inmates than a shilling a day.

But then, they have not my freedom of action, or, at any rate, they imagine they have not my freedom of action, which is perhaps the same thing.

I am content that I am alive to make this experiment. There was a time when I did not think I would be alive in this year of grace, far less happily placed as a bookseller on my own account, but I am grateful for that which has been vouchsafed to me.

Is it not my mission to accept what Providence gives me and not to complain, to count my blessings one by one and find them so many that I have no time to see the disadvantages under which I exist?

These are apparent philosophies, but they are in tune with my outlook to-day. Perhaps this low diet has lowered my spirits. Perhaps it is deficient in nutrition, but anyway it is an interesting experience and one which I like to tell myself I voluntarily undergo from preference—from choice—not under compulsion.

So I write, but how far can a man deceive his own balance sheet?

K

THE BEST OF BENNETT

It is proof that I am a good bookseller, that I am not led away by what reviewers say or even what my customers tell me.

There are not many with whom I can get agreement, but I assert in season and out of season, with or without provocation, that Arnold Bennett is the greatest of our contemporary writers.

And I don't base that only on *The Old Wives' Tale*, though that in my judgment is his greatest work. Well may Messrs Hodder & Stoughton write on the jacket of the new five shilling edition : " It has that internal rhythm which by its pressure lifts a work across the gulf that separates the great from the well-done. To write it—one might say—Bennett grew wings."

Bennett to me is full of passages of wonderful writing and one that I read often and have read again to-day in this edition that has just come from the publishers is the one in *The Old Wives' Tale* where Sophia goes to see her dead husband Gerald. " She saw, in the pale gloom, the face of an aged man peeping out from under a white sheet on a naked mattress. . . ." In her mind she had not pictured Gerald as a very old man. ". . . She knew that he was old ; she said to herself that he must be . . . over seventy. But she had not pictured him . . ." and here enters the description of " this face on the bed " as " painfully, pitiably old. A withered face, with the shiny skin all drawn into wrinkles ! The stretched skin of the jaw was like the skin of a plucked fowl . . ." and then Sophia experiences what Bennett describes as a pure primitive emotion unclouded by any moral or religious quality. She saw how one who had been young was now old and was now dead, and that what had happened to her husband happens to all mankind and would happen to her.

What was the meaning of life? she demanded, and the passage concludes with these words : ". . . The riddle of life itself was killing her and she seemed to drown in a sea of inexpressible sorrow."

But I am not content to let Bennett stand on the reputation of a single book, no matter how great that single book may be.

The man is not only a great novelist but a master of the art of living. Everything which comes within the range of his experience or is within the compass of his imagination is appropriate material for his work, and I come from the Five Towns series to the larger world in which the *Pretty Lady*, *Mr Prohack* and *Lord Raingo* live, with an ever-widening sense of delight. The output of the man is amazing, but no less amazing is the quality of that output. He has written enough to make half a dozen reputations, and it is perhaps because he has written so much and so different that people fail to admit the measure of his greatness.

What vivacity and charm there is in his women—how attractive he found them and how attractive he makes them appear to us. His books are full of the joy of living and the wonderment of existence, and at the same time his sense of the inscrutable riddle of life lies behind them with its supreme question challenging the thoughtful man.

Yes, sir, I recommend you Arnold Bennett—begin at *The Card* or *The Grand Babylon Hotel*, or begin with *The Clayhanger Trilogy*, or begin at *Milestones* or *The Great Adventure* —begin where you like, you cannot begin too soon to admire, enjoy, love and honour the pen and the mind of that great English writer, Arnold Bennett.

MY NEIGHBOUR NEXT DOOR

My neighbour next door is in full sail with his summer sale and I am compelled, a shy figure in the lee of his great bulk, to admire the determination with which he clears out his shabby drapery and *démodé* fashions. It is a recurring problem with me how to clear out my undesired.

And yet I must not be disloyal to my trade. Books never

can be unfashionable. There is always with them the tender grace of the day that is dead. Within their covers somewhere is distilled something of their author's magic, something of the interest they had in life, something of its joy and poignancy, something of its essential quality, and, for the reflective eye, there is always something worth reading in a book no matter how old and unfashionable.

Such a book comes to my hand as I write. It is called *The First Year of a Silken Reign, 1837–38*, published in 1887 by Field & Tuer, the Leadenhall Press, E.C. I bought it for threepence and I doubt if there is a purchaser for it . . . yet how full of interest it is ! There are ten pictures, the first, very properly, being one of Queen Victoria, a delightful picture showing her in a poke bonnet set on the back of her head and her simple, open, girlish countenance facing—for the picture was done on the morning of her accession—the strange vicissitudes which, unknown to her, lay ahead.

The book is beautifully printed and had on one of its front pages the following : ". . . in a palace in a garden, meet scene for youth, and innocence, and beauty—came the voice that told the maiden she must ascend her throne." These words were written by Lord Beaconsfield. Other pictures include " Brighton from the Chain Pier," assuredly an unforgettable picture with gentlemen in high hats and ladies in crinolines, seated or standing in the foreground. Two windmills are to be seen on the horizon.

Then there are pictures of a Lady's Walking Dress, and a Lady's Evening Dress, and these seem so attractive that they inspire me to action.

I must see my neighbour, Mr Evans, and tell him that he should buy this book and that it is worth to him at any rate a guinea.

.   .   .   .

Days have passed since I wrote these words on my counter one depressing day and my neighbour has now changed his windows and is showing his first autumn collection.

Where are the petticoats of the past? What has happened

to the draperies of days gone by? They all went in the summer sale and who knows where they are to-day?

My habit of disparaging my neighbour is unworthy. He is a good business man. He buys what he thinks will sell and when he has made a mistake he cuts his loss and gets on to something else.

I wish I could do as Arnold Bennett has recommended. He says that it is not a bad plan every seven years to get rid of one's possessions—start afresh—a new house, a new business, a new wife, a new life . . . not that he says these things, but that is how I interpret his advice.

I cling to what I have.

I cannot part even with old clothes, and as for papers, catalogues, journals, even the sheets of printed paper in which publishers pack their books, I keep them all. I can throw nothing away, I can give nothing away, and even the temptation to sell something for much-needed money I find easy to resist.

It dawns upon me that I may be a miser, that, like Arnold Bennett's bookseller in *Riceyman Steps* . . . what I have I want to hold. I hope my fate may be more fortunate than that of Mr Earlsforward . . . but it may not be . . . what dark destiny awaits me? And if it waits for me, why should I bother about change? Fate will not pass me by. They say fate only knocks at one's door once—but, when it does come, it comes inevitably and need not knock at all.

DESTROY THE BOOKS

There is no doubt that the problem of the printer, paper-maker, publisher and bookseller is the problem of how to get rid of the books. If people only read more and retained less in these little boxes which are now being built for them all over the country . . . I can see that the demand for books as company is going to be less in the future than it has been in the past. No sensible man of the middle class sat down in his saddlebag chair to sleep after his dinner without a background of books. Though he read little he still had the well-filled bookshelves. Books were an essential part of the furniture and decoration of his establishment. But now a library, public or private—a book borrowed from a friend—a book bought at a bookstall in a cheap edition—or at best a book in the miniature edition of some famous best-seller—these are all the books they seem to want to have and to hold. It is a problem that the Booksellers' Association should take up, and as a contribution to the problem I would direct their attention to the information contained in Dr Herbert A. Giles's book on the Civilization of China. It is in Williams and Norgate's Home University Library, and I should have been dressing my window rather than wasting my time reading it this morning.

Still nothing is lost, least of all time, and the information which Dr Giles gives to the world might be included in the book propaganda of some book society. Dr Giles tells about an extraordinary man who lived two hundred and twenty years before Christ and who became the First Emperor, and here is what he did. He wanted to give a new stimulus to literary effort and he determined that literature should begin anew. He decided to destroy all existing books, but was finally persuaded to spare books dealing with three departments of human knowledge : firstly, books dealing with agricultural operations and the provision of food ; secondly, books of medicine and healing ; and thirdly, books on the methods of foretelling the future. He issued orders that all other books were to be destroyed, and we read that many scholars were put to death for concealing their books. Numbers of valuable works perished in the vast conflagration.

This was two hundred years before Christ, and I. don't know that either China or the world was much worse for the conflagration.

Why should not the world's great age begin anew?

Why should not literature turn over for the first time a new leaf?

What a spurt it would give to the bookselling trade ! What new vigour to the arts of composition and writing, what inspiration to men of genius to feel that the ideas to which they were giving expression were being written in their era for the first time.

" Destroy the books ! "—that should be the slogan. Perhaps the idea might be adopted in another form. Could I not encourage the idea that a book which once has been read should be consigned to the flames? Would it not make one feel a sense of greater value in the printed page over which our eyes now pass so carelessly.

Here I read now but soon I take a final farewell. What makes books seem ordinary and commonplace is their indestructibility. One reads, one's neighbour reads, one's neighbour's neighbour reads, and so on, but the book does not wear out or become exhausted, and it gives and gives and gives. . . .

. . . .

And so an unsuccessful bookseller writes after his shop is closed on a singularly unsatisfactory day. Books that I have bought keep coming in from the publishers and I do not seem to be selling any at all.

No wonder that a desperate bookseller turns to desperate remedies.

Oh, well ! What is one to do?

EATING AND DRINKING

Books on food and drink are better than they used to be—there is almost a spate of them nowadays.

Some which I have bought look like being a long time with me, however. Here are names :

Conduct of the Kitchen, Boulestin ; Heinemann, 3s. 6d.

Tables of Content, Simon ; Constable, 7s. 6d.
A Book of Food, Morton Shand ; Cape, 4s. 6d.

When I bought them I was going to lead a select group of my fellow-citizens (if I could collect them) back to the dining-table as the real altar of human friendliness.

I know better now. I am not a leader in anything—least of all, a leader of others into temptation, and there is authority for my half-baked (what a good culinary metaphor !) endeavours !

" Most people [you will find it quoted on the wrapper of *A Book of Food*] have a foolish way of not minding or pretending not to mind what they eat. For my own part, I mind my belly most studiously and very carefully ; for I look upon it that he who does not mind his belly will hardly mind anything else."

It was Dr Johnson who said it.
He has the last word.

BOOKSELLER AT SCHOOL

These early years of mine have been coming back to me again and again in recent days.

It is, perhaps, because business is dull, or is it because Mrs Jock Johansen—is she a Swede?—brings in her two fair-haired children, and I see once again my own far-off, forgotten childhood? These two kids are really quite marvellous. I am not one who is inclined to sentiment about children.

Perhaps, in the main, I consider them as their parents appear to consider them—rather a nuisance. They run about the shop, up and down, and one day one of them embarrassed me enormously—and his mother too—by clutching my legs suddenly and calling out " Hello, Daddy ! "

Life is like that.

My mind, however, goes back and back and back to these earliest days.

That was a pleasant enough house we lived in with my mother and Liza, and the perambulator with the cracked American cloth cover, and the back yard with its flagstones, and the toad that lived in the ferns in the corner, and the grubbiness and dirtiness of town life, and the clean, scrubbed feeling after I had been thoroughly soaked in boiling water in the zinc bath upstairs.

Those were days, and, perhaps, they were the very heart and core of all my existence.

Childhood is important.

The greatest sentimentalist about children I knew was Perry, and Perry was a barber in my Company in the Shropshire Light Infantry.

Perry, of course, was one of that great class of generous manhood who found in the late War a constant and unexpected relief from the entanglement of existence. Perry had only once been a barber (he was a lather-boy for a few weeks) before he joined the Army, but was confirmed in that calling by the water and the word for the whole period of training at Salisbury Plain.

He held the theory that when our Lord suffered little children to come unto Him, He was in the great tradition of the highest in Godhead. Perry held that as a matter of fact it was only children that God was interested in. He did not care for grown-ups—cherubs were His fancy—small boys and small girls were His delight, and of such stuff are made the angels—and are not the angels the Kingdom of Heaven? Bearded patriarchs, bald-headed, stomach-distended old men, grim witches and other familiar delights, were for earth. Heaven was reserved for the little ones. It is a pleasing fantasy, and as Perry had definitely deserted two wives it came becomingly from him. The problem of Perry's two separation allowances was never, as far as we knew in the Company, solved during his lifetime, for he took his final call in the curtain of fire which descended on the Vimy in 1917. It was a good ending for Perry, and he was one, even in hairdressing, who liked to trim things off neatly.

K 2

Hours have elapsed since I wrote most of what appears on these pages, and since then nothing much has happened. We booksellers can idle and idle and idle and still feel busy. We enjoy our occupation, but the best of us—in which I am included —prefer preoccupation. When I feel that something ought to be done I am always very happy to be able to say that I am pre-occupied. To live in advance is less drastic than cash in advance—an experience, I regret to record, I had this morning from a reluctant publisher who is taking advantage of the new extensions of the services of the General Post Office. I do not like C.O.D. It is not for booksellers.

I was thinking of Mrs Johansen's children, and they have been once again the key to that little land in which, in little rooms, there is infinite riches—the land of childhood.

I was back again at Miss Dawner's school—back again only to recall the days when I left it. It was with real regret that I packed up and took my copy of *The Swiss Family Robinson*, in neatly spaced type for juvenile reading, as my prize—my only one in my Kindergarten career—for regular attendance.

It was kind of the scholastic authorities to give me a prize for the one virtue I had displayed. The bitter business of learning was then, as now, far removed from me, and I was glad, although I could not express it, that I was now to be counted among those who came humbly to the seat of wisdom with fealty and regularity.

There was the prize-giving day and I waddled—for I was a fat child—up to the table and took my prize, making an in-effectual bow to the Vicar or the Bishop, or some Church Dignitary, amid suitable applause, and returned to my seat on the front row with the other scholars who were being rewarded.

Liza, who was my mother's friend and maid-of-all-work—I put the description deliberately in the right order—collected me from the outer gate and led me home. It was the end of an epoch.

I was done with Miss Dawner's school.

The great world of education yawned for me—yawned, I suppose, is in every sense of the term the right word, for I certainly did not detect any eagerness on the part of Craighill College for Boys to absorb me into its planned curriculum.

It was to Craighill College that I ultimately went, but there was a pleasing intermission of idleness—it may have been months but it seemed only like weeks. I was at home with my mother and Liza in my sixth year.

The man who says that he was at Balliol says it with no more pride of recollection than I say " I was at home with my mother and Liza."

Truly delightful creatures, they surrounded me with an affectionate solicitude and regard and comfort which laps me still.

Publishers, I defy you.

Bank managers, I ignore you.

Ill-health, I mock at you.

Shopkeeping, I scoff at you.

These are nothing ; I was happy once when I was six years old and with my mother and Liza.

They took me picnics—does anyone to-day know the delight of such picnics as simple folk had before there were motor-cars or buses or tramways? There were places one went to—not in droves but privately—without difficulty, going a bit by train and walking, what seemed miles but may only have been one, to a place with buttercups and daisies surrounded by hedges garlanded with roses.

There was an Elysium of a field which we called " the rosy place," and we went there and saw the roses, my mother and Liza and I, carrying a basket between us of brown wicker— they surely do not make them nowadays—held together by a lid with a long metal skewer.

This basket was more than Pandora's Box. It contained all the delights of the senses.

They packed, these two guardian angels of mine, pork pie —there are not pork pies made to-day of the same character— they packed delicious bread with crusts and part of a roll of butter—fresh butter—and always fruit and sweets—black-striped balls. We have invented since then six-inch guns, docks, mustard gas, the aeroplane and the submarine, but black-striped balls still, in my judgment, rank high among the prominent achievements of mankind. So I thought in my youth, and if they paraded the whole of the Red Army in all its equipment in front of me in the Square of Moscow, as they are reported to have done last week, I shall still, at the end of eight hours of it, say, even if they threaten me with the knout or the Ogpu—I shall still say that black-striped balls, given to me at " the rosy place " by my mother and Liza, are among the highest achievements of mankind on this dizzy, destruction-designing planet.

The holiday is over.

The end comes to everything earthly and even in paradise, I believe, we know because of our faults, an end must come to every enjoyment, for boredom will supervene.

The end came to it, and, dressed no longer in my red knitted cravat and reefer coat, but instead, in an unsuitable black jacket with a large, uncomfortable collar inadequately tied with a black ribbon bow, I was taken by my mother to the Craighill College. The room in which the Headmaster interviewed me and my mother was frankly repulsive. The furniture consisted mainly of a rude yellow-pine desk at which the Headmaster sat. His name—I now can pronounce with facility, but I never did feel at ease with it when I was his pupil—was Goodenough, and perhaps his name makes him what many described him. If ever a man was damned with faint praise it was Mr Goodenough.

I never knew his Christian name—perhaps because, with all the Bible instruction he gave us, he was as un-Christian as was the Commercial College.

But my mother, poor soul, felt that my father's failure in life was due to his lack of knowledge of commerce. The more I have studied commerce, the more I appreciate my father's contempt for it.

" Getting and spending, we lay waste our powers," wrote Wordsworth, but I would parody and write, " Counting and counting we mis-spend our powers."

BOOKSELLING AND A BACKWARD GLANCE

Days must have elapsed since I wrote these lines. I have had quite a successful time commercially, and I would like to put it on record that I am wrong about Dent's Everyman's Library. There is no doubt it is the university of the half-educated, and I make up my mind to show it more regularly in my window. To-day I have made a new display and have made a special group of " Everyman's " with an attractive ticket—" The Whole Art of Oratory " in a few volumes. I propped this ticket against the following books—William Pitt the Younger's *Orations on the French War* ; Abraham Lincoln's *Letters and Speeches, Introduced by the Right Hon. James Bryce* ; *American Letters and Speeches* by Burke ; *Speeches of John Bright* ; *Anthology of British Historical Speeches*.

I stock the cloth edition of " Everyman " and these volumes are 2s. each.

Every one of them has 400 pages or thereabout, and possibly because of the development of debating societies, or the imminent general election—because of one, or other, or both, or neither—the demand has been considerable.

I like to get bites when I go a-fishing, and I have fished to some purpose this week. For some days I have abandoned altogether the idea that I am a commercial failure, indeed I am rapidly accepting the view that I am a man of real business genius—a man of affairs—a man destined to unique success, not a mere commonplace commercial achievement.

The idea, I recognise, comes probably from the tale I have been told about Mr Woolworth who has recently invaded this country, offering what America makes for sixpence.

This somewhat unpatriotic attitude of his seems to have found ready response with the British public, who never thought highly of the American nation and who are quite willing to believe that most of the commodities which they have to offer are adequately priced at this attractive figure. This Mr Woolworth, however, is no ordinary American. He is, if my informant is to be believed, a man who made several attempts on his own countrymen first to convince them that the normal product of their ingenious factories was not worth more than their equivalent for sixpence.

He spent a number of years unsuccessfully as a farmer and tried his accurate estimate of the value of the manufactured produce of his country in several different ways before he ultimately achieved success. He was, in plain fact, a failure at the beginning but he persisted in his pioneering work and now has reached the position of being a millionaire. Practically everything that America makes can be bought for sixpence and, with others like-minded, Mr Woolworth has come to Britain. One of his shops has been opened in this city, and thousands, they tell me, visit it and make their purchases with enthusiasm and with sixpences. That such an enterprise should be successful is a proof, I think, of the lovable simplicity and gullibility of mankind.

It is a foolish generation that seeketh a sign when signs are everywhere being displayed. Have we not Mr Baldwin, Mr Ramsay MacDonald, Mr Woolworth, Mr Mark—not Saint Mark—and Mr Spencer—signs enough and more?

They tell me in Liverpool that while Louis *le bien aimé* is known to few, Lewis's *le bon marché* is known to many.

Commercial success having come so accidentally and so uselessly to others, the bookseller must be forgiven if he dreams too that it will come to him.

Is there not enough for all of us, and if each of us got his deserts which of us would escape a whipping?

. . . . .

These were brave words but the phase is over—oratory no longer satisfies a demand, and I have changed my window and put in poetry—a neat display, but it is not securing the same response.

I have bought three copies of the *Collected Poems of John Masefield*—8s. 6d. from Heinemann—and haven't sold one yet. I flank it with some books of verses of the Everyman's Library, but these do not seem to attract either. I frankly admit I am a little despondent, and for relaxation turn my mind back from the charms of commerce and the wiles of Woolworth to those far-off days when I was enrolled as a pupil in the Craighill Commercial College. I am again with Mr Goodenough, who conducted us, even in those earliest days of mine, through the Practice of Commerce, which apparently began with shells that were called cowries, and which people exchanged for God-knows-what.

There were later developments, but they were quite irrational.

I only remember the bullock which ran at me in the street. I represented my world of terror. All that Mr Goodenough taught me was as obscure to me then as Madame Blavatsky is to me to-day. I am not one of those who readily assimilate knowledge.

It was an interesting school as schools go, but I was not a popular boy. During the first year or two they used to chase me up and down the playground, and I hated it all.

The playground was covered with black ashes. Many a time I grovelled in it, declining to be dragged to my feet to take part in the rude uninteresting exercises of my companions.

I was a studious lad, but did not like the studies offered to me. I was not a companionable youth—disliked by my companions—and in that unfortunate condition I spent my school-days and those school-days left their stamp upon me for life.

The Goodenough tradition lasted, I suppose, six or seven years, for it was at thirteen I left school. It took me through a curriculum which in retrospect seems to me to have been inspired by what Goodenough and his colleagues knew and not what the pupils of the school ought really to learn.

All the other masters in the school were stodgy figures except one—and these coincidences occur far more frequently in life than novel writers will admit. His name was Badenoch— the spelling was quite different, but the contrast between Goodenough the Headmaster and Badenoch the English, Arithmetic and French Master was too obvious for the simple

minds of schoolboys to resist. We called them cleverly
" Good " and " Bad," but Badenoch was the man who took
my fancy. It was regretted, doubtless, by some of the students,
but not by me—Badenoch drank. I have seen him quite tipsy
at the French class, and hilarious at English Literature. He had
a long, straight, yellow moustache and, from what I know
now, must have been a large consumer of beer. English,
really, was his subject and, inspired by English beer, English
became a hilarious topic. He must then have been a man of
sixty and there was a rumour that he had been once in some
very good school and had been dismissed for intemperance.
When sober he was sad, and it was only when he was in drink
that he found life tolerable and endurable. His history was
splendid and never followed the somewhat bald textbook which
we used—I think they called it *Meiklejohn's English History*.
Badenoch, I believe, was a Scotsman but his speech had long
since been refined to English ears. He had still a strong
Scotch intonation and got carried away sometimes for an hour
at a time by the *Lays of the Scottish Cavaliers*. The title of this
work has been known to me again since I became a bookseller,
and I can think at any moment of the thrill that there was in
it in my school-days. It comes back to me again when I open
the pages of William Edmonstoune Aytoun, who wrote *Edinburgh After Flodden* and the *Execution of Montrose*.

He gave us Scott too—*Marmion* is for me ever one of the
great narrative poems of the language because of the poor
inspired Badenoch.

Shop ! Here is a customer.

CABBAGES AND EMPEROR

Mr Breech is a greengrocer—a good greengrocer. When I am
vitamin- and vegetable-minded—full of the idea that I do not
need the dead flesh of beasts to feed on but the living garment

of God for my nourishment—I go to Breech. He has celery—
so good for rheumatism ; he has lettuce—delicious with vinegar
and sugar ; he has radishes—so satisfying with bread and
butter.

But Breech is more than a greengrocer.

He is a success.

He is a multiple greengrocer.

He has modelled himself on a mind . . . and so he is my
customer. He models himself on a Napoleon—Napoleon who
might have grown spring vegetables in Corsica but who became
an Emperor instead and a Dictator of Europe. Napoleon
appeals to Breech, and who am I to complain?

I have sold him Sir Walter Scott's *Life* (a poor thing, but
I didn't tell him), Oscar Browning's *Napoleon : the First
Phase*, and Lord Rosebery's *Napoleon : the Last Phase*.

He also ordered, and I have still to procure, H. A. L.
Fisher's *Napoleonic Statesmanship*, and J. H. Rose on *Napoleonic
Studies*. His favourite book, however, is the First Edition of
The Table Talk and Opinions of Napoleon Bonaparte done
by Sampson Low, Marston, Low & Searle in 1875. (There
were publishers in those days—a book was a book and a
publishing house more than a morsel.) This book—it has less
than 200 pages—is the kernel of the life of Breech. It is his
guide, his vademecum, his mentor, his fidus Achates, his
familiar, his light, his leading and his reading, and I sold him
the treasure for one shilling.

Mr Thomas Breech deserves his success. He was in the
War—came back—had a wife and two sons—and got a job
as a porter-cum-motorman with a wholesale vegetable ware-
house. In a year he was on his own. In two years he had
two shops. In ten he will have twenty.

He works from four in the morning until ten at night and
studies Napoleon.

It is the recipe for success.

The mortals command it—for they pay the price.

Breech said, " I make myself two men when I study
Napoleon. I am Breech but to Breech I add another greater

than he—Napoleon Bonaparte—the greatest figure in the world of achievement of modern times."

Breech is right.

We can be two men if we will.

We can find an ally if we want to do so—if our egotism will allow us to follow a master. For the Christian the Master is Christ, but as Matthew Arnold said, " Where in Christendom shall I find a Christian? "

Breech will be a Napoleon among the cabbages and why should one not find among the cabbages—the Kings !

" WHO'S WHO "

" The only book I buy nowadays," said my most important customer, " is *Who's Who*. It is my favourite reading for the year. Who wants to read any better biographies than those which are written by those who think they are somebodies and whom Messrs Adam & Charles Black agree shall be included in their carefully compiled volume? " My customer is right. *Who's Who* is an interesting volume and I have spent many an hour turning its pages. Some name in the newspaper sends me to it, and from one name I pass to another and from another to a third and so on, and an hour is whiled away and I have never noticed it.

It is true one does not learn much—this one was educated at Bedford and became General Commissioner in Somaliland, and that one was educated privately and now is a leader-writer on the *Daily Mail*.

It is a strangely fascinating record. There are not many booksellers included in its pages—in fact I have not been able to discover any at all. I scribble out for myself my own record—where I was born—parentage—educated at—served in the Army—commenced business. But it is a bald story—

there isn't much in it ; it is not worth printing, and besides I understand from my customer that the editors are very fastidious about those who are who, and who are permitted to enter its pages. One cannot gate-crash into *Who's Who*, I am informed . . . one has to be invited.

Still it is an attractive book for all that, a good book for a bookseller to sell. Its 3000-odd pages are crammed with interest, not only for those who find their names there but for those who can never hope to be anybody other than nobody.

GREEN-EYED MONSTER

They pass my door.

They ignore my show of the Oxford Poets, the Oxford Book of English Verse, the English Prose, the Religious Verse and the French Verse.

They pass them by. I peer out and wonder. What is it— this commotion, this hurrying along, this eagerness?

They are mostly women, young and old, plump and puny, beautiful as well as forbidding.

I emerge from the doorway, blaming myself for having overslept—blaming myself for not being shaved. I see what it all is about.

The poster on the windows—the red tickets—the appalling clutter of women's clothes—dresses, materials, table-covers, curtains, corsets and camisoles, I suppose—these indescribable things fill my neighbour's windows.

It is the first day of the Summer Sale.

It is monstrous. I withdraw to my back shop, but I am dogged by something.

It is a Green-Eyed Monster.

RANK INJUSTICE

He was an indulgent, genial old buffer and he wanted *Doctor Dolittle* for a little boy. A nice boy, he was holding his hand —restless-footed, large-eyed—grateful because Grand-Uncle Jerry (his name was Jerome Richardson Robertson and he is neither his Grand-Uncle nor his Uncle but secretly, I believe, his mother's friend because he once was his mother's beau) was going to give him a book. That was only ten days ago and to-day the boy is dead of some unknown complication and I daren't write to Jerome Richardson Robertson and tell him that the copy of *Doctor Dolittle* which I ordered at his request awaits his instructions.

It is not bad stock—I can sell my *Dolittle*, but before heaven I think it rank injustice. It can't be explained.

Human minds can't understand it. It may be that all our sins will be forgiven—all our offences purged—all our records duly signed, sealed and delivered, but nothing can give that little boy his *Doctor Dolittle*.

The High Gods themselves cannot—if time is time and eternity eternity—ever bring the time and the place and the loved one all together again. It is the way—the world's way— but Heaven's highest cannot outweigh these unjust balances of earth.

IS IT LIFE ?

Just inside the door on the left-hand side as you enter, I stand.

There is a cool gloom over the doorway and that gloom deepens as you enter the further recesses of the shop. Behind me as I peer out on the street are books of all the ages, books of every type and sort and condition, books that should never have been written ; books, I reflect, that I certainly should never have bought.

Behind me there are those.

And in front of me there is the street full of brightness and sunlight, full of folk coming and going and going and coming.

There are staid matrons—I see one with a stick passing in calm dignity in front of my windows—there are elderly gentlemen enjoying the sun and the air and the movement—there is one Victorian figure with waisted coat and check trousers and a yellow walking-stick with a heavy silver knob—there are young people, gay, laughing, busily making for some objective —and I stand in the gloom on the left-hand side of my door, peering out.

This is life, I suppose, life in all its intensity and vital purpose and endeavour, life in its endless search for something which cannot satisfy it, life in its continuous pursuit of what is not worth pursuing.

It is obvious to-day they do not want books. Books are the last thing they want—perhaps they are quite right in passing by.

This is a melancholy thought but it is all I can give the world, this little service of selling books.

It isn't much—but no man likes to think his all isn't much.

TAKING ONE'S OWN MEDICINE

Some tough old Tory once declared that if at a dinner party or at his club he was told to read some new novel which was thrilling literary London or some book or essay which was titillating the intelligentsia with tremendous delight—when he was told these things he went home and re-read, with gusto, some book of twenty years ago or earlier. Stung with my inability to give a traveller an order—my pride is sore with forced penuries—I, like the tough old Tory, turn to old books.

In 1894 George Allen of Sunnyside, Orpington, published *Selections from the Writings of John Ruskin*. I have the second edition—two volumes—each with a portrait. To these volumes I turn.

Ruskin has been outrun. His was an uncritical world but there are as many critics almost as cats to-day.

Ruskin had more to say, I see—and, if you please, said it much better than his successors. He warned women before they sought to win the vote of their responsibilities : " There is not a war in the world, no, nor an injustice, but you women are answerable for it : not in that you have provoked it, but in that you have not hindered." And he goes on in another place to assert that " war was the foundation of all great art."

Here are sentences from the same passage supporting the argument :

" The greatest works produced [in ancient Egypt] are sculptures of their Kings going out to battle or receiving the homage of conquered armies."

" The rudiments of art . . . and of all science were laid first by this warrior nation which held in contempt all mechanical trades and in absolute hatred the peaceful life of shepherds."

He amazes me !

" As peace is established or extended in Europe, the arts decline," he asserts, but declares that strange though it is— and very dreadful—it is an undeniable fact.

I found in brief that all great nations learned their truth of word and strength of thought in war : that they were nourished in war and wasted by peace : taught by war and deceived by peace : trained by war and betrayed by peace : in a word, that they were born in war and expired in peace.

War, war, war. . . .

On the Embankment one night What-*was*-his-name? (a clergyman who had left the Church and quoted Swinburne to me) pointed an eager finger over the parapet of the river and showed me these words in red letters—WAR—WAR—WAR.

I hadn't seen it before. He laughed at me.

" Walk along a bit," he said, and we saw the whole word. It wasn't War over London—it was DEWAR—a different story.

It absorbs me, this warring world, and, as has been so often pointed out, we find in literature as in life what we look for. I find war—over London, among the nations, in my memories, in the heavens above threatening, in the waters beneath menacing, in my innocent books. . . . To the shelves I go. There is an *Imitation of Christ*. I'll never sell it : prayer books, Bibles—these will stay with me.

British Soldier Heroes by Spencer Wilkinson, *Ordeal by Battle* by F. S. Oliver, *Medicine and Duty* by Harold Dearden, *Expansion of England* by Sir John Seeley, *British Battles of Destiny* by Boyd Cable, Napier's *Battles in the Peninsula*—these are my stock-in-trade. I am ready for the war mind when it turns to buy books.

How well Napier writes ". . . the enemy retired : but Ridge fell, and no man died that night with more glory—yet many died, and there was much glory." There is an epitaph for a soldier. Even Casper—and there are Caspers to-day—would admit, as at Hohenlinden, that it was a glorious victory.

We booksellers who cannot give orders to travellers because we have too much stock have our compensations. If we cannot buy new books and cannot sell our old books, we can read them.

What happiness can my neighbour have in contemplating his out-moded corsets or faded fancy work?

What joy can a greengrocer have in the greens of months gone by?

What inspiration can an ironmonger find in his unsold pots and rejected pans?

The answer is, " None."

The best of all worlds—ancient and modern : ascending, descending or falling—is the world of books and its high priest is the bookseller. He, like a good doctor, takes his own medicine, and in my case—to tell the truth—likes it.

What is there in his list anyway ! I can do without the lot. My own stock is as well selected as that of any publisher ;

and more, I know something about the contents of my books. I read, and so am able to recommend. I find good things in books and am able to quote them. "You should buy this book," I say, "because of this . . ." and I notice that my nails are dirty and my hands grubby!

It is a sad downfall and I must refrain from pointing until my hands are more refined.

I resolve to do better but I must read no more—nor think no more of war. I must sober my mind. I will read the unsaleable *Imitation of Christ* and be at peace.

SHOPKEEPING PROMOTES PHILOSOPHY

Shopkeeping promotes philosophy—that is true. I do not think there is any other calling which is more successful. It is the natural forcing-bed for philosophy, and if those other people whom I see in shops don't look like philosophers, I am persuaded that despite their disappointing externals they are philosophers in deed and in word.

To-night I am headache-stricken and feel less able to stand up to existence than usual.

It is the War and my headaches—or something—something —anything but myself.

It will not do. I must brace myself.

I have committed myself to bookselling, shopkeeping, bills, and the determination to establish and hold a place for myself in life.

I am too given to thinking life has to be faced—lived out hour by hour. It is no use planning or forcing or conjecturing or romancing about it. I must do something and go on doing something. Work is justification and anodyne and the only true Nunc dimittis is " It is finished. . . ." Under no other terms can the good Lord let His servant depart in peace.

I WONDER

I wonder.

I wonder how things are with me—how things are with the universe.

It is no business of mine, but it is now almost two o'clock and I have sold only two Edgar Wallaces and a copy of *Book-keeping and Accounts*, Cropper (Macdonald & Evans).

I wonder where I am drifting and whether, though I don't know where I am going, when I get there, I shall be glad.

Shall I ever be glad? Was I ever glad?

Yes, I have been glad. It was after the Battle of Arras in 1917. We went into rest. The Colonel had us up at five, running and drilling, but we were finished by ten. I had my billet with the rest of the platoon in Zwitze's Farm—we called it Witches' Farm—and it was a home to soldiers.

We had the run of the Kitchen—bought eggs—used the stove with the Madam—swopped bully beef and bread—for omelettes and coffee. The dunghill troubled us not: we loafed in the fields—slept under the hedges—bathed in the ditches—and hardly noticed the rumble of shell-fire far away.

A sausage balloon hung between us and heaven—it was the only emphatic reminder of the War. I was glad then—but gladness departed. The magic went.

A red German plane one morning swooped down on our sausage balloon and it fell in flames, the Observer breaking his legs in a bad landing with his parachute. That tore it—the balloon and everything.

I was never glad again in quite that way.

War was behind me then. I had done well and got my medal. I had fought not Germans but fear, and felt I could do it again.

I had friends. My Company Commander understood me. I had a comrade.

Then the glory departed.

It was just a wretched French farmhouse with a disgusting dunghill.

The farm folk were greedy and clutching.

We would soon go back to the line.

War was futile, detestable, silly.

Yet I was glad once and I will be again.

Two Edgar Wallaces and Cropper are not less than three in a loaf and a pannikin of tea.

I have grounds for gladness, I assert,—but they are not very convincing.

I don't know why.

I just wonder—

WIT AND WISDOM

There is a good title—" The Wit and Wisdom of Queen Bess "—what we want are not biographies, dates of births, marriages and deaths—what we want are the distillations of wit and wisdom from the wittiest and the wisest.

The publishers ought to get out a whole series beginning, if you like, with the Wit and Wisdom of the Bible down to— what should it be?—the Wit and Wisdom of Arnold Bennett.

I would be delighted to co-operate, and if I were only on better terms financially with the traveller I would give them the suggestion.

How these overdue accounts freeze the free transports of the imagination and compel me to dismiss these companionable gentlemen with the cold words yet so all-embracing, " Nothing to-day."

" Alas, nothing to-day—nothing I can buy, nothing I can say, nothing I can pay, nothing to-day."

It is almost a poem—a sad one at that.

But I have bought—and paid for—*The Wit and Wisdom of Queen Bess.*

Its author—or is it compiler?—is Frederick Chamberlain and its publisher is John Lane (5s.)—not much bulk—only 133 pages—for the money. I declare, however, it is good value, and when I sell it I am going to order a bigger book from which it takes its origin—*The Sayings of Queen Elizabeth*—same author, same publisher—demy 8vo, 16s. nett.

She was Queen and woman both.

Here is the Queen—to her Court before the Armada sailed from Spain : " By God's death, I would send my fleet to disperse the Armada even if it were in the interior of Spain." .

Here is the woman—to Fénelon, the French Ambassador : " I do not want a husband who honours me as a Queen, if he does not love me as a woman."

I reflect on the observation that a country is best governed by a woman.

When a man governs—a woman behind the throne rules. When a woman governs—a man behind the throne rules.

I wonder—but why should an all but bankrupt bookseller reflect on such things? He should attend to his business.

THE TEMPORARY GENTLEMAN

He is a good fellow but all has not gone well with him. He would be twenty-five in 1914 and apparently had no serious occupation prior to that year, or, if he had an occupation, it was of such little moment that he gladly resigned it on the call of King and Country. After a few months in the ranks, he attained or obtained a commission.

Life began for him.

He had status and clothes and money. He had an occupation in which his colleagues and competitors were amateurs like himself. He was also a hero.

France found him with the first of the New Armies and he marvellously survived those experiments in war which characterised the years of 1915 and 1916. He became a Temporary Captain and in 1917 won a Military Cross.

Experience, boredom, habit, the lowered standard of his fellow-soldiers, the weakening of the enemy, his inability to get trench fever, shell-shock or serious wounds kept him at the front till the end of the War. He passed the Armistice in Germany.

He was reluctantly demobilised and, at an age under thirty, faced the Peace.

He had a holiday, spending most of his time and nearly all his money, in London. He got a job in the motor-car world—what a world—and lost it.

He sold petrol, newspaper space, insurance, cattle food, fire-extinguishers, carpet-sweepers, books . . . and now he comes into my life.

I have given him money but was denied the pleasure of feeling I had given it to him—as he got it from me as a loan. He has slept in my back shop more than once. He has swept out my front shop and is now—poor goat—at the end of his tether.

Nobody wants him.

Neither his King nor his Country want him.

His Military Cross is as little use as his Temporary Captaincy.

He is a man without a place in life and, short of another war, one can't imagine one for him.

What is he to do?

What am I—his keeper—to do for my brother in arms? I give it up.

He knows I can do no more. He knows he is not wanted.

Yet it is someone's business surely.

We took him—used him—made him our tool for our purposes—would have honoured him and given him a neat grave if he had only died on the job—but as he didn't he is just scrap war material and unsaleable at that.

He should have a pension—enough to keep him—two pounds a week would do.

Why not?—on what grounds shouldn't he have the two pounds?

They have been wonderfully docile these Temporary Gentlemen : perhaps it is because they were not just Temporary Gentlemen after all.

I'LL TAKE THE HIGH ROAD

The books issued from the Bodley Head have always a sort of mystical attraction for me and I was glad I had two of theirs this afternoon for the young lady with the knapsack who intends to take the high road.

She admitted that she was an Honours woman in the University, and she admitted that she had been told to take a holiday of not less than a month entirely in the open air, and she admitted that she had bought the short-kilted skirt that she wore from my neighbour next door. She came to me for a guide-book and perhaps a map, but I had neither.

It is lamentable to me how I never seem to have what the people want—perhaps the public are really like young children, what they want is really not good for them.

I like the book buyer who buys what I have—the book buyer who comes to my shop like a housewife to a baker, asking for a loaf of bread, goes hungry away—I like the book buyer who thinks he wants a book, who comes in prepared to buy something he sees, something which interests him. . . .

But I must get back to my books which I sold Miss Justinia Brookes Blair.

The books I sold her were *Agricola's Road in Scotland* and *In Roman Scotland*, both by Jessie Mothersole and both published by John Lane at The Bodley Head.

They have coloured illustrations of which I am never very fond, but in this instance as they are done apparently by the author they are less objectionable than most.

Miss Blair, anyway, is off with the two of them, and skirt, pack, staff and all I wish her well with her knowledge and her holiday. For half a split second—the phrase is not mine but one used by a publisher's young traveller—for half a split second I thought I would like to go with her, but, fortunately, I restrained myself.

The High Road is not for me.

The High Street will have to do meanwhile.

REGRET

He was a dilapidated figure. The woman with him was worse than that. Such sights ought not to be allowed. I have had my troubles but I did not parade them. Where are the police? What do we pay rates for?

Anyway they are impostors—no one could be so miserable as they look. They have no right. . . . And so I thought, rather above myself because the Dean (a Rural one at that—I like the country air) had bought a good parcel from me.

I needn't have felt so superior to a sinning, not always successful world.

The Dean was my only customer to-day.

I ought to have shown mercy and given the dilapidated ones a sixpence. It wouldn't have hurt. My conscience would have been easier.

The chance has gone. The same water never runs twice under the same bridge. What was it I read and cut out of a paper the other day? I find the cutting. Here it is—I write it for penance :

> " One troubling thought stands out, alone,
> As I reflect on Time's swift glass!
> The kindnesses I might have shown
> But let them pass."

BOOKSELLER RECOLLECTS HOSPITAL DAYS
. . . AND HOW HE WENT TO WAR AGAIN

The poet Shenstone declared that in all his travels round the weary world he had found the warmest welcome of life in an Inn.

He put it poetically but I feel I must put it prosaically because, prosaic though it was, I found hospital life comfortable and, in retrospect, an enjoyable experience. Everything, of course, is relative in this related world and perhaps it was the contrast from the discomfort of the trenches that made it appeal so attractively to me. They landed me at Mudros and for some time I lay in a marquee with other dysenterics. I was in a bad way. Dysentery makes one feel that the life has dropped from one's body and that the flesh is falling from one's bones.

Whether it was because I got better or I got worse, I don't know, but one bright morning I saw the last of those sunny Mediterranean skies. They carried me on a stretcher and, after much discomfort, I reached Alexandria. For a month I lay in some building there, the exterior of which I never saw, as I arrived in the dark and left in the dark. A good many died who shared beds in my ward, but I cared not at all.

I had complications. Dysentery had joined hands with malaria and, duly married, without benefit of clergy, they wedded themselves in my attenuated person. I became thin, wasted, yellow, weary, ashamed to look at myself in the three-inch steel mirror which remained to me from my trench days. I was moved again and in a suburb of Cairo I found myself recovering health. I got better quickly—too quickly some of my fellow-soldiers told me.

But in one week I recollect I was born again. Life seemed to come back into my body again. I ate better, the malaria diminished, the dysentery disappeared, and with the coming of the spring in Egypt I became a new man.

What had happened in the world from the time I left Gallipoli to the time I left Cairo I really never knew. I read

The Lady of the Barge by W. W. Jacobs, Sir Walter Scott's *Journal* and a little book which I still have, called *The Right Joyous and Pleasant History of the Feats, Gests and Prowesses of the Chevalier Bayard, The Good Knight without Fear and without Reproach*, by the Loyal Servant, Translated by Sara Coleridge. This little volume is published by George Newnes, Limited, in their pocket classics and for an adventurer like me it was high-spirited, stimulating stuff.

I would go to the wars again. The greatest cataclysm of history had descended upon humanity, my kith and kin and country were engaged in a life-and-death struggle, and who was I to spend the forenoons in climbing the Pyramids or the afternoons in sipping tea at Groppi's? I would tell the Board that I was fit and ready. It was all in that one week and I found the Board made up of one Englishman, one Australian and one Scotsman, and they signed me off as convalescent right away.

Down to the sea I went again and travelled as a light-duty convalescent passenger back to England and Home and Duty and Beauty. I remember the journey through the Mediterranean, from Alexandria to Southampton was the pinnacle, the keynote of my enjoyment in life . . . it was all behind me, my childhood days, the collapse of my life which came when my mother, the keystone of it, dropped out, the dullness of an Insurance Office, the call of War, the thrill of one's first experience in France, the heavy, desperate routine of Gallipoli, the lassitude of sickness, the glory of getting better, the feeling that life had not left me yet and that death was still an enemy being held at arm's length . . . these whirling, inspiring ideas made me a hero, another Ulysses sailing too westward in the Mediterranean towards the " western stars before I die."

These were historic waters and I was the centre of the historic scene. The Gates of Hercules as we passed through them had a new meaning and the callow youth who a few months before had sailed for Gallipoli was now a man, proved, to his own satisfaction at any rate, to be a man among men.

I was in the beginning of 1917 one of those who cared

nothing for their own welfare but cared only that, as long as the Cause required service, hands and head and body and brain were one's country's to command. There was an accepting spirit these days among those lovely lads of whom I was one and of whom now many are dead and rotten.

Landed in England there was a slight set-back. They sent me to hospital but it was as a convalescent, not as a bed-patient. I was getting better and got better rapidly, and in Wandsworth Hospital, where I lay, a good deal of liberty was permitted.

I learned for the first time a lot about London.

London in early 1917 was beginning to fill up with Canadians and Australians. The country was entering its third year of war with experience, disillusionment and the knowledge of how grim the business upon which it was engaged really was to be.

There was gaiety in the streets. There was food in the restaurants. There was money in my pocket. There was comradeship among all of us who wore the khaki, and like lovely phantasms before my memory I see again Buster Brown and Sister Joyce and Sergeant Macaulay and Brother Drummond. They were among my immediate associates. Sister Joyce was a nurse of two years' experience and had her troubles and trials and, like me, was now level with life—nothing could put her down and nothing could greatly lift her. She had met too many, endured too much, and seen through it all.

If this were a diary I might write of hours we spent together at places of amusement, on Wandsworth Common, on Putney Heath, and one unforgettable run down to see some friends of hers (whom she missed) leave from Folkestone—but this is not a diary and Sister Joyce, all unwritten, is the most unfading of all the women I met in the War.

Buster Brown has been an Ironmonger's Traveller and from that inglorious walk in life had stepped to the very height of things. He had an amazing gift in the air and, with D.S.O. and Bar, Military Cross and three Bars, was spending—and perhaps he knew it—the last few months of his life in a hectic round of intensive gaiety in London. Buster died in September

L

1917 above Passchendaele Ridge, and I think I saw his 'plane fall, whirling like a red autumn leaf, in flames.

Sergeant Macaulay was a different sort—an Old Sweat wounded at Mons, wounded at Loos, recovering from wounds on the Somme, knowing that he could not face the terrible music of war again and again with impunity. I don't know what happened to him. If he came through he will stand, I suppose, with his D.C.M. and M.M., in front of the palatial entrance of some bank—

> " Think what 'e's been,
> Think what 'e's seen.
> Think of his pension an'——
> GAWD SAVE THE QUEEN !"

Brother Drummond was a gentle soul, bred for the Church which he had abandoned for photography. Photography found him at the moment when he was compelled to face a greater realism. Although he was taught to look on life in terms of black and white, or, at best, brown and cream, he never would be a realist.

A leader among men (the most reasoned, the most erudite of these my friends), he has gone far, and I read the political news of the day not, as perhaps some may imagine, to know the latest trials of the ex-enemy countries or the provocations of the victors, but to see what Brother Drummond is doing in this post-War world. He was then, as he is now, one of those men who make the theory of Socialism attractive, likeable, commanding sacrifices—not because he was a good Socialist but because he was a good and a great man.

We called him Brother Drummond because he had, and has, please God, the brotherhood of man in his heart and in his life.

And here I am interrupted by the customer who comes in —a customer, I remember, interrupted John Gilpin

> " . . . of credit and renown,
> A trainband captain eke was he,
> Of famous London Town."

I folded up my papers and laid impressively on top of them a copy of John H. Burton's *The Book Hunter*. Hill Burton was an astonishing fellow, telling about mighty book hunters and their clubs and the members of them, telling it all in the edition published by Blackwood in 1863.

"John Galt Mackay, Edinburgh, 1871" is written on the title-page. Who the gentleman was I don't know. Anyway, I put Hill Burton on top of my scribble paper and faced the front.

It was a book hunter who demanded my attention. "I am a collector," he said, "and I am a collector of original editions. I am desirous of completing my collection of the works of Robert Louis Stevenson. I have," he continued, "the 1894–1903 edition, 34 volumes, T. & A. Constable, including the *Life* by Graham Balfour, *Stevensoniana* by Hammerton. I want, however, first editions, particularly *Familiar Studies of Men and Books*, 1882, *Kidnapped*, 1886; they must be in first-class condition." I blankly look at my would-be patron.

Alas, I have no first editions of Robert Louis Stevenson. He is deeply entrenched in my affection; I bound him to my heart; I hold him to my bosom; his essays slip from my fingers while I close my eyes in sleep, but I have no first editions, not one in all my shop.

"Have you ever heard of Stevenson?" demands the lofty purchaser of first editions.

"Yes," I say, "I think I can tell you the names of everything he wrote." I am on the defensive.

I mentioned *The Wrecker, Treasure Island, The Master of Ballantrae*. . . . I thought I mentioned them all, but he glanced sideways at me with a scoffing sneer as he made for the door : "You have omitted one." And to be honest with myself I had never heard of the book before. The book is *Alma Mater's Mirror*, St. Andrews, 1887.

The original, I learned since from an obliging catalogue, is in white-and-gold boards with silk ties and contains the first edition of *The House Beautiful*, 10s. 6d.

Personally I think it a little hard of him to catch me thus, but there it is, and we slaves of the shop must expect sometimes hard words from our indulgent masters.

It is with pleasure that I turn again to those days that are past, with a feeling that even in memory they are more real and gratifying than the most present realities of to-day.

Where was I?

I read.

I was at Wandsworth in the convalescent block in the society of some of the brightest and best. I was passed in the glorious month of April to light duty.

I had not calculated on the determined offensive against the French and I did not know that the pressure must be relieved by an attack in front of Arras. The attack took place on 9th April 1917, and I found myself quickly recovering from my illness, my spell of light duty sharply curtailed, and for the third time leaving the shores of England.

This time we left by Folkestone and a different France greeted me from that which I had seen in 1915. France was a British Camp; Hospitals, Dumps, British Troops everywhere seemed settled as if they were there until Judgment Day, and through these permanent features of the landscape moved ever forward drafts for the Front and, from the Front, drafts for the hospitals and home. It was clock-work.

There was no moaning at the bar.

I left Britain before the end of April and stood up in front of a square wood with a Scottish Division. The Scotch were new to me in the collective sense. I had lived in England and moved and worked among English people, but these Scotch were to me a revelation. They do not take foreigners willingly to their bosom—in fact I have come to the conclusion they mean what they say when they assert that they are a different race. There was a Scotch Doctor who held strenuously that the Scotch had conquered England and had imposed their king upon the English—a king whose descendant reigned to-day. I never quite followed that but I accepted it; the vehemence of the man was too overpowering for simple argument.

He said in my hearing, I remember, when the English

Division on our right had been heavily raided and thrown back in the attack which followed the raid, " I am afraid our English Allies are letting us down again."

He recognised the War in which the Scotch were fighting the Germans almost single-handed, but had the support of certain Allies among whom the English, French, Canadians, Australians were included. No too great reliance must be placed upon these willing and gallant friends of ours. They had their essential weakness and here, apparently, they had failed, although he was not unaccustomed to, nor indeed had been wholly unexpectant of, such occurrences.

About the beginning of May I was involved in some mixed, confused sort of fighting and I think I fired my rifle and ran in the direction of the enemy. I never reached them, nor indeed did any of my comrades.

War was becoming a long-range business.

German gentlemen some miles away directed their heavy artillery against the British Infantry. Equally obliging English gentlemen, several miles away, directed their artillery against German Infantry. And this agreeable game in which the British and German Infantry were the objectives was one which made the opposing Infantry more sympathetic to each other than well disposed to the respective artilleries. It was said that the trench troops had more in common with the enemy than with the back-country people on either side and, personally, it would not have surprised me if the hand-to-hand fighters made a separate peace. But these are half-forgotten whimsies, recollected from the early summer of '17, and if I remember these vaguely I hardly remember the remainder of that summer at all.

After Arras we went out to train and long, glorious days, sultry nights and billets in villages and in farms was our tremendous good fortune in the 9th Scottish Division. We were told we were being fattened up for something, and true enough in September 1917 they had us in the Line at Paschendaele. There we took our share in what was the second blood bath of the British Army. Winston Spencer Churchill

in *The World Crisis* tells it better than any other author told it.
The book ought to be in a cheap edition. If I knew him I
would write to him and tell him that among the great services
he has done his country—in all his varied life he has done
many—he might also do this further one and provide an edition,
abridged if you like, of his book so that those who served and
knew would also have the opportunity of reading. He must
know too well that ordinary soldiers in the peace which we now
enjoy cannot afford large-volume works, but if he would allow
me I would provide him with the excerpts which would make a
first-class anthology of the War . . . the piece of writing, for
example, in which he sums up the First Battle of the Somme
is—I care not what the critic says—fine prose. Those who
say that it is turgid rhetoric—I read someone who wrote that
the other day—did not know the War, did not know the
emotions which it inspired in us.

This idea of writing an anthology is worth consideration.

I often have good ideas about books. An anthology of
War Poetry, I believe, is in existence, but what about an
anthology of War Prose?

Churchill's *World Crisis* would make a very substantial
contribution.

To these papers I come again. It is weeks ago since I
wrote and they are dusty and dirty. Still, I persist.

" Sorrow's crown of sorrow is remembering happier things."
Hendrik Van Loon has written *The Story of Mankind* with
illustrations, and I have a customer for it. I am anxious to
see the book and he wants it as soon as possible, but I fear
that when it does come in I shall have to hand it over without
a chance of reading it. It seems rather hard luck. Van Loon,
I am told by my customer, is a writer in the H. G. Wells'
" World History " vein and, although Dutch by birth, is an
American citizen. I look forward to Van Loon and hope my
customer does not come too early to collect his book.

It occurs to me I may tell him that it hasn't come in.
That will give me twenty-four hours for its enjoyment.

These perverse thoughts should not come to a bookseller

whose business it is to serve the public. I should be ashamed that I did not have the book in stock and had to try to procure it. . . . I shall do so with the utmost expedition, and deliver it by hand if necessary to his home. I remind myself of my duties as distributor of literature.

Passchendaele—what a story I could write about that if I could write ! . . . but then I cannot write. I only register experiences. I only recollect events, and even for those I have little exact memory.

September 21st was the date. Zonnebeke Redoubt, marvellous barrage, clock-work advance on objectives, Jerry attacking, General killed—he had a V.C. this General—return to billets behind Ypres, five days out . . . up the Line again, another attack, unsuccessful, held the Line, sweated, strove, ate, drank, slept, worked, lived, died . . . these words make the picture of Passchendaele which saw the end of a gallant little group of Scotsmen—mostly Scotsmen and some Welshmen and Irishmen—Jerry burst the lot up and we will meet no more this side of Jordan. It was a good comradeship and I am told most of them lie in Tyne Cot Cemetery. One day I must go there, if my creditors will let me and my funds will permit it ; but they tell me, returned soldiers from the Battlefields, the place is not what it was. It is evidently a true story the story of the ex-officer with his ex-batman who journeyed together to see, after the War had finished, the Salient. For half an hour or so they walked about tidied-up ruins of places ; they talked to, they asked questions of villagers—and then the ex-batman turned to his officer and said as they approached the estaminet, standing on the side of the Potege Road, " Beg pardon, sir," relapsing into war-time phraseology—" beg pardon, sir, they seem to have *messed* this place about a bit since we left it."

It is quite true.

The War background has been messed about.

The worst elements have disappeared. Some good things that the War brought have gone too. It is a " fair itchibod," as Mr Polly is made to say by H. G. Wells. The glory is departed.

This is enough of this writing.

Passchendaele was followed by a great retreat and I have written of that before.

I will not put any more of my past into words to-night.

THE BOOKSELLER

RECOLLECTS THE RETREAT

Always the War—I come back to that when business won't come to me.

The Retreat in the Somme which began in March 1918 was the biggest experience of my life.

" What did you do in the Great War? " they ask.

" I retreated! I was defeated at Loos! I was evacuated at Gallipoli! I was stalemated at Ypres and I retreated in March 1918."

Someone has said that the English lose every battle but the last and that is the only one that matters. It is true. It possibly is true of life, that life is a losing game. We lose every trick except the last when we win the crown eternal because we hold to the King of Hearts.

I would like to believe that.

Something like it is said by John Bunyan—is it in *Grace Abounding*? I give too little time to religious reading. It is a fault with me. I ought to turn my mind to holier things. We are God's creatures and we forget it too often, putting food in a hole in our faces, as Chesterton tells us.

I say life is real ; life is earnest.

Life was real and earnest in 1918. The reality and the earnestness have departed. I will try and remember these days. I will be yet another Historian of the Great War.

The beginning of 1918 we were down in the Somme country right on the forward part which had been evacuated the year before. There was a great empty canal in front of us and this formed the defence of our front.

January and February I seem to have spent there, although one lost count of days and weeks and months. One night they put me down a rope ladder into the Canal, and it was one of the eeriest experiences of my life to find myself sixty feet below the level of the front line.

The idea was that the enemy was mining and I and two others had to explore the tangle of wire and other discards of war in order to see what was afoot. Really, there was nothing afoot and it was with tremendous satisfaction that I clambered back over the side into the comparative security of the trench. They were cosy places, these trenches, for all the rigours of the weather. I often think I was never so warm as I used to be in some cubby-hole cut out of the chalk, at the door of which stood an asphyxiating charcoal brazier. Three men in a loaf, three men in a cubby-hole, one scrounged blanket between us, *there* was comradeship, contentment, comfort. They have talked about deplorable housing conditions a great deal, and perhaps what they say is true, but without sanitation, without furniture, without hot and cold water laid on, without fireplaces and without a chimney, we had health, comfort, security and happiness.

I am not recommending a return to Cave Dwelling by our urban population, but there is something to be said for it. There must be many left like me who can say it, who can say a good deal in favour of a comfortable dug-out on the enemy side of the trench.

Apart from my descent into the empty canal, I took part in two raids—miserable affairs they were—across no-man's-land trying to capture some terror-stricken Boche and bring him back for identification. One of us caught our man all right, but he was so badly wounded that he expired before we got him through the wire. He served his purpose, however, as he had a pocket-book and—his shoulder straps : these apparently gave all the information required by the obscure pundits who lived in the back regions and who we knew by

L 2

their green tabs but by no other sign as Intelligence. It was a cold winter, for all the recollections I have of warmth and comfort. One day we did a raid in white night-gowns bought from some still enterprising shopkeeper away back behind us at Amiens. The idea of the white night-gowns was that we would be less noticeable in the snow, but it did not prevent the Boche from seeing us and taking two of my platoon—two of the best at that—prisoners. One of them died in their hands, so that his white night-shirt was indeed his winding sheet too.

The quietness of the Line and the inactivity of the soldiers on both sides stirred the not always active imaginations of our leaders. We had a General—we were told it was a General, anyhow—who believed that the enemy was starving and who purchased three crowing cocks which he sent up to us in the front line. Our instructions were to place the first of these in no-man's-land and sight thereon the Lewis guns. The theory was that the hunger-stricken Germans would crawl out and seize this attractive delicacy, it having announced its presence. The cock crew at dawn. . . . I don't know what happened but each of the three experiments was a failure. We took the cocks out all right, they dutifully crowed as far as I know, but Jerry secured them for himself without the watchful sentinels ever seeing them disappear. I think there must have been something of a conjurer in the German Lines. Anyway they went, a cock on three successive mornings. (What is that in Plato?—" a cock for Aesculapius "—I can't find it.) The General went on leave and consumed, let us hope, a belated Christmas dinner.

At the end of February we went into rest but it was not for long. It was a pleasant fortnight—if it was as long as a fortnight—and we spent our time in getting fit—physical exercises, bayonet-fighting, marching, and, in the evenings, drinking thin French beer and attending concert parties the performers at which were fellow-soldiers. We never had in the 9th Division the services of Mr Leslie Henson or Mr Harry Lauder or Mr Ivor Novello. These bright lights of the Musical World apparently for the most part twinkled for others.

We heard of them but they were as remote as Sirius from our view. The Captain of my Company, a bumptious but quite likeable Scotsman, thought he was something of a comic singer. It was a dreary experience to listen to him, supplemented as he was by a number of others no better as singers and less interesting in that they were either more modest or press-ganged for the performance.

I must not be too hard on the Captain. Like Mary, he did what he could, and it was something to his credit that with no adequate preparation for the leadership of men—he had been a shop-walker in the south-east of London—he did the job as well as he did. Anyway, when the big barrage fell on 21st March he stood up to his audience and, I take it, now plays an important part in the place where brave men go and have their reward.

There was no sign of that ultimate fate for him and for hundreds of others in these latter days of February.

Life went on from hour to hour and day to day, and the wisest of us spoke neither of the past nor of the future but took the present for what it was at its face value, and it seemed to be good.

Early in March we were in the Line in front of Heudicourt and many distinguished people came to see us there. Gough himself came and Winston Churchill, and Divisional and Brigade Generals called almost as regularly every morning as the milkman does in happier days. There was a tremendous calm. The enemy never fired his artillery and we never fired. We stood, day after day, facing each other. Some thought the enemy had gone home in the opposite trenches, and as far as we were concerned our good behaviour might have given him a similar impression. Scabs, which was the name we gave to a young subaltern whose real name was Scobie, held the view that the real War was over and the Peace had been signed and the troops were all demobbed . . . except us ; we had been overlooked, we had been left behind, and the rations we were getting would keep on reaching us until the dumps at Nurlu were exhausted.

Scabs imagined a story that not only was the War over but

the world had come to an end and the Divine Host had not included moppers-up, and so we had been left until the Roll was called to the bitter end up yonder.

These ideas had a ready acceptance among the simple soldiers. Were we not descendants of those who had seen the angels at Mons and who, generations before, had been awed by the martyrdom of Joan of Arc?

Soldiers believe anything because they must believe in themselves.

Alarms and excursions, interruptions and business, I find myself almost protesting against customers! Who are they to disturb the thread of thought of one who is an historian of the Great War? I seem to serve nothing but tourists . . . have I a copy of William Graham's *One Pound Note and the Rise and Progress of Banking in Scotland*?

I admit I haven't.

I receive the information that it was published in 1886 and I offer to procure it.

It will be an interesting book for me to read.

Is the One Pound Note referred to the only pound they ever had in Scotland? Was it responsible for the rise and progress of that ubiquitous country, I wonder?

They say that money is tight with the Scotch but I cannot believe they had only one pound. Yet, on reflection, it might have been what the Gold Standard is to-day, a standard which is never used for currency but is kept in the Central Bank of Scotland, whatever it is called, to let the cautious Scots know that they can get money for their goods if and when they want it.

It may be so, I don't know.

I am asked, too, have I a copy of *The School for Scandal*. What a business this is; there are literally millions of books and I am expected to be able to supply immediately or on very short notice anything that was ever printed or published.

I must not complain. I have had luck.

I sold to-day the complete set of Swinburne's Poems, six volumes in all, including *Songs before Sunrise*, for 17s. 6d.

Songs before Sunrise—as I write it reminds me of *The Pilgrims*. I wish I had re-read the poem before I packed the books up and parted with them. I feel I will go along to the man's hotel and ask him to let me have that volume back again. It is really too absurd to have given it away before I had committed that to memory. I always intended to learn *The Pilgrims* by heart, and now here am I, an historian of the Great War, lamenting.

Only a few words remain in my recollection . . . what are they again . . .?

> ". . . And ye shall die before your thrones be won,
> Yea—and the changed world and the liberal sun
> Shall move and shine without us. . . ."

. . . something like that. What a pity! I wish I had had a copy of the book on the Scotch Pound and put that down the capacious maw of my customer rather than my *Songs before Sunrise*!

THE BOOKSELLER STILL ON THE RETREAT

That was a trying day when I had to interrupt my recollections about The Retreat in 1918 because of the invasion of customers.

"Really, one would think that this was a shop," I found myself saying. "Who are they to disturb my quietude?" Let me get on with the War!

For months now I have been accustomed to doing practically no business and I have been in the habit of looking upon my premises as my private study. I must get rid of that mood.

It is all wrong—I am here to serve the public. And yet it is not very blameable that I should seek to disinter the past when the present is so dull and dreary and unprofitable.

(Yesterday's takings were eight and sixpence.)

It was the days before 21st March about which I wrote, and the warm vision I had of them when last I wrote seems to have departed.

I would like to have set down then, as I think I could have done, what I felt and saw and remembered of the Revillon Farm and Gauche Wood and the Havrincourt sector generally.

The glory has departed, the vision has faded, the dream has been obscured by other dreams.

I remember, none the less, the quietness before the attack, the talking, the endless rumours, the latrine stories, what they had heard at the ration dump, what they saw coming back from leave and what the Signallers at Divisional H.Q. had told the Quartermaster's servant—all these made up the atmosphere in which that part of the Fifth Army in which I served awaited the German attack.

It came, having been three times prophesied, unexpectedly. The ordinary soldier had begun to believe it was just one more rumour and in any case the attack might not be upon our front. It was a dead quiet night, the night of the 20th. There was a little shelling on our left down Arras way but complete quietness to the right towards Bapaume. I did a patrol about ten o'clock with the sergeant and two other fellows, but the line was quiet in front of us although we thought we heard more talking than it was usual to hear on our nightly meanderings.

We did not know that the trenches opposite us held ten men for every one that stood in ours, nor did we know that within the next three days ten fresh divisions would be hurled against the division in which we served.

It was fortunate. It is as well that we know even less about the future than we remember of the past. I got down to it about midnight, I imagine, and slept—as only men who lived as soldiers did in these days knew how to sleep. I could sleep standing on my feet, unpropped. I could sleep with comfort leaning against the back wall of the trench, and from such slumbers I could awake almost as quickly as one could fire a rifle. The night of the 20th/21st I slept long and soundly, and it must have been half-past four or five when I was awakened by the hellish bombardment which seemed to me to be made up of every conceivable kind of projectile. We had trench mortars on our front line, pipsqueaks on our support line, heavy machine-gun fire seemed almost to spray our front and over our heads, and singing sadly towards Divisional Headquarters or even Corps went shells from the long-range artillery. They say that never such a bombardment was ever before contemplated on any front, and I am willing enough to believe it.

Our people—and by them I mean not distinguished Generals or even Colonels, but Captains and Subalterns, Sergeants, Corporals and private soldiers—our people were handicapped a good deal by the mist which may have been smoke or may have been the ordinary dank miasma that rose in the Somme country. It confused us, at any rate, but it did not deter us from taking proper action.

My Captain saw first to his flanks, reassured himself that they were established, sent back messages to Battalion Headquarters, and threw out a dozen men well into no-man's-land with a couple of Lewis guns. Through the mist they fired and kept on firing, apparently with such effect that as far as our Battalion was concerned, and those on our left and right, our lines were still being held at eleven o'clock.

We were ordered retiral to the support line about midday and with reinforcements from the Divisional School, cooks and runners, spare officers and a very stout-hearted but physically enfeebled Padre, we held the support line until late that afternoon. About five we were ordered to withdraw to Sorel-le-Grand where we saw some of the Divisional " Enjoyment " Company, old crocks, baths, stores and concert party, veterans armed with D.P. rifles. All embodied themselves with us and conformed to our movements. Up to this time we had had a good many casualties but had evacuated all our wounded. My Company alone had taken four prisoners, all young boys who were employed by one of my officers to carry the surplus kit of the Company. During the night we fell back to Nurlu and took over the green line. The King's Own Scottish Borderers —I think one of the Battalions of the Division—undertook the rear-guard action and most courageously they filled this rôle, taking prisoners and killing many of the enemy every few hundred yards in their rear-guard movement. Much has been written about this March Retreat, and even the Prime Minister thought fit to say in the House of Commons that units of the Fifth Army had failed to stand up to their duty. Doubtless Prime Ministers are better informed than private soldiers, but it is a gross libel on the Division that I served in, and the men of other Divisions whom I saw later in the Retreat, to say that they did other than their duty. There was not a Division in the whole of the Fifth Army that was not under strength and there was not a Division in the Army that did not take, at one time or another, odds of from three to ten to one. Far from showing the white feather, those half-trained men proved once again that in retreat the British soldier is more dangerous to his enemy than in attack. When one comes to think of it, some of the most glorious episodes in British history are associated with rear-guard fighting.

What has happened to my Napier's *History of the Peninsular War*? I break off this writing to go and look for it. John Murray is the publisher. A dark thought crosses my mind—one which has recently occurred to me more than once—Has the book been pinched? I must be more careful. Some people are so fond of books that they are kleptomaniacs—a strange but to me easily forgivable sin—but they are inconveniencing an historian of the Great War who desires to make a comparison between the retreat of Wellington in the Peninsula and the retreat in which he himself played a part in France.

There is no doubt, at any rate, that the 9th Division for the first twenty-four hours of the battle remained as a division completely intact, took punishment and gave punishment to the enemy and retired according to plan.

It was the following day, when the Divisions on the right, fewer in personnel than the 9th, were forced to a more rapid and less orderly retirement . . . it was when they lost their original organisation that the front began to disintegrate.

A hard thing was said then by a Scotch doctor who, having

torn off his Red Cross brassard, carried a rifle and bayonet as well as a bandage-box.   This was what he said on being asked what had happened to the Division on the right.   " I am afraid," he declared, " oor English Allies have let us doon again."

I had heard the gibe before.   It was a stock joke with the Scotch.   It was true, however, this time.   I remember reflecting at Trones Wood, many hours later, on the odd insularity of the Scots, as I did often.   They were in this War as an independent nation, assisted by another nation with whom they had frequently been at war before but who, in this particular European adventure, happened to be on the same side.   The Scotch are like that.   Where do they get their individuality?

Is it from Robert Burns or Thomas Carlyle, Adam Smith, David Hume or Sir Walter Scott?   It certainly was not from Robert Louis Stevenson, who had the good fortune to travel with a donkey on the Continent.   The Scotch are only comprehensible when they have travelled either with or without donkeys.   The Scots abroad I have found more polished than those Scots whom I have seen on their native heaths, but the polish was very superficial and, to do them justice, they were not proud of what they had acquired by friction rather than by choice.

The outstanding recollection of the big retreat was the fact that none of us seemed to get any sleep.   At first you were tired and dead weary, and then later you forgot that you were tired and dead weary because you seemed never to have been anything else.   Men staggered backward or forward as creatures doped or drugged, weariness was complete . . . entire . . . the weariness of exhaustion.   Men obeyed orders when they got them—took up positions—loaded—fired—and then fell asleep—spurred into wakefulness again—loaded again and fired and fell asleep—this happened half a dozen times, and in the platoon in which I served from Havrincourt back to the Somme every hour had its adventure, every quarter of an hour had its thrill.   The Cavalry had been seen on the horizon . . . in the rear the South African Brigade had been surrounded and taken, killed to a man . . . an attack had been launched at Ypres

. . . we had driven the Germans out of the whole of the north of Belgium . . . the French Cavalry were six hours away . . . tanks were at the banks of the Somme awaiting the German advance . . . we were bait, luring the German Army on to destruction . . . Paris had fallen—these and many other tales and rumours were freely circulated among the troops, and I myself, feeling that this was an opportunity for real invention, gave it out that I had heard from a Runner that he had heard from his Colonel who had heard it from a Staff Officer that the Fleet were out in the North Sea and in a three days' battle had overwhelmed and destroyed every ship in the German Navy. The satisfaction of telling this story and its elaboration remains as one of the brighter recollections of these crowded days. In two or three hours the tale had come back to me from an entirely different authority, much embellished and embroidered but still good enough in its essentials for me to recognise it as my own. I told it to every stranger with whom I came in contact. An artilleryman heard it greedily on his way back to rejoin his battery. Several members of the R.A.M.C., hurriedly collecting their wounded from Field Ambulances, were told the good tidings, and I do claim that in a welter of uncertainty I did contribute a positive if somewhat fictional note which was not without its value in steadying the defence of Britain. Men must have something wherewith to occupy their minds. I know that now as a bookseller. I learned it long ago as a soldier.

These roaring, tearing hours came to an end when we reached Bray. There we understood we had withdrawn from the line. The Somme Salient had been given up. The Third Army had taken over our front. The French had reinforced and we were in billets to be refitted. All that information we got between four one afternoon and midnight, and the whole of the Division, from General to private soldier, were dead asleep, dreaming that for them at any rate the battle for the time was over. It was the supreme delusion of that phase of the campaign, because a couple of hours after midnight the whole Division was on its feet, on the road again to defend the

line of the Somme beside Albert. Some Division had failed
to hold its front and we were out to take its place. Gone were
our reassuring stories of the Third Army, gone were the tales
of the French. What was left of the Division lined itself along
the valley of the Somme, dead from lack of sleep, tired beyond
the meaning of the word, no ammunition, without rations,
without water, but with definite, clear instructions that this
line was to be held beyond any doubt whatever at all costs.
The day began for me, I suppose, at two o'clock in the morning,
but its brighter possibilities became apparent at nine o'clock.
I found myself with a number of others near a large Expeditionary Force Canteen which had had to be abandoned. There
a Scotch officer was disbursing without money and without
price, as he said, biscuits and beer and, indeed, anything that
a man demanded. There never was such a sight. " No money,
sonny? " he said. " What will you have? A hundred Abdullas,
a table lamp, cheese, a pair of nurse's shoes . . . what's
yours? " This time it was an officer and he was given a case
of whisky to take to the artillery. This Scotch officer and his
batman were the only two salesmen in this remarkable building
but by two o'clock most of its movables and eatables had been
removed, and the last I saw of him was emptying some palliasses
and spreading the straw all round the outside of the wooden
building. By three that afternoon, whether by enemy fire or
by intention, the Expeditionary Force Canteen was a blazing
mass. Having read a German Officer's account of the Retreat
I would like to tell the Scots officer that he made a mistake, or
whoever instructed him made a mistake. Binding, the German
writer, tells us that the cause of the disorganisation of the
German Army was the discovery that the British whom they
thought were on their last legs, who had been starved to death
by their " U " boats, had in fact enormous stores of every kind
of luxury—food and drink and, what was more striking to them,
dumps of any amount of rubber tyres, munitions of war,
vehicles, hospital supplies . . . everything which the Germans
had believed was no longer obtainable by his enemies. This
experience brought home to the rank and file of the German

Army, so this writer states and so I believe, more forcibly than we can imagine how false had been the propaganda upon which he had been fed for the last year.

Anyway, I had a thousand cigarettes—good cigarettes, not " Trumpeter " of which I had been a reluctant smoker for nearly a year before.

That night saw the last of the German attacks. We counter-attacked that evening, drove them off the railway embank-ment. . . . I lost friends that night, men who had gone through five or six days of continuous retreat, but who caught it then in what was the last day of that fighting. It was the worst thing of the War, the getting to know a man so well, so utterly and completely in a day or two, and then lose him as utterly and completely in half an hour. It was ill to be borne. It is ill to be remembered and *Dulce et decorum est* . . . doesn't help one much, the personal loss is too considerable, too un-endurable.

The Australians relieved us, but we were so tired and they were so tired that we lay in our poor trenches for twenty-four hours before they could take over or we could hand over.

And then we were withdrawn.

We had held the position on the left of the Fifth Army from the beginning of the Retreat to the end. We had done what none of us believed we could do, but we were too tired, too worn, too wearied to have any pride but thankfulness . . . thankfulness that no longer we had to march, halt, about-turn, lie down, fire, get up, march, halt, about-turn, lie down, fire . . . thankfulness for no more of that was possibly the feeling that held most of us—and it was one of unspeakable gratitude.

JUST LIKE HIM

He was just like him—that is all.

He wasn't Brough Hall and I am sad for the thought that this side of Jordan I won't see him again. But I will see him there—he loved riversides, even the shores of the Ancre and the Somme, not to speak of the unspeakable Hannabeke !

He and I parted just after demobilisation. He had bought a ticket to some out-back place in the Northern Territory of Australia, and had lodged a sum of money with the Shipping Company for travelling expenses. The balance of his " demob " money he was spending as rapidly as he could. He had only ten days to spend before he left Europe for ever. And these ten days and what was left of his money he was spending at the Cecil.

The man who walked in an hour ago was just like him— just like him, that is true. He was not Brough Hall.

Brough began the War with a commission and threw it up over an argument with his colonel about Ireland. He had been and done a lot of things before that—banking, writing, acting, hotel-keeping—in the Greek War in 1897—in the South African one in 1900—in some mixed business in South America, and now in France after Gallipoli.

His life had two passions—fighting for lost causes, countries or individuals—he brought an equal passion to each—and the reading of Montaigne.

He agreed with Robert Louis Stevenson when he declared that Montaigne was the man of all men who had survived himself most completely and who had left behind him a personal seduction which made friendship irresistible. He quoted him in lumps and chunks—I remember when I re-read Montaigne in my favourite edition on my shelves just now—in such passages as :

" ' When once forty years old, we should consider it as an age to which few arrive. . . .' " (Crash, cr-rump, came the heavy stuff just behind the front line which we held.)

" Few arrive," I remarked.

He would go on calmly : " ' For seeing that men do not usually proceed so far, it is a sign that we are pretty well advanced. We have exceeded the ordinary bounds which make the just measure of life. We ought not to expect to go much further.' (Tell the Captain to put that into his report to the

Colonel.) ' Having escaped so many precipices of death ' [note how the wise Montaigne foresaw the futility of mining in attack], ' we should acknowledge that so extraordinary a fortune as that which has saved us from these imminent perils and kept us alive beyond the ordinary term of living ' (You have been out over six months, Jimmy) ' is not at all likely to continue long.' "

He desired death, did Brough Hall.

He had had enough, he used to declare ; he was no glutton at the Banquet of Life—the sweets are never worth waiting for if the Burgundy has been good—that was Brough Hall.

And yet he came through it and I will never see him again. He recites his Montaigne to a lucky audience in some back blocks of Northern Queensland, I believe, and I may only see his like.

A poor similitude, this passer-by—but he has made it a day again for me, a day in which I can recall Brough Hall— the bravo—the Fronter of Fate—the challenger of death who claimed Montaigne as comrade-in-arms in the trenches of France.

I remind myself I am a bookseller.

This writing has no justification merely as a reminiscence.

I catalogue.

MONTAIGNE—Lucas Collins.
   Foreign Classics for English Readers.
   Blackwood.
   Second Hand—not over clean.   1/-
MONTAIGNE—Charles Cotton's translation—
   Navarre Society—5 vols.   10/- each.
MONTAIGNE—John Florio—3 vols.
   Everyman's Library. Cloth.   2/- each.
MONTAIGNE—*Select Essays*.
   T. N. Foulis.   2/-

That's my stock, and pretty good I think it is too—the dirty book at a shilling is my favourite. I have had it longest. My superior customers don't like dirty books, but I don't mind.

Brough Hall wasn't too clean himself and his trench copy was so dirty as to be unsaleable.

I hope he has it still.

I hope he has kept his Montaigne. I will likely keep mine.

PITY THE POOR

It is not, I am sure, generally known how much blackmail there is in business.

I do not mean the man who comes to me and tells me that what I did in London ten years ago is now discovered and all is lost unless I will pay for silence and discretion—it is not that sort of blackmail from which booksellers suffer, it is blackmail on behalf of the poor.

There is the society for poor children's country holidays, the organisation for poor mothers, the society for the upraising of poor fathers, every society of every sort to help the poor, and well-to-do folk who take up their cause come to wretched shopkeepers such as I am and demand that we help them.

Sometimes I demand to know for what I pay rates. That is the Tory in me which so blusters and rants.

Sometimes I tell the fair beggars what Tolstoy has written —how he has said :

" We will do anything for the poor, we will educate them, we will teach them religion, we will give them holidays, we will find them work, we will do anything for them, in fact, except get off their backs."

Tolstoy wrote that somewhere but I quote it uncertainly, although I have used it with considerable effect. Somehow I don't pity the poor as much as I used to. Is it cynicism or ignorance which makes me think I am right when I assert that poverty in this land is no longer absolute but relative?

.Frankly, I think it is not the poverty of the pitiful nor

grinding kind that one saw twenty years ago ; *that* poverty has gone and gone ; it is no idle phrase to use, gone for good.

If Society cannot afford to clothe all her citizens, then the well-fed and the well-to-do should go overcoat-less or shoe-less and give to the children of the poor.

I agreed with that, but I cannot now accept the view that we have not gone too far in the other direction.

Whether we like it or not, life is a warfare and, mask it as much as we can, it still remains at bottom the plain fact that upon the basis of struggle God has planned His world.

To continue, therefore, the rewards or the pains of struggle is to continue something which is apparently essential to all life, especially human life.

No, pity for the poor is not what it was. My pity I hold for persons not very unlike myself, half-broken members of the lower middle class who find it is as easy to abandon our standards of decency as it would be for us to lose our legs or lose our heads.

The shopman who collects his pence to buy a book is to me a figure that wants pity and encouragement, not the casual user of the Public Library secure in the knowledge that what he demands will come from taxes paid by others.

There must be something of the outlook of George Gissing in me, although heaven forgive me if it is a fault. He and Henry Ryecroft are probably as close friends as I can find in the pages of contemporary literature.

Poverty of the Middle Ages seems at this distance almost a blessed thing, but the poverty of these days is at best a mean poverty—a poverty filled more with envy than with real necessity—and it is a poverty for which I can find no sympathy.

These are smug words from an insecure shopkeeper, scribbling idly on a July afternoon in his front shop. He should be up and doing. He should be aspiring in a big way to be Britain's best and biggest bookseller. If he really holds this view, if success is a thing to be striven for, let him strive for it with all his heart, with all his soul and with all his strength.

Or if not, then he ought to join the class-conscious proletariat who recognise, or think they recognise, that they are mere pawns on the chessboard of the capitalist system, doomed to be cast aside at the behest of kings and queens and knights.

Oddly enough neither of these positions seems to me so reasonable.

I exist as I am, as I often remind myself in Walt Whitman's words—perhaps I don't fit into the economic system, perhaps I don't want to try. But why should I? What is the economic system? Some theoretical shape which is imposed upon certain facts by some external observer. . . .

"What books have you by William J. Locke?" was the interruption which brought an end to these musings. I was able to sell three to one who loved *The Morals of Marcus Ordeyne*: they were *The Beloved Vagabond*, *The Glory of Clementina Wing* and *The Joyous Adventures of Aristide Pujol*. William J. Locke, when I come to think of it, would decline classification by the economic theorist and I would like to be declined with him.

Perhaps after all the artist only is free and a bookseller at best may claim to be an artist's batman.

But this business "pity the poor" keeps recurring to me.

The poor as I meet them across the threshold of this shop are very much the same as other people. They say they want a good time, whatever that may mean. Perhaps Carlyle could give them an answer with his story of the immortal shoeblack.

I can't. I am too indolent or too incompetent to preach them the doctrine that having a good time is not possible in the evil days that are always with the children of men.

ANOTHER BOOKSELLER

This morning an oddish man browsed about the place for an unconscionable length of time and eventually bought a Burton's

Anatomy, two books on Costume, and what I think is a very stupid book called *Pannell's Reference Book*.

He was a real bibliomaniac and I am sure bought books because he must, just as some, I am told, drink gin because they can't help it.

He told me he was a Don and for a moment I was on the Spanish Main. My education led me to think of Dons as some sort of Spanish Grandee—a kind of gay, debonair, decorative figure against the squalid background of duller days.

But my friend was not a Don of that sort. He was a Don of Cambridge. How he functioned, what he did, I did not learn. He told me something, however, of vital and personal interest. He suggested that I was rather a character—a rôle which I am not disinclined to assume—he went on to tell me about another but greater, it was obvious he thought, in Cambridge itself.

He told me of David—a remarkable story of a Frenchman who came to this country while quite a youth and embarked upon bookselling somewhere in the Midlands and later in London, and ultimately started a book-stand in the open air in Cambridge Market.

A real bookman this M. David seems to have been—a collector—a man of letters—a man who bought fairly and sold cheaply—a man of the world of books. Frankly, I warmed to him and would have known more of M. David.

I see him with the eye of the imagination—happier than I in that he pays no rent, or next to none—happier than I in that he deals only with books which are second-hand—happier than I in that lives in a town where some store is set on literature.

Perhaps I will write to him. Perhaps I will not.

It is a happiness to know that there is one with whom a Don of Cambridge thinks I have affinity.

It is an empty and passionless world for booksellers. We ought to get together more, but how can I go to Cambridge?

The world is too much for me ; getting and spending I lay waste my powers.

RETREAT

To-night I am renegade.

I lower my flag. I almost admit that I made a mistake and should not have taken on this bookshop. It was fancy. It was because my mother left me that bit of money and I had not the courage just to squander it and have nothing again.

This was respectability, intellectuality, this buying of a bookseller's business. I wonder if it is too late now : Is this to be my end, is this to be my tomb—a long, long range of human lives which began God knows where and has reached out to me as its most recent manifestation?

Is it to go on and on in this back shop of a bookshop?

Have I courage to get out and away or must I fight it out here with unpaid rates, bad debts, dirty windows, tiresome customers, dusty shelves, bank overdrafts, bills—are these the beasts with which I have to fight at Ephesus?

I would not mind if I saw the day when on some sunny shore I would sit reflecting in peace, contented that I had fought the beasts at Ephesus and escaped—but what I fear is that I shall not live to tell the tale. Here destiny may get me down and here I am tied, at any rate, fast.

It is perfectly ridiculous to pose in this fashion. I am merely an unsuccessful tradesman and there have been many such— the bankruptcy reports indicate that there are thousands of men such as I who, in every sort of business, from farming and innkeeping to greengrocery and drapery, come to this fortune which I seem shortly to attain.

From what I know, they do not pine or fume or despair. They wind up their affairs, get rid of their little businesses for what they will fetch, close the shop door and with brief English succinctness say, " That is that," and get on with the next.

But I am reminded, what is the next?

The next may be anything ; it may be living on one's wife who keeps lodgers, or it may be taking up an insurance book, or it may be persuading one's creditors to give one once more credit and start again, or it may be taking a job as an employee in the kind of business in which one once was master.

Life emphatically goes on, and although it may never be my fate to sail beyond the sunset and the baths of all the western seas until I die, I may yet—astonishing possibility—be able to continue to face up to twenty shillings in the pound here.

The Bank Manager tells me that I ought to make the most of where I am in place of planning something else.

I am always planning, and to-day I thought of books on wheels—a book barrow. The world goes round—why shouldn't I push my books round the world in a book barrow?

(*Round the World on a Wheel* by Sir John Foster Fraser— Pearson—out of stock !)

My idea is that I will buy or get books from anywhere and everywhere and not pay more than threepence each for them. There are enough books in the world to supply my modest need in this direction, and my plan would then be to put them on the barrow, wheel them about and offer them for the uniform price of sixpence. Neil Lyons wrote a book called *Sixpenny Pieces*. Perhaps the name which he chose for his book might do for my book barrow. That's an idea.

These new housing areas which fringe this city, what have they to do with literature?—they need it badly, for although literature is no substitute for life, life is a little thing without literature and they have no bookshops—in fact they have no shops at all—no pubs even—such is the eagerness of the civic authorities to prevent the people being led into temptation.

There are acres of new houses in London which ought to supply customers for books and no one seems to be going for them. I must talk this over.

I must think it over—but I must not think it aloud— someone else might be there before me and my books and wheelbarrow—the new book revolution might be the child of someone else.

I must keep pushing my idea of books on wheels.

CHOICE IS ALL

There is not any doubt now. There was a time but not now. I am satisfied.

We have choice. We can do what we will within the limits set.

I may sweep only the front of the counters. I may sweep both the front and the back of the counters. I may sweep the back shop as well as all the front shop—more, I may sweep right across the pavement down to the gutter.

I am free to choose any one of these—free to choose, too, to do none of them at all.

I take it further.

I may buy or I may not—happier thought—I may sell or I may not. I am free.

There was a time when I was a dreary determinist, when I thought that God had it all laid out and planned for us—one to Hell—one to Heaven—one for Damnation—one for Salvation —I was silly enough to believe that once.

But a child showed me differently—a child among other miracles.

I gave a kid sixpence—too much—my mother thought a penny enough but I am not as wise as my mother was. I gave this kid a sixpence and *she* was free to do what she liked with that sixpence. Hoard it, give it away, put it in her bank, buy cakes or sweets or papers or toys with it—she had sixpenny-worth of opportunity—unlimited, unfettered, uncontrolled.

Life, I was told (I would not claim I thought it), Life, I was told, is *that*—sixpennyworth of opportunity. [A. N. Lyons has a book *Sixpenny Pieces*.] Hoard it or spend it, wisely or ill, it is yours—your sixpence—God has given it to you. It is yours absolutely. You have your sixpence.

Free will must have limits. We don't seriously claim that we ought to be free to make footballs of the stars if we willed it. We admit the limits as inevitable but, within these inevitable limits, we have choice.

Choice is all. On choice depends happiness, progress, life ever more abundantly.

I wonder if we can be sure of these—I have freedom of intelligence to see that these desirable things may not necessarily be inevitable.

Must I choose the good?

The darker moment comes over me. I have doubts. Do I will to choose life, even more abundantly? Lately I have felt that I don't want it. I am not in love with life any more.

There have been times—this green earth—the sweet security of the streets—friends—I had a comrade—food—dawn and sunset—but the salt of life has lost its savour and wherewith shall it be salted?

Why should I choose life when my mind turns to the Unknown more hopefully? What is there in the familiar, hectic embraces of life that I should prefer them to the " sure-enwinding arms of cool-enfolding Death "?

To-night, then, if I am just to choose—if I am passively to receive my heart's desire, it must be " *lovely and soothing death, sooner rather than later, delicate death.*"

Ah! if I am just to choose passively—but why wait? This urging question keeps coming to me. Why wait?

Life is over for you, my lover, health gone, business not worth while, why wait?

There are no loose ends to join up—no theatrical questions —" Ay, there's the rub "—there's no rub for me.

I should be a chooser if mine were no coward soul. The best have chosen the time of their going—" On! gallant heart, as thou wert wont," shouted the Douglas as he charged to death with the Heart of the Bruce in his arms; " We shall this day light such a candle by God's grace in England as shall never be put out," cried the saintly Latimer, finding peace in willing death; " Sic itur ad astra," declared the great Marquis of Montrose as he went up the hangman's steps to take his seat with the Immortals—these were choosers.

There was the Great Chooser. He did not dally with death

when His hour was come. He chose to die. He chose to die at the right time.

Sufficient has not been made of that aspect of Christ's example. Suicide and sacrifice are not so far removed—indeed they are, in deepest sincerity, blood brothers.

How dare a bookseller write like this?

I have books to sell ; alas, too, I have books for which I ought to pay and see not the day when I will be able to pay.

There is little choice there, I tell my *alter ego.*

Where is your Free Will theory now?

Choice is all?—fudge !

THE END

DATE DUE

JAN 15 1988			

Lightning Source UK Ltd.
Milton Keynes UK
UKHW022021150223
417096UK00020B/256

9 781014 430830